**Introduction
to
Special Relativity**

Introduction
to
Special Relativity

Robert Resnick
Professor of Physics
Rensselaer Polytechnic Institute

John Wiley & Sons, Inc.   New York   London   Sydney

To

Trudy Resnick

In loving memory

Preface

This book can be regarded as the first part of a text on "modern physics." Indeed, it is the basis for the treatment of relativity in such a text that I am now writing with Robert Eisberg. That text will be the third and concluding volume of a series on introductory physics, the first two volumes of which I have written with David Halliday.

However, the material in this *Introduction to Special Relativity* has a coherence of its own and can be used in many ways. In the two-year introductory physics course at Rensselaer, for example, these chapters build upon the background in electromagnetism and optics of the Halliday-Resnick text and precede the full development of quantum physics. Applications of relativity to certain areas, such as high-energy physics, are given when, as in our third volume, those areas are presented later. There are other ways to use these chapters, as well. For instance, they can be integrated easily with the classical material. The early chapters on the experimental background and kinematic aspects of relativity could follow immediately the development of Newtonian mechanics, as could much of the relativistic dynamics, whereas the electromagnetic aspects of relativity could follow the presentation of Maxwell's equations. Or, this book could replace the brief and sketchy treatment of the foundations of relativity characteristic of modern physics courses of the immediate past. Still other uses will suggest themselves to physics instructors.

A good deal of optional material is presented here not only because of its intrinsic interest but also to permit the instructor to vary the length and depth of his treatment. Thus, in separate appendices, there are supplementary topics on the geometrical representation of space-time, on the twin paradox, and on the principle of equivalence and general relativity. Also, in the body of the text, some material of an historical, an advanced, or a special nature is printed in reduced type for optional use. Similarly, the problems and thought questions, nearly 250 in number, span a wide range of content and level of difficulty so that the impact of the course can be altered significantly by the choice of which ones and how many are assigned. Many references are cited especially to encourage students to read widely in relativity. The writing is expansive, however, so that the book is self-contained. Pedagogic aids, such as summary tables and worked-out examples, are employed to help the student to learn on his own.

Writing this book has been a labor of love. Relativity has always been a favorite subject of mine, and Einstein was one of the heroes of my youth. Over two decades ago, Franco Rasetti impressed the beauty of the subject upon me in a course at The Johns Hopkins University. Also I was much influenced by the relativity treatments in the classic advanced texts of Peter Bergmann and of Wolfgang Panofsky and Melba Phillips. In revising my notes through successive drafts, classroom trials, and production, I have received constructive criticism or other valuable assistance from many individuals, especially Richard Albagli, Kenneth Brownstein, Benjamin Chi, Robert Eisberg, David Halliday, and Roland Lichtenstein. I am grateful to Mrs. Cassie Young for her skill and dedication in typing the many versions of the notes and to the publishers, John Wiley and Sons, Inc., for their outstanding cooperation. To my wife and daughters, whose forbearance over years of writing is nearly habitual, my deepest thanks. My release from some other duties during the preparation of the manuscript was made possible in part by a Ford Foundation grant to the Engineering School at Rensselaer for curricular development.

It is my earnest hope that this effort will make relativity accessible to beginning students and arouse in them some of the excitement that is physics.

Robert Resnick

Troy, New York
January 1968

Contents

**Introduction
to
Special Relativity**

Chapter One

The Experimental Background
of the Theory of Special Relativity

1.1 *Introduction*

To send a signal through free space from one point to another as fast as possible, we use a beam of light or some other electromagnetic radiation such as a radio wave. *No faster method of signaling has ever been discovered.* This experimental fact suggests that the speed of light in free space, c ($= 3.00 \times 10^8$ m/sec),* is an appropriate limiting reference speed to which other speeds, such as the speeds of particles or of mechanical waves, can be compared.

In the macroscopic world of our ordinary experiences, the speed u of moving objects or mechanical waves with respect to any observer is always less than c. For example, an artificial satellite circling the earth may move at 18,000 mph with respect to the earth; here $u/c = 0.000027$. Sound waves in air at room temperature move at 332 m/sec through the air so that $u/c = 0.0000010$. It is in this ever-present, but limited, macroscopic environment that our ideas about space and time are first formulated and in which Newton developed his system of mechanics.

In the microscopic world it is readily possible to find particles whose speeds are quite close to that of light. For an electron accelerated through a 10-million-volt potential difference, a value reasonably easy to obtain, the speed u equals $0.9988c$. We cannot be certain without direct experimental test that Newtonian mechanics can be safely extrapolated from the ordinary region of low speeds ($u/c \ll 1$) in which it was developed to this high-speed region ($u/c \rightarrow 1$). Experiment shows, in fact, that Newtonian mechanics does *not* predict the correct answers when it is applied to such fast particles. Indeed, in Newtonian mechanics there is no limit in principle to the speed attainable by a particle, so that the speed of light c should play no special role at all. And yet, if the energy of the 10 Mev electron above is increased by a factor of four (to 40 Mev) experiment [1] shows that the speed is not doubled to $1.9976c$, as we might

*The presently accepted value of the speed of light is $2.997925 \pm 0.000003 \times 10^8$ m/sec.

expect from the Newtonian relation $K = \frac{1}{2}Mv^2$, but remains below c; it increases only from $0.9988c$ to $0.9999c$, a change of 0.11 percent. Or, if the 10 Mev electron moves at right angles to a magnetic field of 2.0 weber/m², the measured radius of curvature of its path is not 0.53 cm (as may be computed from the classical relation $r = m_e v/qB$) but, instead, 1.8 cm. Hence, no matter how well Newtonian mechanics may work at low speeds, it fails badly as $u/c \rightarrow 1$.

In 1905 Albert Einstein published his special theory of relativity. Although motivated by a desire to gain deeper insight into the nature of electromagnetism, Einstein, in his theory, extended and generalized Newtonian mechanics as well. He correctly predicted the results of mechanical experiments over the complete range of speeds from $u/c = 0$ to $u/c \rightarrow 1$. Newtonian mechanics was revealed to be an important special case of a more general theory. In developing this theory of relativity, Einstein critically examined the procedures used to measure length and time intervals. These procedures require the use of light signals and, in fact, an assumption about the way light is propagated is one of the two central hypotheses upon which the theory is based. His theory resulted in a completely new view of the nature of space and time.

The connection between mechanics and electromagnetism is not surprising because light, which (as we shall see) plays a basic role in making the fundamental space and time measurements that underlie mechanics, is an electromagnetic phenomenon. However, our low-speed Newtonian environment is so much a part of our daily life that almost everyone has some conceptual difficulty in understanding Einstein's ideas of spacetime when he first studies them. Einstein may have put his finger on the difficulty when he said "Common sense is that layer of prejudices laid down in the mind prior to the age of eighteen." Indeed, it has been said that every great theory begins as a heresy and ends as a prejudice. The ideas of motion of Galileo and Newton may very well have passed through such a history already. More than a half-century of experimentation and application has removed special relativity theory from the heresy stage and put it on a sound conceptual and practical basis. Furthermore, we shall show that a careful analysis of the basic assumptions of Einstein and of Newton makes it clear that the assumptions of Einstein are really much more reasonable than those of Newton.

In the following pages, we shall develop the experimental basis for the ideas of special relativity theory. Because, in retrospect, we found that Newtonian mechanics fails when applied to high-speed particles, it seems wise to begin by examining the foundations of Newtonian mechanics. Perhaps, in this way, we can find clues as to how it might be generalized to yield correct results at high speeds while still maintaining its excellent agreement with experiment at low speeds.

1.2 *Galilean Transformations*

Let us begin by considering a physical *event*. An event is something that happens independently of the reference frame we might use to describe it. For concreteness, we can imagine the event to be a collision of two particles or the turning-on of a tiny light source. The event happens at a point in space and at an instant in time. We specify an event by four (space-time) measurements in a particular frame of reference, say the position numbers x, y, z and the time t. For example, the collision of two particles may occur at $x = 1$ m, $y = 4$ m, $z = 11$ m, and at time $t = 7$ sec in one frame of reference (e.g., a laboratory on earth) so that the four numbers (1, 4, 11, 7) specify the event in that reference frame. The same event observed from a different reference frame (e.g., an airplane flying overhead) would also be specified by four numbers, although the numbers may be different than those in the laboratory frame. Thus, if we are to describe events, our first step is to establish a frame of reference.

We define an *inertial system* as a frame of reference in which the law of inertia—Newton's first law—holds. In such a system, which we may also describe as an *unaccelerated* system, a body that is acted on by zero net external force will move with a constant velocity. Newton assumed that a frame of reference fixed with respect to the stars is an inertial system. A rocket ship drifting in outer space, without spinning and with its engines cut off, provides an ideal inertial system. Frames accelerating with respect to such a system are not inertial.

In practice, we can often neglect the small (acceleration) effects due to the rotation and the orbital motion of the earth and to solar motion.* Thus, we may regard any set of axes fixed on the earth as forming (ap-

---

*Situations in which these effects are noticeable are the Foucault pendulum experiment or the deflection from the vertical of a freely falling body. The order of magnitude of such effects is indicated by the result that in falling vertically 100 ft (1200 in.) a body at the Equator is deflected less than $\frac{1}{8}$ in. from the vertical.

proximately) an inertial coordinate system. Likewise, any set of axes moving at uniform velocity with respect to the earth, as in a train, ship, or airplane, will be (nearly) inertial because motion at uniform velocity does not introduce acceleration. However, a system of axes which accelerates with respect to the earth, such as one fixed to a spinning merry-go-round or to an accelerating car, is *not* an inertial system. A particle acted on by zero net external force will not move in a straight line with constant speed according to an observer in such noninertial systems.

The special theory of relativity, which we consider here, deals only with the description of events by observers in inertial reference frames. The objects whose motions we study may be accelerating with respect to such frames but the frames themselves are unaccelerated. The general theory of relativity, presented by Einstein in 1917, concerns itself with all frames of reference, including noninertial ones, and we shall discuss it briefly in Topical Appendix C.

Consider now an inertial frame S and another inertial frame S' which moves at a constant velocity $\mathbf{v}$ with respect to S, as shown in Fig. 1-1. For convenience, we choose the three sets of axes to be parallel and allow their relative motion to be along the common x, x' axis. We can easily generalize to arbitrary orientations and relative velocity of the frames later, but the physical principles involved are not affected by the particular simple choice we make at present. Note also that we can just as well

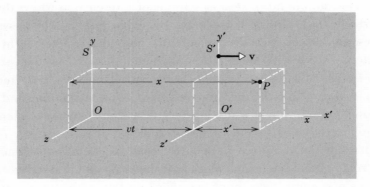

Fig. 1-1. Two inertial frames with a common x-x' axis and with the y-y' and z-z' axes parallel. As seen from frame S, frame S' is moving in the positive x-direction at speed v. Similarly, as seen from frame S', frame S is moving in the negative x'-direction at this same speed. Point P suggests an *event*, whose space-time coordinates may be measured by each observer. The origins O and O' coincide at time $t = 0$, $t' = 0$.

regard S to be moving with velocity $-\mathbf{v}$ with respect to S' as we can regard S' to move with velocity $\mathbf{v}$ with respect to S.

Let an event occur at point P, whose space and time coordinates are measured in each inertial frame. An observer attached to S specifies by means of meter sticks and clocks, for instance, the location and time of occurrence of this event, ascribing space coordinates x, y, and z and time t to it. An observer attached to S', using his measuring instruments, specifies the *same* event by space-time coordinates x', y', z', and t'. The coordinates x, y, z will give the position of P relative to the origin O as measured by observer S, and t will be the time of occurrence of P that observer S records with his clocks. The coordinates x', y', and z' likewise refer the position of P to the origin O' and the time of P, t', to the clocks of inertial observer S'.

We now ask what the relationship is between the measurements x, y, z, t and x', y', z', t'. The two inertial observers use meter sticks, which have been compared and calibrated against one another, and clocks, which have been synchronized and calibrated against one another. The classical procedure, which we look at more critically later, is to assume thereby that length intervals and time intervals are absolute, that is, that they are the same for all inertial observers of the same events. For example, if meter sticks are of the same length when compared at rest with respect to one another, it is implicitly assumed that they are of the same length when compared in relative motion to one another. Similarly, if clocks are calibrated and synchronized when at rest, it is assumed that their readings and rates will agree thereafter, even if they are put in relative motion with respect to one another. These are examples of the "common sense" assumptions of classical theory.

We can show these results explicitly, as follows. For simplicity, let us say that the clocks of each observer read zero at the instant that the origins O and O' of the frames S and S', which are in relative motion, coincide. Then the *Galilean coordinate transformations*, which relate the measurements x, y, z, t to x', y', z', t', are

$$
\begin{aligned}
x' &= x - vt \\
y' &= y \\
z' &= z.
\end{aligned}
\qquad (1\text{-}1a)
$$

These equations agree with our classical intuition, the basis of which is easily seen from Fig. 1-1. It is assumed that time can be defined independently of any particular frame of reference. This is an implicit assumption of classical physics, which is expressed in the transformation equations by the absence of a transformation for t. We can make this assumption of the universal nature of time explicit by adding to the Galilean transformations the equation

$$t' = t. \tag{1-1b}$$

It follows at once from Eqs. 1-1a and 1-1b that the time interval between occurrence of two given events, say P and Q, is the same for each observer, that is

$$t_P' - t_Q' = t_P - t_Q, \tag{1-2a}$$

and that the distance, or space interval, between two points, say A and B, measured at a given instant, is the same for each observer, that is

$$x_B' - x_A' = x_B - x_A. \tag{1-2b}$$

This result (Eq. 1-2b) is worth a more careful look. Let A and B be the end points of a rod, for example, which is at rest in the S-frame. Then, the primed observer, for whom the rod is moving with velocity $-\mathbf{v}$, will measure the end-point locations as x_B' and x_A', whereas the unprimed observer locates them at x_B and x_A. Using the Galilean transformations, however, we find that $x_B' = x_B - vt_B$ and $x_A' = x_A - vt_A$, so that $x_B' - x_A' = x_B - x_A - v(t_B - t_A)$. Since the two end points, A and B, are measured at the same instant, $t_A = t_B$ and we obtain $x_B' - x_A' = x_B - x_A$, as found above.

Or, we can imagine the rod to be at rest in the primed frame, and moving therefore with velocity $\mathbf{v}$ with respect to the unprimed observer. Then the Galilean transformations, which can be written equivalently as

$$\begin{aligned} x &= x' + vt \\ y &= y' \\ z &= z' \\ t &= t', \end{aligned} \tag{1-3}$$

give us $x_B = x_B' + vt_B'$ and $x_A = x_A' + vt_A'$ and, with $t_A' = t_B'$, we once again obtain $x_B - x_A = x_B' - x_A'$.

Notice carefully that two measurements (the end points x_A', x_B' or x_A, x_B) are made for each observer and that we assumed they were made at the *same time* ($t_A = t_B$, or $t_A' = t_B'$). The assumption that the measurements are made at the same time—that is, simultaneously—is a crucial part of our definition of the length of the moving rod. Surely we should not measure the locations of the end points at different times to get the length of the moving rod; it would be like measuring the location of the tail of a swimming fish at one instant and of its head at another instant in order to determine its length (see Fig. 1-2).

The time-interval and space-interval measurements made above are absolutes according to the Galilean transformation; that is, they are the same for all inertial observers, the relative velocity **v** of the frames being arbitrary and not entering into the results. When we add to this result the assumption of classical physics that the mass of a body is a constant, independent of its motion with respect to an observer, then we can conclude that classical mechanics and the Galilean transformations imply that length, mass, and time—the three basic quantities in mechanics—are all independent of the relative motion of the measurer (or observer).

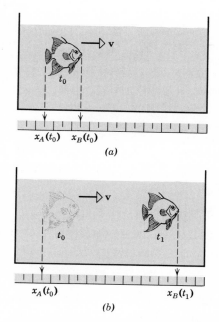

Fig. **1-2.** To measure the length of a swimming fish one must mark the positions of its head and tail simultaneously (*a*), rather than at arbitrary times (*b*).

1.3   *Newtonian Relativity*

How do the measurements of different inertial observers compare with regard to *velocities* and *accelerations* of objects? The position of a particle in motion is a function of time, so that we can express particle velocity and acceleration in terms of time derivatives of position. We need only carry out successive time differentiations of the Galilean transformations. The *velocity* transformation follows at once. Starting from

$$x' = x - vt,$$

differentiation with respect to t gives

$$\frac{dx'}{dt} = \frac{dx}{dt} - v.$$

But, because $t = t'$, the operation d/dt is identical to the operation d/dt', so that

$$\frac{dx'}{dt} = \frac{dx'}{dt'}.$$

Therefore,

$$\frac{dx'}{dt'} = \frac{dx}{dt} - v.$$

Similarly,

$$\frac{dy'}{dt'} = \frac{dy}{dt}$$

and

$$\frac{dz'}{dt'} = \frac{dz}{dt}.$$

However, $dx'/dt' = u_x'$, the x-component of the velocity measured in S', and $dx/dt = u_x$, the x-component of the velocity measured in S, and so on, so that we have simply the *classical velocity addition theorem*

$$\begin{aligned} u_x' &= u_x - v \\ u_y' &= u_y \\ u_z' &= u_z. \end{aligned} \tag{1-4}$$

Clearly, in the more general case in which **v**, the relative velocity of the frames, has components along all three axes, we would obtain the more general (vector) result

$$\mathbf{u}' = \mathbf{u} - \mathbf{v}. \tag{1-5}$$

The student has already encountered many examples of this. For example, the velocity of an airplane with respect to the air (**u**′) equals the velocity of the plane with respect to the ground (**u**) minus the velocity of the air with respect to the ground (**v**).

◆ *Example* 1. A passenger walks forward along the aisle of a train at a speed of 2.2 mi/hr as the train moves along a straight track at a constant speed of 57.5 mi/hr with respect to the ground. What is the passenger's speed with respect to the ground?

Let us choose the train to be the primed frame so that $u_x' = 2.2$ mi/hr. The primed frame moves forward with respect to the ground (unprimed frame) at a speed $v = 57.5$ mi/hr. Hence, the passenger's speed with respect to ground is

$$u_x = u_x' + v = 2.2 \text{ mi/hr} + 57.5 \text{ mi/hr} = 59.7 \text{ mi/hr}.$$

◆ *Example* 2. Two electrons are ejected in opposite directions from radioactive atoms in a sample of radioactive material at rest in the laboratory. Each electron has a speed $0.67c$ as measured by a laboratory observer. What is the speed of one electron as measured from the other, according to the classical velocity addition theorem?

Here, we may regard one electron as the S frame, the laboratory as the S' frame, and the other electron as the object whose speed in the S-frame is sought (see Fig. 1-3). In the S'-frame, the other electron's speed is $0.67c$, mov-

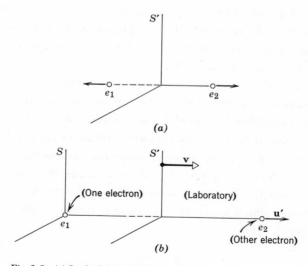

Fig. **1-3.** (*a*) In the laboratory frame, the electrons are observed to move in opposite directions at the same speed. (*b*) In the rest frame, S, of one electron, the laboratory moves at a velocity **v**. In the laboratory frame, S', the second electron has a velocity denoted by **u'**. What is the velocity of this second electron as seen by the first?

ing in the positive x'-direction say, and the speed of the S-frame (one electron) is $0.67c$, moving in the negative x'-direction. Thus, $u_x' = +0.67c$ and $v = +0.67c$, so that the other electron's speed with respect to the S-frame is

$$u_x = u_x' + v = +0.67c + 0.67c = +1.34c,$$

according to the classical velocity addition theorem.   ◀

To obtain the acceleration transformation we merely differentiate the velocity relations (Eq. 1-2). Proceeding as before, we obtain

$$\frac{d}{dt'}(u_x') = \frac{d}{dt}(u_x - v),$$

or
$$\frac{du_x'}{dt'} = \frac{du_x}{dt}, \qquad v \text{ being a constant,}$$

$$\frac{du_y'}{dt'} = \frac{du_y}{dt},$$

and
$$\frac{du_z'}{dt'} = \frac{du_z}{dt}.$$

That is, $a_x' = a_x$, $a_y' = a_y$, and $a_z' = a_z$. Hence, $\mathbf{a'} = \mathbf{a}$. The measured components of acceleration of a particle are unaffected by the uniform relative velocity of the reference frames. The same result follows directly from two successive differentiations of Eqs. 1-1 and applies generally when $\mathbf{v}$ has an arbitrary direction, as long as $\mathbf{v} = $ constant.

We have seen that different velocities are assigned to a particle by different observers when the observers are in relative motion. These velocities always *differ by* the relative velocity of the two observers, which in the case of inertial observers is *a constant velocity*. It follows then that when the particle velocity changes, the *change will be the same* for both observers. Thus, they each measure the *same acceleration* for the particle. The acceleration of a particle is the same in *all* reference frames which move relative to one another with constant velocity; that is

$$\mathbf{a'} = \mathbf{a}. \tag{1-6}$$

In classical physics the *mass* is also unaffected by the motion of the reference frame. Hence, the product $m\mathbf{a}$ will be the same for all inertial observers. If $\mathbf{F} = m\mathbf{a}$ is taken as the definition of force, then obviously each observer obtains the same measure for each force. If $\mathbf{F} = m\mathbf{a}$, then $\mathbf{F}' = m\mathbf{a}'$ and $\mathbf{F} = \mathbf{F}'$. *Newton's laws of motion and the equations of motion of a particle would be exactly the same in all inertial systems.* Since, in mechanics, the conservation principles—such as those for energy, linear momentum, and angular momentum—all can be shown to be consequences of Newton's laws, it follows that *the laws of mechanics are the same in all inertial frames.* Let us make sure that we understand just what this paragraph says, and does not say, before we draw some important conclusions from it.

First, concerning the *invariance* of Newton's laws (that is, the statement that they are the same for all inertial observers), we should recall that a complete statement of the laws includes the assertions (1) that particles interact in pairs (third law) and (2) that the action-reaction forces are directed along the straight line connecting the interacting particles. For many forces that we deal with, it is also true that their magnitude is a function only of the separation of the particles (see Example 3). Thus, these laws apply to such phenomena as gravitation, Van der Waals' forces, and electrostatics. Furthermore, by considering a collection of interacting mass points, we can include the mechanics of rigid bodies, of elastic bodies, and hydrodynamics. Notice, however, that electrodynamics is *not* included because the interaction between moving electric charges (that is, between charges and magnetic fields) involves forces whose directions are not along the line connecting the charges; notice too, that these forces depend not only on the positions of the charges but also on their velocities. We shall return later (Chapter Four) to the electrodynamic situation.

Second, although different inertial observers will record different velocities for the same particle, and hence different momenta and kinetic energies, they will agree that momentum is conserved in a collision or not conserved, that mechanical energy is conserved or not conserved, and so forth. The tennis ball on the court of a moving ocean liner will have a different velocity to a passenger than it has for an observer on shore, and the billiard balls on the table in a home will have different velocities to the player than they have for an observer on a passing train. But, whatever the values of the particle's or system's momentum or mechanical energy may be, when one observer finds that they do not change in an interaction, the other observer will find the same thing. Although the numbers assigned to such things as velocity, momentum, and kinetic energy may be different for different inertial observers, the laws of mechanics (e.g., Newton's laws and the conservation principles) will be the same in all inertial systems (see Problems 2 to 6).

▶ *Example* 3. A particle of mass $m_1 = 3$ kg, moving at a velocity of $u_1 = +4$ m/sec along the x-axis of frame S, approaches a second particle of mass $m_2 = 1$ kg, moving at a velocity $u_2 = -3$ m/sec along this axis. After a head-on collision, it is found that m_2 has a velocity $U_2 = +3$ m/sec along the x-axis.

(*a*) Calculate the expected velocity U_1 of m_1, after the collision.

We use the law of conservation of momentum.

Before the collision the momentum of the system of two particles is

$$P = m_1 u_1 + m_2 u_2 = (3 \text{ kg})(+4 \text{ m/sec}) + 1 \text{ kg} (-3 \text{ m/sec})$$
$$= +9 \text{ kg-m/sec.}$$

After the collision the momentum of the system,

$$P = m_1 U_1 + m_2 U_2,$$

is also $+9$ kg-m/sec, so that

$$+9 \text{ kg-m/sec} = (3 \text{ kg})(U_1) + 1 \text{ kg} (+3 \text{ m/sec})$$
or $$U_1 = +2 \text{ m/sec along the x-axis.}$$

(*b*) Discuss the collision as seen by observer S' who has a velocity **v** of $+2$ m/sec relative to S along the x-axis.

The four velocities measured by S' can be calculated from the Galilean velocity transformation equation (Eq. 1-5), $\mathbf{u'} = \mathbf{u} - \mathbf{v}$, from which we get

$$u_1' = u_1 - v = +4 \text{ m/sec} - 2 \text{ m/sec} = 2 \text{ m/sec,}$$
$$u_2' = u_2 - v = -3 \text{ m/sec} - 2 \text{ m/sec} = -5 \text{ m/sec,}$$
$$U_1' = U_1 - v = +2 \text{ m/sec} - 2 \text{ m/sec} = 0,$$
$$U_2' = U_2 - v = +3 \text{ m/sec} - 2 \text{ m/sec} = 1 \text{ m/sec.}$$

The system momentum in S' is

$$P' = m_1 u_1' + m_2 u_2' = (3 \text{ kg})(2 \text{ m/sec}) + (1 \text{ kg})(-5 \text{ m/sec})$$
$$= +1 \text{ kg-m/sec}$$

before the collision, and

$$P' = m_1 U_1' + m_2 U_2' = (3 \text{ kg})(0) + (1 \text{ kg})(1 \text{ m/sec})$$
$$= +1 \text{ kg-m/sec}$$

after the collision.

Hence, although the velocities and momenta have different numerical values in the two frames, S and S', when momentum is conserved in S it is also conserved in S'. ◀

An important consequence of the above discussion is that *no mechanical experiments carried out entirely in one inertial frame can tell the observer what the motion of that frame is with respect to any other inertial frame.* The billiard player in a closed box-car of a train moving uniformly along a straight track cannot tell from the behavior of the balls what the motion of the train is with respect to ground. The tennis player in an enclosed court on an ocean liner moving with uniform velocity (in a calm sea) cannot tell from his game what the motion of the boat is with respect to the water. No matter what the relative motion may be (perhaps none), so long as it is constant, the results will be identical. Of course, we *can* tell what the *relative* velocity of two frames may be by comparing measurements *between* frames—we can look out the window of a train or compare the data different observers take on the very same event—but then we have not deduced the relative velocity from observations *confined to a single frame.*

Furthermore, there is no way at all of determining the *absolute* velocity of an inertial reference frame from our mechanical experiments. No inertial frame is preferred over any other, for the laws of mechanics are the same in all. Hence, there is no physically definable absolute rest frame. We say that all inertial frames are equivalent as far as mechanics is concerned. The person riding the train cannot tell absolutely whether he alone is moving, or the earth alone is moving past him, or if some combination of motions is involved. Indeed, would you say that you on earth are at rest, that you are moving 30 km/sec (the speed of the earth in its orbit about the sun) or that your speed is much greater still (for instance, the sun's speed in its orbit about the galactic center)? Actually, no mechanical experiment can be performed which will detect an absolute velocity through empty space. This result, that we can only speak of the *relative* velocity of one frame with respect to another, and not of an absolute velocity of a frame, is sometimes called *Newtonian relativity.*

▶ *Example* 4. Consider the forces that two particles exert on each other to lie along their connecting straight line, the magnitude of these equal and opposite forces being a function only of the separation distance of the particles. Under these conditions, forces can always be represented by the negative space derivatives of the potential energy. Show that the equation of motion of such a particle remains unchanged under a Galilean transformation.

Let the distance between the two particles be r_{12} in the S frame, and r_{12}' in the S' frame. Then the potential energy U of the system in S will be a function of r_{12}, which we write as $U(r_{12})$. Hence, the components of force are given by

$$F_x = -\frac{\partial U}{\partial x}, \qquad F_y = -\frac{\partial U}{\partial y} \qquad \text{and} \qquad F_z = -\frac{\partial U}{\partial z}.$$

The equations of motion in frame S for particle 1, say, of mass m_1 will therefore be

$$m_1\frac{d^2x_1}{dt^2} = -\frac{\partial U}{\partial x_1}$$

$$m_1\frac{d^2y_1}{dt^2} = -\frac{\partial U}{\partial y_1} \qquad (1\text{-}7a)$$

$$m_1\frac{d^2z_1}{dt^2} = -\frac{\partial U}{\partial z_1}.$$

Now the mass of a body is assumed to be independent of the inertial reference frame in which it is measured in classical physics. Also, we have seen that under a Galilean transformation the S' observer obtains the same acceleration for a body as the S observer does. Hence (using x', y', z', and t' for the primed observer's variables to describe the motion of the same particle that the unprimed observer described with x, y, z, and t), we have already found that $m_1' = m_1$, and that

$$\frac{d^2x_1}{dt^2} = \frac{d^2x_1'}{dt'^2}, \frac{d^2y_1}{dt^2} = \frac{d^2y_1'}{dt'^2}, \qquad \text{and} \qquad \frac{d^2z_1}{dt^2} = \frac{d^2z_1'}{dt'^2}.$$

Furthermore, we have seen that both observers measure the same separation of the two particles. That is, $x_2' - x_1' = x_2 - x_1, y_2' - y_1' = y_2 - y_1$, and $z_2' - z_1' = z_2 - z_1$ so that

$$r_{12}' = \sqrt{(x_2' - x_1')^2 + (y_2' - y_1')^2 + (z_2' - z_1')^2}$$
$$= \sqrt{(x_2 - x_1)^2 + (y_2 - y_1)^2 + (z_2 - z_1)^2} = r_{12}.$$

The potential energy of the system is represented by $U(r_{12})$, which is some function of the separation of the particles, such as k/r_{12}^2 for example. Because $r_{12} = r_{12}'$, $U(r_{12})$ simply becomes (transforms to) the same function of r_{12}'. Hence, $U(r_{12}) = U(r_{12}')$, where $U(r_{12}')$ expresses the potential energy in the primed system's variables.

Remember that we are trying to prove that the equations of motion of particle 1 in one inertial frame S will have the identical form as the equations of motion of the same particle in another inertial system S', if the relation between the different observer's variables is given by the Galilean transformation. That is, we are trying to show that each inertial observer uses the same laws of mechanics. So far we have found that the left side of Eqs. 1-7a, when transformed from S to S', has the identical form and that $U(r_{12})$ and $U(r_{12}')$ are identical.

It remains now to show that

$$-\frac{\partial U}{\partial x_1} = -\frac{\partial U}{\partial x_1'}, \quad -\frac{\partial U}{\partial y_1} = -\frac{\partial U}{\partial y_1'}, \quad \text{and} \quad -\frac{\partial U}{\partial z_1} = -\frac{\partial U}{\partial z_1'}$$

and we shall have completed our proof. Let us do the x differentiation only (the y and z differentiations proceed identically). We have

$$-\frac{\partial U}{\partial x_1} = -\frac{dU}{dr_{12}}\frac{\partial r_{12}}{\partial x_1} = \frac{dU}{dr_{12}}\frac{x_2 - x_1}{r_{12}},$$

and

$$-\frac{\partial U}{\partial x_1'} = -\frac{dU}{dr_{12}'}\frac{\partial r_{12}'}{\partial x_1'} = -\frac{dU}{dr_{12}'}\frac{x_2' - x_1'}{r_{12}'}.$$

But $r_{12} = r_{12}'$; $x_2 - x_1 = x_2' - x_1'$; and $U(r_{12}) = U(r_{12}')$ so that

$$-\frac{\partial U}{\partial x_1} = -\frac{\partial U}{\partial x_1'}.$$

Hence, by applying the Galilean transformation equations to the equations of motion of particle 1 in S, we obtain the identical equations of motion for this same particle 1 in S', namely,

$$m_1\frac{d^2 x_1'}{dt'^2} = -\frac{\partial U}{\partial x_1'}$$

$$m_1\frac{d^2 y_1'}{dt'^2} = -\frac{\partial U}{\partial y_1'} \tag{1-7b}$$

$$m_1\frac{d^2 z_1'}{dt'^2} = -\frac{\partial U}{\partial z_1'}$$

in which the variables x_1, y_1, z_1, and t of S in Eqs. 1-7a simply become the corresponding variables x_1', y_1', z_1', and t' of S' in Eqs. 1-7b. Obviously, we would obtain similar results for particle 2, and indeed the procedure is easily generalized to a large collection of mass particles.

This example illustrates explicitly the statement that Newton's laws of mechanics and the equations of motion are the same in all inertial frames when the frames are related by the Galilean transformation equations. Under a Galilean transformation $\mathbf{F} = m\mathbf{a}$ becomes $\mathbf{F}' = m\mathbf{a}'$. ◀

Transformation laws, in general, will change many quantities but will leave some others unchanged. These unchanged quantities are called invariants of the transformation. In the Galilean transformation laws for the relation between observations made in different inertial frames of

reference, for example, acceleration is an invariant and—more important—so are Newton's laws of motion. A statement of what the invariant
quantities are is called a relativity principle; it says that for such quantities the reference frames are equivalent to one another, no one having
an absolute or privileged status relative to the others. Newton expressed
his relativity principle as follows: "The motions of bodies included in
a given space are the same amongst themselves, whether that space is
at rest or moves uniformly forward in a straight line."

1.4 *Electromagnetism and Newtonian Relativity*

Let us now consider the situation from the electrodynamic point
of view. That is, we inquire now whether the laws of physics other than
those of mechanics (such as the laws of electromagnetism) are invariant
under a Galilean transformation. If so, then the (Newtonian) relativity
principle would hold not only for mechanics but for all of physics. That
is, no inertial frame would be preferred over any other and *no type of
experiment* in physics, not merely mechanical ones, carried out in a
single frame would enable us to determine the velocity of our frame
relative to any other frame. There would then be no preferred, or absolute, reference frame.

To see at once that the electromagnetic situation is different from the
mechanical one, as far as the Galilean transformations are concerned,
consider a pulse of light (i.e., an electromagnetic pulse) traveling to the
right with respect to the medium through which it is propagated at a
speed c. The "medium" of light propagation was given the name "ether,"
historically, for when the mechanical view of physics dominated physicists' thinking (late 19th century and early 20th century) it was not
really accepted that an electromagnetic disturbance could be propagated
in empty space. For simplicity, we may regard the "ether" frame, S,
as an inertial one in which an observer measures the speed of light to be
exactly $c = (1/\sqrt{\epsilon_0 \mu_0}) = 2.997925 \times 10^8$ m/sec. In a frame S' moving
at a constant speed v with respect to this ether frame, an observer would
measure a different speed for the light pulse, ranging from $c + v$ to
$c - v$ depending on the direction of relative motion, according to the
Galilean velocity transformation.

Hence, the speed of light is certainly *not* invariant under a Galilean
transformation. If these transformations really do apply to optical or
electromagnetic phenomena, then there is one inertial system, and only

one, in which the measured speed of light is exactly c; that is, there is a unique inertial system in which the so-called ether is at rest. We would then have a physical way of identifying an absolute (or rest) frame and of determining by optical experiments carried out in some other frame what the relative velocity of that frame is with respect to the absolute one.

A more formal way of saying this is as follows. Maxwell's equations of electromagnetism, from which we deduce the electromagnetic wave equation for example, contain the constant $c = 1/\sqrt{\mu_0 \epsilon_0}$, which is identified as the velocity of propagation of a plane wave in vacuum. But such a velocity cannot be the same for observers in different inertial frames, according to the Galilean transformations, so that electromagnetic effects will probably not be the same for different inertial observers. In fact, Maxwell's equations are not preserved in form by the Galilean transformations, although Newton's laws are. In going from frame S to frame S', the form of the wave equation, for example, changes if the substitutions of Eqs. 1-1 are made (see Problem 8). But if we accept both the Galilean transformations and Maxwell's equations as basically correct, then it automatically follows that there exists a unique privileged frame of reference (the "ether" frame) in which Maxwell's equations are valid and in which light is propagated at a speed $c = 1/\sqrt{\mu_0 \epsilon_0}$.

The situation then seems to be as follows.* The fact that the Galilean relativity principle *does* apply to the Newtonian laws of mechanics but *not* to Maxwell's laws of electromagnetism requires us to choose the correct consequences from amongst the following possibilities.

1. A relativity principle exists for mechanics, but *not* for electrodynamics; in electrodynamics there *is* a preferred inertial frame; that is, the ether frame. Should this alternative be correct the Galilean transformations would apply and we would be able to locate the ether frame experimentally.

2. A relativity principle exists *both* for mechanics and for electrodynamics, but the laws of electrodynamics as given by Maxwell are *not* correct. If this alternative were correct, we ought to be able to perform experiments that show deviations from Maxwell's electrodynamics and reformulate the electromagnetic laws. The Galilean transformations would apply here also.

---

*The treatment here follows closely that of Ref. 2.

3. A relativity principle exists *both* for mechanics and for electro-dynamics, but the laws of mechanics as given by Newton are *not* correct. If this alternative is the correct one, we should be able to perform experiments which show deviations from Newtonian mechanics and reformulate the mechanical laws. In that event, the correct transformation laws would not be the Galilean ones (for they are inconsistent with the invariance of Maxwell's equations) but some other ones which are consistent with classical electromagnetism and the new mechanics.

We have already indicated (Section 1-1) that Newtonian mechanics breaks down at high speeds so that the student will not be surprised to learn that alternative 3, leading to Einsteinian relativity, is the correct one. In the following sections, we shall look at the experimental bases for rejecting alternatives 1 and 2, as a fruitful prelude to finding the new relativity principle and transformation laws of alternative 3.

1.5 *Attempts to Locate the Absolute Frame—The Michelson-Morley Experiment*

The obvious experiment* would be one in which we can measure the speed of light in a variety of inertial systems, noting whether the measured speed is different in different systems, and if so, noting especially whether there is evidence for a single unique system—the "ether" frame—in which the speed of light is c, the value predicted from electromagnetic theory. A. A. Michelson in 1881 and Michelson and E. W. Morley in 1887 carried out such an experiment [4]. To understand the setting better, let us look a bit further into the "ether" concept.

When we say that the speed of sound in dry air at $0°C$ is 331.3 m/sec, we have in mind an observer, and a corresponding reference system, fixed in the air mass through which the sound wave is moving. The speed of sound for observers moving with respect to this air mass is correctly given by the usual Galilean velocity transformation Eq. 1-1. However, when we say that the speed of light in a vacuum is 2.997925×10^8 m/sec $(= 1/\sqrt{\mu_0\epsilon_0})$ it is not at all clear what reference system is implied. A reference system fixed in the medium of propagation of light presents difficulties because, in contrast to sound, no medium seems to exist. However, it seemed inconceivable to 19th century physicists that

---

*Of the two famous experiments, the Trouton-Noble and the Michelson-Morley, we discuss only the latter. See Ref. 3 for a discussion of the Trouton-Noble experiment.

light and other electromagnetic waves, in contrast to all other kinds of waves, could be propagated without a medium. It seemed to be a logical step to postulate such a medium, called the ether, even though it was necessary to assume unusual properties for it, such as zero density and perfect transparency, to account for its undetectability. The ether was assumed to fill all space and to be the medium with respect to which the speed c applies. It followed then that an observer moving through the ether with velocity **v** would measure a velocity **c**′ for a light beam, where $\mathbf{c}' = \mathbf{c} + \mathbf{v}$. It was this result that the Michelson-Morley experiment was designed to test.

If an ether exists, the spinning and rotating earth should be moving through it. An observer on earth would sense an "ether wind," whose velocity is **v** relative to the earth. If we were to assume that v is equal to the earth's orbital speed about the sun, about 30 km/sec, then $v/c \approx 10^{-4}$. Optical experiments, which were accurate to the first order in v/c, were not able to detect the absolute motion of the earth through the ether, but Fresnel (and later Lorentz) showed how this result could be interpreted in terms of an ether theory. This interpretation had difficulties, however, so that the issue was not really resolved satisfactorily with first-order experiments. It was generally agreed that an unambiguous test of the ether hypothesis would require an experiment that measured the "second-order" effect, that is, one that measured $(v/c)^2$. The first-order effect is not large to begin with ($v/c = 10^4$, an effect of one part in 10,000) but the second-order effect is really very small ($v^2/c^2 = 10^{-8}$, an effect of one part in 100 million).

It was A. A. Michelson (1852–1931) who invented the optical interferometer whose remarkable sensitivity made such an experiment possible. Michelson first performed the experiment in 1881, and then—in 1887, in collaboration with E. W. Morley—carried out the more precise version of the investigation that was destined to lay the experimental foundations of relativity theory. For his invention of the interferometer and his many optical experiments, Michelson was awarded the Nobel Prize in Physics in 1907, the first American to be so honored.

Let us now describe the Michelson-Morley experiment. The Michelson interferometer (Fig. 1-4) is fixed on the earth. If we imagine the "ether" to be fixed with respect to the sun, then the earth (and interferometer) moves through the ether at a speed of 30 km/sec, in different directions in different seasons (Fig. 1-5). For the moment, neglect the earth's spin-

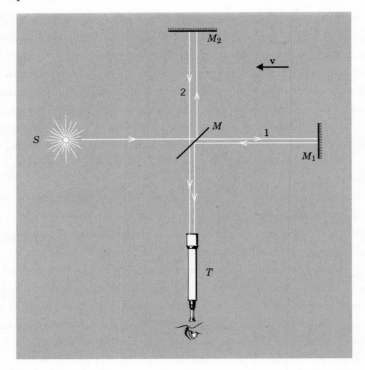

Fig. **1-4.** A simplified version of the Michelson interferometer showing how the beam from the source S is split into two beams by the partially silvered mirror M. The beams are reflected by mirrors 1 and 2, returning to the partially silvered mirror. The beams are then transmitted to the telescope T where they interfere, giving rise to a fringe pattern. In this figure, **v** is the velocity of the ether with respect to the interferometer.

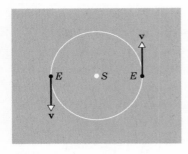

Fig. **1-5.**   The earth E moves at an orbital speed of 30 km/sec along its nearly circular orbit about the sun S, reversing the direction of its velocity every six months.

ning motion. The beam of light (plane waves, or parallel rays) from the laboratory source S (fixed with respect to the instrument) is split by the partially silvered mirror M into two coherent beams, beam 1 being transmitted through M and beam 2 being reflected off of M. Beam 1 is reflected back to M by mirror M_1 and beam 2 by mirror M_2. Then the returning beam 1 is partially reflected and the returning beam 2 is partially trans-

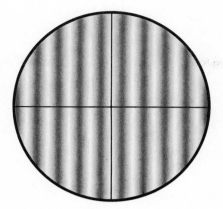

Fig. **1-6.** A typical fringe system seen through
the telescope T when M_1 and M_2 are not quite
at right angles.

mitted by M back to a telescope at T where they interfere. The interference is constructive or destructive depending on the phase difference of the beams. The partially silvered mirror surface M is inclined
at $45°$ to the beam directions. If M_1 and M_2 are very nearly (but not quite)
at right angles, we shall observe a fringe system in the telescope (Fig. 1-6)
consisting of nearly parallel lines, much as we get from a thin wedge of
air between two glass plates.

Let us compute the phase difference between the beams 1 and 2. This
difference can arise from two causes, the different path lengths traveled,
l_1 and l_2, and the different speeds of travel with respect to the instrument
because of the "ether wind" v. The second cause, for the moment, is the
crucial one. The different speeds are much like the different cross-stream
and up-and-down-stream speeds with respect to shore of a swimmer in
a moving stream. The time for beam 1 to travel from M to M_1 and back is

$$t_1 = \frac{l_1}{c - v} + \frac{l_1}{c + v} = l_1\left(\frac{2c}{c^2 - v^2}\right) = \frac{2l_1}{c}\left(\frac{1}{1 - v^2/c^2}\right)$$

for the light, whose speed is c in the ether, has an "upstream" speed of
$c - v$ with respect to the apparatus and a "downstream" speed of $c + v$.
The path of beam 2, traveling from M to M_2 and back, is a cross-stream
path through the ether, as shown in Fig. 1-7, enabling the beam to return

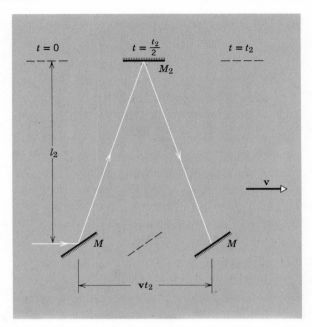

Fig. 1-7. The cross-stream path of beam 2. The mirrors move through the "ether" at a speed v, the light moving through the "ether" at speed c. Reflection from the moving mirror automatically gives the cross-stream path. In this figure, $\mathbf{v}$ is the velocity of the interferometer with respect to the "ether."

to the (advancing) mirror M. The transit time is given by

$$2\left[l_2{}^2 + \left(\frac{vt_2}{2}\right)^2 \right]^{1/2} = ct_2$$

or

$$t_2 = \frac{2l_2}{\sqrt{c^2 - v^2}} = \frac{2l_2}{c}\,\frac{1}{\sqrt{1 - v^2/c^2}}.$$

The calculation of t_2 is made in the ether frame, that of t_1 in the frame of the apparatus. Because time is an absolute in classical physics, this is perfectly acceptable classically. Note that both effects are second-order ones ($v^2/c^2 \simeq 10^{-8}$) and are in the same direction (they *increase* the transit time over the case $v = 0$). The difference in transit times is

$$\Delta t = t_2 - t_1 = \frac{2}{c}\left[\frac{l_2}{\sqrt{1 - v^2/c^2}} - \frac{l_1}{1 - v^2/c^2} \right]$$

Suppose that the instrument is rotated through $90°$, thereby making l_1

the cross-stream length and l_2 the downstream length. If the corresponding times are now designated by primes, the same analysis as above gives the transit-time difference as

$$\Delta t' = t_2' - t_1' = \frac{2}{c}\left[\frac{l_2}{1 - v^2/c^2} - \frac{l_1}{\sqrt{1 - v^2/c^2}}\right].$$

Hence, *the rotation changes the differences* by

$$\Delta t' - \Delta t = \frac{2}{c}\left[\frac{l_2 + l_1}{1 - v^2/c^2} - \frac{l_2 + l_1}{\sqrt{1 - v^2/c^2}}\right].$$

Using the binomial expansion and dropping terms higher than the second-order, we find

$$\Delta t' - \Delta t \cong \frac{2}{c}(l_1 + l_2)\left[1 + \frac{v^2}{c^2} - 1 - \frac{1}{2}\frac{v^2}{c^2}\right] = \left(\frac{l_1 + l_2}{c}\right)\frac{v^2}{c^2}.$$

Therefore, the rotation should cause a shift in the fringe pattern, since it changes the phase relationship between beams 1 and 2.

If the optical path difference between the beams changes by one wavelength, for example, there will be a shift of one fringe across the crosshairs of the viewing telescope. Let ΔN represent the number of fringes moving past the crosshairs as the pattern shifts. Then, if light of wavelength λ is used, so that the period of one vibration is $T = 1/\nu = \lambda/c$,

$$\Delta N = \frac{\Delta t' - \Delta t}{T} \cong \frac{l_1 + l_2}{cT}\frac{v^2}{c^2} = \frac{l_1 + l_2}{\lambda}\frac{v^2}{c^2}. \tag{1-8}$$

Michelson and Morley were able to obtain an optical path length, $l_1 + l_2$, of about 22 m. In their experiment the arms were of (nearly) equal length, that is, $l_1 = l_2 = l$, so that $\Delta N = (2l/\lambda)(v^2/c^2)$. If we choose $\lambda = 5.5 \times 10^{-7}$ m and $v/c = 10^{-4}$, we obtain, from Eq. 1-8,

$$\Delta N = \frac{22 \text{ m}}{5.5 \times 10^{-7} \text{ m}}10^{-8} = 0.4,$$

or a shift of four-tenths a fringe!

Michelson and Morley mounted the interferometer on a massive stone slab for stability and floated the apparatus in mercury so that it could be rotated smoothly about a central pin. In order to make the light path as long as possible, mirrors were arranged on the slab to reflect the beams back and forth through eight round trips. The fringes were observed

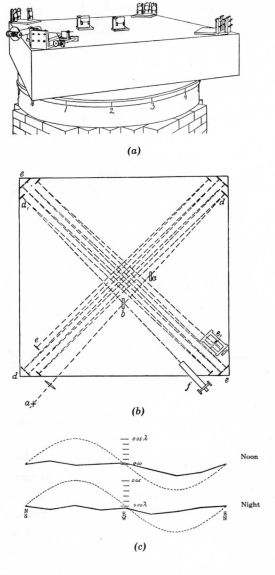

(a)

(b)

(c)

Fig. **1-8.** (*a*) Mounting of the Michelson-Morley apparatus. (*b*) Plan view. (*c*) Observed results. The broken solid lines show the observed fringe shift in the Michelson-Morley experiment as a function of the angle of rotation of the interferometer. The smooth dashed curves—which should be *multiplied by a factor* of 8 to bring it to the proper scale—show the fringe shift predicted by the ether hypothesis. (From "On the Relative Motion of the Earth and the Luminiferous Aether" by Albert A. Michelson and Edward W. Morley, *The London, Edinburgh, and Dublin Philosophical Magazine and Journal of Science,* December 1887.)

under a continuous rotation of the apparatus and a shift as small as 1/100 of a fringe definitely could have been detected (see Fig. 1-8). Observations were made day and night (as the earth spins about its axis) and during all seasons of the year (as the earth rotates about the sun), but the expected fringe shift was not observed. Indeed, the experimental conclusion was that *there was no fringe shift at all.*

TABLE **1-1**   TRIALS OF THE MICHELSON-MORLEY EXPERIMENT

OBSERVER	YEAR	PLACE	l METERS	FRINGE SHIFT PREDICTED BY ETHER THEORY	UPPER LIMIT OF OBSERVED FRINGE SHIFT
Michelson	1881	Potsdam	1.2	0.04	0.02
Michelson and Morley	1887	Cleveland	11.0	0.40	0.01
Morley and Miller	1902–1904	Cleveland	32.2	1.13	0.015
Miller	1921	Mt. Wilson	32.0	1.12	0.08
Miller	1923–1924	Cleveland	32.0	1.12	0.030
Miller (sunlight)	1924	Cleveland	32.0	1.12	0.014
Tomaschek (starlight)	1924	Heidelberg	8.6	0.3	0.02
Miller	1925–1926	Mt. Wilson	32.0	1.12	0.088
Kennedy	1926	Pasadena and Mt. Wilson	2.0	0.07	0.002
Illingworth	1927	Pasadena	2.0	0.07	0.0004
Piccard and Stahel	1927	Mt. Rigi	2.8	0.13	0.006
Michelson et al	1929	Mt. Wilson	25.9	0.9	0.010
Joos	1930	Jena	21.0	0.75	0.002

Source. From Shankland, McCuskey, Leone, and Kuerti, *Rev. Mod. Phys.*, **27**, 167 (1955).

This null result ($\Delta N = 0$) was such a blow to the ether hypothesis that the experiment was repeated by many workers over a 50-year period. The null result was amply confirmed (see Table 1-1) and provided a great stimulus to theoretical and experimental investigation. In 1958 J. P. Cedarholm, C. H. Townes et al [5] carried out an "ether-wind" experiment using microwaves in which they showed that if there is an ether and the earth is moving through it, the earth's speed with respect to the ether would have to be less than 1/1000 of the earth's orbital speed. This is an improvement of 50 in precision over the best experiment of the Michelson-Morley type. The null result is well established.

The student should note that the Michelson-Morley experiment depends essentially on the 90° rotation of the interferometer, that is, on interchanging the roles of l_1 and l_2, as the apparatus moves with a speed v through an "ether." In predicting an expected fringe shift, we took **v** to be the earth's velocity with respect to an ether fixed with the sun. However, the solar system itself might be in motion with respect to the hypothetical ether. Actually, the experimental results themselves determine the earth's speed with respect to an ether, if indeed there is one, and these results give $v = 0$. Now, if at some time the velocity were zero in such an ether, no fringe shift would be expected, of course. But the velocity cannot always be zero, since the velocity of the apparatus is *changing* from day to night (as the earth spins) and from season to season (as the earth rotates about the sun). Therefore, the experiment does not depend solely on an "absolute" velocity of the earth through an ether, but also depends on the changing velocity of the earth with respect to the "ether." Such a changing motion through the "ether" would be easily detected and measured by the precision experiments, if there were an ether frame. The null result seems to rule out an ether (absolute) frame.

One way to interpret the null result of the Michelson-Morley experiment is to conclude simply that the measured speed of light is the same, that is, c, for all directions in every inertial system. For this fact would lead to $\Delta N = 0$ in the (equal arm) experiment, the "downstream" and "cross-stream" speeds being c, rather than $|\mathbf{c} + \mathbf{v}|$, in any frame. However, such a conclusion, being incompatible with the Galilean (velocity) transformations, seemed to be too drastic philosophically at the time. If the measured speed of light did not depend on the motion of the observer, all inertial systems would be equivalent for a propagation of light and there could be no experimental evidence to indicate the existence of a unique inertial system, that is, the ether. Therefore, to "save the ether" and still explain the Michelson-Morley result, scientists suggested alternative hypotheses. We explore these alternatives in succeeding sections.

1.6 *Attempts to Preserve the Concept of a Preferred Ether Frame—*
The Lorentz-Fitzgerald Contraction Hypothesis

Fitzgerald (in 1892) proposed a hypothesis, which was elaborated upon by Lorentz, to explain the Michelson-Morley null result and still to retain the concept of a preferred ether frame. Their hypothesis was that all bodies are contracted in the direction of motion relative to the stationary ether by a factor $\sqrt{1 - v^2/c^2}$. For convenience, let the ratio v/c be represented by the symbol β, so that this factor may be written as $\sqrt{1 - \beta^2}$. Now, if l° represents the length of a body at rest with respect to the ether (its rest length) and l its length when in motion with respect to the ether, then in the Michelson-Morley experiment

$$l_1 = l_1{}^\circ \sqrt{1 - \beta^2} \quad \text{and} \quad l_2 = l_2{}^\circ.$$

This last result follows from the fact that in the hypothesis it was assumed that lengths at right angles to the motion are unaffected by the motion. Then

$$\Delta t = \frac{2}{c} \frac{1}{\sqrt{1 - \beta^2}} (l_1{}^\circ - l_2{}^\circ)$$

and, on 90° rotation,   (1-9)

$$\Delta t' = \frac{2}{c} \frac{1}{\sqrt{1 - \beta^2}} (l_1{}^\circ - l_2{}^\circ).$$

Hence, no fringe shift should be expected on *rotation* of the interferometer, for $\Delta t' - \Delta t = 0$.

Lorentz was able to account for such a contraction in terms of his electron theory of matter, but the theory was elaborate and somewhat contrived and other results predicted from it could not be found experimentally. As for the interferometer result of the contraction hypothesis, it too can be demolished as a correct explanation. Recall that, in the original experiment, the arms were of (nearly) equal length ($l_1 = l_2 = l$). Consider now an interferometer in which $l_1 \neq l_2$. In that case, *even including the Lorentz contraction effect,* we should expect a fringe shift when the velocity of the interferometer changes with respect to the ether from v to v'. The predicted shift in fringes (to second-order terms; see Problem 11) is

$$\Delta N = \frac{l_1{}^\circ - l_2{}^\circ}{\lambda} \left(\frac{v^2}{c^2} - \frac{v'^2}{c^2} \right).$$ (1-10)

Kennedy and Thorndike [6], using an interferometer with unequal arms (the path difference was about 16 cm, as great as permitted by coherence of the source), carried out the appropriate experiment. Although the difference $(v^2 - v'^2)/c^2$ should change as a result of the earth's spin (the biggest change occurring in twelve hours) and the earth's rotation (the biggest change occurring in six months), neither effect was observed (i.e., $\Delta N = 0$) in direct contradiction to the contraction hypothesis.

1.7   *Attempts to Preserve the Concept of a Preferred Ether Frame—*
The Ether-Drag Hypothesis

Another idea advanced to retain the notion of an ether was that
of "ether drag." This hypothesis assumed that the ether frame was
attached to all bodies of finite mass, that is, dragged along with such
bodies. The assumption of such a "local" ether would automatically give
a null result in the Michelson-Morley experiment. Its attraction lay in
the fact that it did not require modification of classical mechanics or
electromagnetism. However, there were two well-established effects
which contradicted the ether-drag hypothesis: stellar aberration and the
Fizeau convection coefficient. Let us consider these effects now, since
we must explain them eventually by whatever theory we finally accept.

The aberration of light was first reported by Bradley [see Ref. 7] in
1727. He observed that (with respect to astronomical coordinates fixed
with respect to the earth) the stars appear to move in circles, the angular
diameter of these circular orbits being about 41 seconds of arc. This can
be understood as follows. Imagine that a star is directly overhead so that
a telescope would have to be pointed straight up to see it if the earth
were at rest in the ether. That is (see Fig. 1-9a), the rays of light coming
from the star would proceed straight down the telescope tube. Now,
imagine that the earth is moving to the right through the ether with a
speed v. In order for the rays to pass down the telescope tube without
hitting its sides—that is, in order to see the star—we would have to tilt
the telescope as shown in Fig. 1-9b. The light proceeds straight down
in the ether (as before) but, during the time Δt that the light travels the
vertical distance $l = c\,\Delta t$ from the objective lens to the eyepiece, the telescope has moved a distance $v\,\Delta t$ to the right. The eyepiece, at the time
the ray leaves the telescope, is on the same vertical line as the objective
lens was at the time the ray entered the telescope. From the point of view
of the telescope, the ray travels along the axis from objective lens to
eyepiece. The angle of tilt of the telescope, α, is given by

$$\tan \alpha = \frac{v\,\Delta t}{c\,\Delta t} = \frac{v}{c}. \tag{1-11}$$

It was known that the earth goes around the sun at a speed of about
30 km/sec, so that with $c = 3 \times 10^5$ km/sec, we obtain an angle
$\alpha = 20.5$ sec of arc. The earth's motion is nearly circular so that the
direction of aberration reverses every six months, the telescope axis

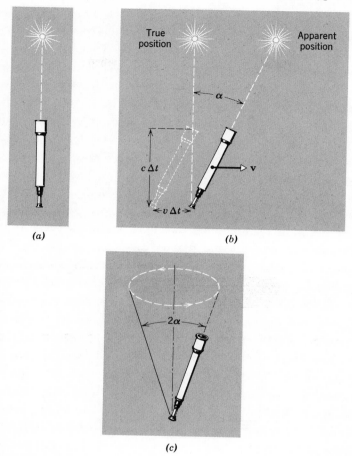

Fig. **1-9.** (*a*) The star and telescope have no relative motion (i.e., both are at rest in the ether); the star is directly overhead. (*b*) The telescope now moves to the right at speed *v* through the ether; it must be tilted at an angle α (greatly exaggerated in the drawing) from the vertical to see the star, whose apparent position now differs from its true position. ("True" means with respect to the sun, i.e., with respect to an earth that has no motion relative to the sun.) (*c*) A cone of aberration of angular diameter 2α is swept out by the telescope axis during the year.

tracing out a cone of aberration during the year (Fig. 1-9*c*). The angular diameter of the cone, or of the observed circular path of the star, would then be $2\alpha = 41$ sec of arc, in excellent agreement with the observations. For stars not directly overhead, the analysis, although more involved, is similar and identical in principle (see Problem 12).

The important thing we conclude from this agreement is that the ether is *not* dragged around with the earth. If it were, the ether would be at rest with respect to the earth, the telescope would not have to be tilted, and there would be no aberration at all. That is, the ether would be moving (with the earth) to the right with speed v in Fig. 1-9c, so there would be no need to correct for the earth's motion through the ether; the light ray would be swept along with the ether just as a wind carries a sound wave with it. Hence, *if* there is an ether, it is *not* dragged along by the earth but, instead, the earth moves freely through it. Therefore, we cannot explain the Michelson-Morley result by means of an ether-drag hypothesis.

Another well-established effect that contradicts the ether-drag hypothesis involves the propagation of electromagnetic waves in moving media. J. A. Fresnel, in 1817, predicted that light would be partially dragged along by a moving medium and derived an exact formula for the effect on the basis of an ether hypothesis. The effect was confirmed experimentally by Fizeau in 1851. The set-up of the Fizeau experiment is shown diagrammatically in Fig. 1-10. Light from the source S falls on a partially silvered mirror M which splits the beam into two parts. One part is transmitted to mirror M_1 and proceeds in a counterclockwise sense back to M, after reflections at M_1, M_2, and M_3. The other part is reflected to M_3 and proceeds in a clockwise sense back to M, after reflections at M_3, M_2, M_1. At M, part of the returning first beam is transmitted and part of the returning second beam is reflected to the telescope T. Interference fringes, representing optical path differences of the beams, will be seen in the telescope. Water flows through the tubes (which have flat glass end sections) as shown, so that one light beam always travels in the direction of flow and the other always travels opposite to the direction of flow. The flow of water can be reversed, of course, but outside the tubes conditions remain the same for each beam.

Let the apparatus be our S-frame. In this laboratory frame the velocity of light in still water is c/n and the velocity of the water is v_w. Does the flow of water, the medium through which the light passes, affect the velocity of light measured in the laboratory? According to Fresnel the answer is yes. The velocity of light, v, in a body of refractive index, n, moving with a velocity v_w relative to the observer (i.e., to the frame of reference S in which the free-space velocity of light would be c) is given by Fresnel as

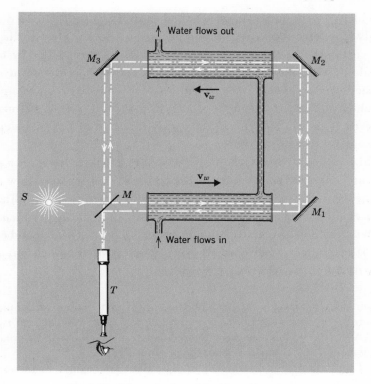

Fig. **1-10.** Schematic view of the Fizeau Experiment.

$$v = \frac{c}{n} \pm v_w\left(1 - \frac{1}{n^2}\right).$$ (1-12)

The factor $(1 - 1/n^2)$ is called the Fresnel drag coefficient. The speed of light is changed from the value c/n because of the motion of the medium but, because the factor is less than unity, the change (increase or decrease) of speed is less than the speed v_w of the medium—hence the term "drag." For yellow sodium light in water, for example, the speed increase (or decrease) is 0.565 v_w. Notice that for $n = 1$ ("a moving vacuum") Eq. 1-12 reduces plausibly to $v = c$.

This result can be understood by regarding the light as being carried along both by the refractive medium and by the ether that permeates it. Then, with the ether at rest and the refractive medium moving through the ether, the light will act to the rest observer as though only a part of the velocity of the medium were added to it. The result can be derived directly from electromagnetic theory. There we use the electric displacement vector **D** which is a sum ($\epsilon_0\mathbf{E} + \mathbf{P}$) of two terms. The first term depends on the free-space electric field **E** and the second term is the polarization **P,** which relates to the refractive medium. In computing the velocity of electromagnetic waves in a moving refractive medium compared to that in a stationary one, only that part of **D** which depends on **P** contributes to the difference.

In Fizeau's experiment, the water flowed through the tubes at a speed of about 7 m/sec. Fringe shifts were observed from the zero flow speed to flow speeds of 7 m/sec, and on reversing the direction of flow. Fizeau's measurements confirmed the Fresnel prediction. The experiment was repeated by Michelson and Morley in 1886 and by P. Zeeman and others after 1914 under conditions allowing much greater precision, again confirming the Fresnel drag coefficient.

▶ *Example* 5. In Fizeau's experiment, the approximate values of the parameters were as follows: $l = 1.5$ m, $n = 1.33$, $\lambda = 5.3 \times 10^{-7}$ m, and $v_w = 7$ m/sec. A shift of 0.23 fringe was observed from the case $v_w = 0$. Calculate the drag coefficient and compare it with the predicted value.

Let d represent the drag coefficient. The time for beam 1 to traverse the water is then

$$t_1 = \frac{2l}{(c/n) - v_w d}$$

and for beam 2

$$t_2 = \frac{2l}{(c/n) + v_w d}.$$

Hence,

$$\Delta t = t_1 - t_2 \doteq \frac{4lv_w d}{(c/n)^2 - v_w{}^2 d^2} \cong \frac{4ln^2 v_w d}{c^2}$$

The period of vibration of the light is $T = \lambda/c$ so that

$$\Delta N \cong \frac{\Delta t}{T} = \frac{4ln^2 v_w d}{\lambda c}$$

and, with the values above, we obtain

$$d = \frac{\lambda c\, \Delta N}{4ln^2 v_w} = 0.47.$$

The Fresnel prediction (see Eq. 1-12) is

$$d = 1 - \frac{1}{n^2} = 0.44 . \quad \blacktriangleleft$$

If the ether were dragged along with the water, the velocity of light in the laboratory frame, using the Galilean ideas, would have been $(c/n) + v_w$ in one tube and $(c/n) - v_w$ in the other tube. Instead, the Fizeau experiment, as we have seen, is interpreted most simply in terms of no ether drag at all, either by the apparatus or the water moving through it, and a partial drag due to the motion of the refractive medium. Indeed, the aberration experiment, when done with a telescope filled with water (see Question 15), leads to exactly the same result and interpretation. Hence, the ether-drag hypothesis is contradicted by the facts.

There appears to be no acceptable experimental basis then for the idea of an ether, that is, for a preferred frame of reference. This is true whether we choose to regard the ether as stationary or as dragged along. We must now face the alternative that a principle of relativity is valid in electrodynamics as well as in mechanics. If this is so, then either electrodynamics must be modified, so that it is consistent with the classical relativity principle, or else we need a new relativity principle that is consistent with electrodynamics, in which case classical mechanics will need to be modified.

1.8 *Attempts to Modify Electrodynamics*

Let us consider now the attempts to modify the laws of electromagnetism. A possible interpretation of the Michelson-Morley result (one that contradicts the classical relativity principle) is that the velocity of light has the same value in all inertial frames. If this is so, then the velocity of light surely cannot depend on the velocity of the light source relative to the observer. Hence, one modification of electromagnetism that suggests itself, if we wish to avoid the principle of the invariance of the velocity of light as the correct interpretation of the Michelson-Morley results, is to assume that the velocity of a light wave *is* connected with the motion of the source rather than with an ether. The various theories that are based on this assumption are called *emission* theories. Common to them all is the hypothesis that the velocity of light is c relative to the original source and that this velocity is independent of the state of motion of the medium transmitting the light. This would automatically explain the null result of the Michelson-Morley experiment. The theories differ in their predictions as to what the velocity of light becomes on reflection from a moving mirror.* Nevertheless, all emission theories are contradicted directly by two types of experiment. The first is typified by the de Sitter observations on double (or binary) stars (see Ref. 9 and Problem 14), the second by a Michelson-Morley experiment using an extraterrestrial light source.

Two stars that are close to one another and move in orbits about their common center of mass are called double stars. Imagine the orbits to be circles. Now assume that the velocity of the light by which we see them through the empty space is equal to $c + v_s$, where v_s is the component of the velocity of the source relative to the observer, at the time the light is emitted, along the line from the source to the observer. Then, the time for light to reach the earth from the approaching star would be smaller than that from the receding star. As a consequence, the circular orbits of double stars should appear to be eccentric as seen from earth. But measurements show no such eccentricities in the orbits of double stars observed from earth.

The results are consistent with the assumption that the velocity of the light is independent of the velocity of the source.** DeSitter's conclusion was that, if the velocity of light is not equal to c but is equal instead to $c + kv_s$, then k experimentally must be less than 2×10^{-3}. More recent experiments [11], using fast-moving terrestrial sources, confirm the conclusion that the velocity of electromagnetic radiation is independent of the velocity of the source. In the most recent experiment (1964), measurements are made of the speed of electromagnetic radiation from the decay of rapidly moving π° mesons produced in the CERN synchrotron. The mesons had energies greater than 6 GeV ($v_s = 0.99975c$) and the speed of the γ-radiation emitted from these fast-moving sources was measured absolutely by timing over a known distance. The result corresponded to a value of k equal to $(-3 \pm 13) \times 10^{-5}$.

The Michelson-Morley experiment, using an extraterrestrial source, has been performed by R. Tomaschek, who used starlight, and

---

*The *original source* theory assumes that the velocity remains c relative to the source; the *ballistic* theory assumes that the velocity becomes c relative to the mirror; and *the new source* theory assumes that the velocity becomes c relative to the mirror image of the source. See Refs. 8.

**For an analysis and a discussion of alternate interpretations of the de Sitter experiment, see Ref. 10.

D. C. Miller, who used sunlight [12]. If the source velocity (due to rotational and translational motions relative to the interferometer) affects the velocity of light, we should observe complicated fringe-pattern changes. No such effects were observed in either of the experiments.

We saw earlier that an ether hypothesis is untenable. Now we are forced by experiment to conclude further that the laws of electrodynamics are correct and do not need modification. The speed of light (i.e., electromagnetic radiation) is the same in all inertial systems, independent of the relative motion of source and observer. Hence, a relativity principle, applicable both to mechanics *and* to electromagnetism, is operating. Clearly, it cannot be the Galilean principle, since that required the speed of light to depend on the relative motion of source and observer. We conclude that the Galilean transformations must be replaced and, therefore, the basic laws of mechanics, which were consistent with those transformations, need to be modified.

1.9   *The Postulates of Special Relativity Theory*

In 1905, before many of the experiments we have discussed were actually performed (see Question 18), Albert Einstein (1879–1955), apparently unaware of several earlier important papers on the subject, provided a solution to the dilemma facing physics. In his paper "On the Electrodynamics of Moving Bodies" [13], Einstein wrote ". . . no properties of observed facts correspond to a concept of absolute rest; . . . for all coordinate systems for which the mechanical equations hold, the equivalent electrodynamical and optical equations hold also . . . . In the following we make these assumptions (which we shall subsequently call the Principle of Relativity) and introduce the further assumption—an assumption which is at the first sight quite irreconcilable with the former one—that light is propagated in vacant space, with a velocity c which is independent of the nature of motion of the emitting body. These two assumptions are quite sufficient to give us a simple and consistent theory of electrodynamics of moving bodies on the basis of the Maxwellian theory for bodies at rest."

We can rephrase these assumptions of Einstein as follows.

1. *The laws of physics are the same in all inertial systems. No preferred inertial system exists.* (The Principle of Relativity.)

2. *The speed of light in free space has the same value c in all inertial systems.* (The Principle of the Constancy of the Speed of Light.)

Einstein's relativity principle goes beyond the Newtonian relativity principle, which dealt only with the laws of mechanics, to include *all* the laws of physics. It states that it is impossible by means of *any* physical measurements to designate an inertial system as intrinsically stationary or moving; we can only speak of the *relative* motion of two systems. Hence, no physical experiment of *any* kind made entirely *within* an inertial system can tell the observer what the motion of his system is with respect to any other inertial system. The second principle above, which flatly contradicts the Galilean velocity transformation (Eq. 1-5), is clearly consistent with the Michelson-Morley (and subsequent) experiments. The entire special theory of relativity is derived directly from these two assumptions. Their simplicity, boldness, and generality are characteristic of Einstein's genius. The success of his theory can only be judged by comparison with experiment. It not only was able to explain all the existing experimental results but predicted new effects which were confirmed by later experiments. No experimental objection to Einstein's special theory of relativity has yet been found.

In Table 1-2 we list the seven theories proposed at various times and compare their predictions of the results of thirteen crucial experiments, old and new. Notice that only the special theory of relativity is in agreement with *all* the experiments listed. We have already commented on the successes and failures of the ether and emission theories with most of the light-propagation experiments and it remains for us to show how special relativity accounts for their results. In addition, several experiments from other fields—some suggested by the predictions of relativity and in flat contradiction to Newtonian mechanics—remain to be examined. What emerges from this comparative preview is the compelling *experimental* basis of special relativity theory. It alone is in accord with the real world of experimental physics.

As is often true in the aftermath of a great new theory, it seemed obvious to many in retrospect that the old ideas had to be wrong. For example, in discussing the concept of an ether as a substance, a concept that persisted long after relativity, Max Born [14] made the point that the elastic properties of matter were being derived with increasing success from electromagnetic forces so that it was quite inconsistent to try, in

TABLE **1-2**   EXPERIMENTAL BASIS FOR THE THEORY OF SPECIAL RELATIVITY

Theory		Aberration	Fizeau convection coefficient	Michelson-Morley	Kennedy-Thorndike	Moving sources and mirrors	De Sitter spectroscopic binaries	Michelson-Morley, using sunlight	Variation of mass with velocity	General mass-energy equivalence	Radiation from moving charges	Meson decay at high velocity	Trouton-Noble	Unipolar induction, using permanent magnet
		LIGHT PROPAGATION EXPERIMENTS							EXPERIMENTS FROM OTHER FIELDS					
Ether theories	Stationary ether, no contraction	A	A	D	D	A	A	D	D	N	A	N	D	D
	Stationary ether, Lorentz contraction	A	A	A	D	A	A	A	A	N	A	N	A	D
	Ether attached to ponderable bodies	D	D	A	A	A	A	A	D	N	N	N	A	N
Emission theories	Original source	A	A	A	A	A	D	D	N	N	D	N	N	N
	Ballistic	A	N	A	A	D	D	D	N	N	D	N	N	N
	New source	A	N	A	A	D	D	A	N	N	D	N	N	N
Special theory of relativity		A	A	A	A	A	A	A	A	A	A	A	A	A

Legend. A, the theory agrees with experimental results.
      D, the theory disagrees with experimental results.
      N, the theory is not applicable to the experiment.
Source. From Panofsky and Phillips, *Classical Electricity and Magnetism* (2nd ed.), Addison-Wesley, New York (1962).

turn, to explain electromagnetic phenomena in terms of the elastic properties of some hypothetical medium. In the same spirit Herman Bondi [15] has said:

"The special theory of relativity is a necessary consequence of any assertion that the unity of physics is essential, for it would be intolerable for all inertial systems to be equivalent from a dynamical point of view yet distinguishable by optical measurements. It now seems almost incredible that the possibility of such a discrimination was taken for granted in the nineteenth century, but at the same time it was not easy to see what was more important—the universal validity of the Newtonian principle of relativity or the absolute nature of time."

It was his preoccupation with the nature of time that led Einstein to his revolutionary proposals. We shall see later how important a clear picture of the concept of time was to the development of relativity theory. However, the program of the theory, in terms of our discussions in this chapter, should now be clear. First, we must obtain equations of transformation between two uniformly moving (inertial) systems which will keep the velocity of light constant. Second, we must examine the laws of physics to check whether or not they keep the same form (i.e., are invariant) under this transformation. Those laws that are not invariant will need to be generalized so as to obey the principle of relativity.

The new equations of transformation obtained in this way by Einstein are known for historical reasons as a Lorentz transformation. We have seen (Section 1-3) that Newton's equation of motion is invariant under a Galilean transformation, which we now know to be incorrect. It is likely then that Newton's laws—and perhaps other commonly accepted laws of physics—will not be invariant under a Lorentz transformation. In that case, they must be generalized. We expect the generalization to be such that the new laws will reduce the old ones for velocities much less than that of light, for in that range both the Galilean transformation and Newton's laws are at least approximately correct.

In Table 1-3, for perspective, we compare relativity theory to the older emission and ether theories in terms of their basic assumptions and conclusions.

1.10 *Einstein and the Origin of Relativity Theory*

It is so fascinating a subject that one is hard-pressed to cut short a discussion of Albert Einstein, the person. Common misconceptions of the man, who quite properly symbolized for his generation the very height of intellect, might be shattered by such truths as these: Einstein's parents feared for a while that he might be mentally retarded for he learned to speak much later than customary; one of his teachers said to him "You will never amount to anything, Einstein," in despair at his daydreaming and his negative attitude toward formal instruction; he failed to get a high-school diploma and, with no job prospects, at the age of fifteen he loafed like a "model dropout"; Einstein's first attempt to gain admission to a polytechnic institute ended when he failed

TABLE **1-3** BASIC ASSUMPTIONS AND CONCLUSIONS OF ALTERNATIVE THEORIES

	EMISSION THEORY	CLASSICAL ETHER THEORY	SPECIAL THEORY OF RELATIVITY
Reference system	No special reference system	Stationary ether is special reference system	No special reference system
Velocity dependence	The velocity of light depends on the motion of the source	The velocity of light is independent of the motion of the source	The velocity of light is independent of the motion
Space-time connection	Space and time are independent	Space and time are independent	Space and time are interdependent
Transformation equations	Inertial frames in relative motion are connected by a Galilean transformation	Inertial frames in relative motion are connected by a Galilean transformation	Inertial frames in relative motion are connected by a Lorentz transformation

Source. From Panofsky and Phillips, *Classical Electricity and Magnetism* (2nd Ed.), Addison-Wesley, New York (1962).

to pass an entrance examination; after gaining admittance he cut most of the lectures and, borrowing a friend's class notes, he crammed intensively for two months before the final examinations. He later said of this " . . . after I had passed the final examination, I found the consideration of any scientific problem distasteful to me for an entire year." It was not until two years after his graduation that he got a steady job, as a patent examiner in the Swiss Patent Office at Berne; Einstein was very interested in technical apparatus and instruments, but—finding he could complete a day's work in three or four hours—he secretly worked there, as well as in his free time, on the problems in physics which puzzled him. And so it goes.*

The facts above are surprising only when considered in isolation, of course. Einstein simply could not accept the conformity required of him, whether in educational, religious, military, or governmental institutions. He was an avid reader who pursued his own intellectual interests, had a great curiosity about nature, and was a genuine "free-thinker" and independent spirit. As Martin Klein (Ref. 16) points out, what is really surprising about Einstein's early life is that none of his "elders" recognized his genius.

But such matters aside, let us look now at Einstein's early work. It is appropriate to quote here from Martin Klein [16].

"In his spare time during those seven years at Berne, the young patent examiner wrought a series of scientific miracles; no weaker word is adequate. He did nothing less than to lay out the main lines along which twentieth-century theoretical physics has developed. A very brief list will have to suffice.

*See Refs. 16–21 for some rewarding articles and books about Einstein.

Einstein in 1905

Einstein in 1920

Einstein in later life

Einstein playing the violin in concert   **Einstein and a student**

"The only thing that gives me pleasure, apart from my work, my violin and my sailboat, is the appreciation of my fellow workers."

Einstein leaning against the mast of his boat

He began by working out the subject of statistical mechanics quite independently and without knowing of the work of J. Willard Gibbs. He also took this subject seriously in a way that neither Gibbs nor Boltzman had ever done, since he used it to give the theoretical basis for a final proof of the atomic nature of matter. His reflections on the problems of the Maxwell-Lorentz electrodynamics led him to create the special theory of relativity. Before he left Berne he had formulated the principle of equivalence and was struggling with the problems of gravitation which he later solved with the general theory of relativity. And, as if these were not enough, Einstein introduced another new idea into physics, one that even he described as 'very revolutionary,' the idea that light consists of particles of energy. Following a line of reasoning related to but quite distinct from Planck's, Einstein not only introduced the light quantum hypothesis, but proceeded almost at once to explore its implications for phenomena as diverse as photochemistry and the temperature dependence of the specific heat of solids.

"What is more, Einstein did all this completely on his own, with no academic connections whatsoever, and with essentially no contact with the elders of his profession. Years later he remarked to Leopold Infeld that until he was almost thirty he had never seen a real theoretical physicist. To which, of course, we should add the phrase (as Infeld almost did aloud, and as Einstein would never have done), "except in the mirror!"

The discussion thus far emphasizes Einstein's independence of other contemporary workers in physics. Also characteristic of his work is the fact that he always made specific predictions of possible experiments to verify his theories. In 1905, at intervals of less than eight weeks, Einstein sent to the *Annalen der Physik* three history-making papers. The first paper [22] on the quantum theory of light included an explanation of the photoelectric effect. The suggested experiments, which gave the proof of the validity of Einstein's equations, were successfully carried out by Robert A. Millikan nine years later! The second paper [23] on statistical aspects of molecular theory, included a theoretical analysis of the Brownian movement. Einstein wrote later of this: "My major aim in this was to find facts which would guarantee as much as possible the existence of atoms of definite size. In the midst of this I discovered that, according to atomistic theory, there would have to be a movement of suspended microscopic particles open to observation, without knowing that observations concerning the Brownian motion were already long familiar."* The third paper [13], on special relativity, included applications to electrodynamics such as the relativistic mass of a moving body, all subsequently confirmed experimentally.

Under these circumstances, it is not particularly fruitful to worry about whether, or to what extent, Einstein was aware of the Michelson-Morley ex-

---

*Robert Brown, in 1827, had published these observations.

periment* (the evidence is that he had heard of the result but not the details) or the directly relevant 1904 papers of Lorentz and Poincare** (the evidence is strong that he had not read them)—all the more so since all the participants acknowledge Einstein as the original author of relativity theory. Instead, we should note another characteristic of Einstein's work, which suggests why his approach to a problem was usually not that of the mainstream; namely, his attempt to restrict hypotheses to the smallest number possible and to the most general kind. For example, Lorentz, who never really accepted Einstein's relativity, used a great many *ad hoc* hypotheses to arrive at the same transformations in 1904 as Einstein did in 1905 (and as Voigt did in 1887); furthermore, Lorentz had assumed these equations *a priori* in order to obtain the invariance of Maxwell's equations in free space. Einstein on the other hand *derived* them from the simplest and most general postulates—the two fundamental principles of special relativity. And he was guided by his solution to the problem that had occupied his thinking since he was 16 years old: the nature of time. Lorentz and Poincaré had accepted Newton's universal time $(t = t')$, whereas Einstein abandoned that notion.

Newton, even more than many succeeding generations of scientists, was aware of the fundamental difficulties inherent in his formulation of mechanics, based as it was on the concepts of absolute space and absolute time. Einstein expressed a deep admiration for Newton's method and approach and can be regarded as bringing many of the same basic attitudes to bear on his analysis of the problem. In his Autobiographical Notes [18], after critically examining Newtonian mechanics, Einstein writes:

"Enough of this. Newton, forgive me; you found the only way which, in your age, was just about possible for a man of highest thought and creative power. The concepts, which you created, are even today still guiding our thinking in physics, although we now know that they will have to be replaced by others farther removed from the sphere of immediate experience, if we aim at a profounder understanding of relationships."

It seems altogether fitting that Einstein should have extended the range of Newton's relativity principle, generalized Newton's laws of motion, and later incorporated Newton's law of gravitation into his space-time scheme. In subsequent chapters we shall see how this was accomplished.

Questions

1. Can a particle move through a medium at a speed greater than the speed of light *in that medium?* Explain. (See R. Resnick and D. Halliday, *Physics*, p. 517–518.)

---

*See Refs. 24 and 25 for a fascinating analysis of this issue and of Einstein's early work.

**See Ref. 26 for a careful study of the historical situation and the characteristics of Einstein's work.

2. Is the sum of the interior angles of a triangle equal to $180°$ on a spherical surface? On a plane surface? Under what circumstances does spherical geometry reduce to plane geometry? Draw an analogy to relativistic mechanics and classical mechanics.

3. Would observers on the North Pole agree with those on the South Pole as to the direction of "up" and "down?" What definition of the terms could they agree on?

4. Give examples of non-inertial reference frames.

5. How does the concept of simultaneity enter into the measurement of the length of a body?

6. Could a mechanical experiment be performed in a given reference frame which would reveal information about the *acceleration* of that frame relative to an inertial one?

7. Discuss the following comment, which applies to most of the figures: "The figure *itself* belongs to some particular reference frame, that is, the picture represents measurements made in some particular frame." Can we look omnipotently at moving frames, wave fronts, and the like, without realizing first what frame *we* are in?

8. In an inelastic collision, the amount of thermal energy (internal mechanical kinetic energy) developed is independent of the inertial reference frame of the observer. Explain why, in words.

9. Describe an acoustic Michelson-Morley experiment by analogy with the optical one. What differences would you expect, and what similarities, in comparing the acoustical and the optical experiment?

10. Does the Lorentz-Fitzgerald contraction hypothesis contradict the classical notion of a rigid body?

11. A simple way to test the Lorentz contraction theory would be to make one-way measurements of the speed of light (rather than round trips). That is, we could measure the speed along a straight line in the direction of the earth's motion through the ether and compare it with the speed along the same line in the opposite direction. Explain how this would make possible the detection of an ether wind, if one existed. (Such a high precision experiment, using the Mössbauer effect, can be done today.)

12. If the earth's motion, instead of being nearly circular about the sun, were uniformly along a straight line through the "ether," could an aberration experiment measure its speed?

13. How can we use the aberration observations to refute the Ptolemaic model of the solar system?

14. Does the fact that stellar aberration is observable contradict the principle of the relativity of uniform motion (i.e., does it determine an absolute velocity)? How, in this regard, does it differ from the Michelson-Morley experiment?

15. If the "ether" were dragged along with water, what would be the expected result of the aberration experiment when done with a telescope filled with water? (The actual results were the same with as without water. The experiment was done by Sir George Airy in 1871 and confirmed Eq. 1-12. For a complete analysis see Rosser [3].)

16. Of the various emission theories, only the original source one is consistent with the ordinary optical result of the Doppler effect for a moving mirror. Explain.

17. What boxes in Table 1-2 have been accounted for in this chapter?

18. Of the experiments discussed in this chapter, which ones were not available at the time of Einstein's 1905 paper? (See references.)

Problems

1. Justify the relations $y = y'$ and $z = z'$ of Eq. 1-1a by symmetry arguments.

2. Momentum is conserved in a collision of two objects as measured by an observer on a uniformly moving train. Show that momentum is also conserved for a ground observer.

3. Repeat Problem 2 under the assumption that after the collision the masses of the two objects are different from what they were before; that is, assume a transfer of mass took place in the course of the collision. Show that for momentum to be conserved for the ground observer, conservation of mass must hold true.

4. Kinetic energy is conserved in an elastic collision by definition. Show, using the Galilean transformation equations, that if a collision is elastic in one inertial frame it is elastic in all inertial frames.

5. Consider two observers, one whose frame is attached to the ground and another whose frame is attached, say, to a train moving with uniform velocity **u** with respect to the ground. Each observes that a particle, initially at rest with respect to the train, is accelerated by a constant force applied to it for time t in the forward direction. (a) Show that for each observer the work done by the force is equal to the gain in kinetic energy of the particle, but that one observer measures these quantities to be $\frac{1}{2}ma^2t^2$, whereas the other observer measures them to be $\frac{1}{2}ma^2t^2 + maut$. Here a is the common acceleration of the particle of mass m. (b) Explain the differences in work done by the same force in terms of the different distances through which the observers measure the force to act during

the time t. Explain the different final kinetic energies measured by each observer in terms of the work the particle could do in being brought to rest relative to each observer's frame.

6. Suppose, in the previous problem, that there is friction between the particle and, say, the train floor, and that the applied force gives the particle the same acceleration over the same time as before. Note that there is no change in the initial and final kinetic energies but an extra force is needed to oppose friction.) (*a*) Show that the amount of heat energy developed is the *same* for each observer. (*Hint.* Work done against friction depends on the *relative* motion of the surfaces.) (*b*) The applied force does work on the train itself, according to the ground observer, in addition to developing heat energy and increasing the kinetic energy of the particle. Compute the amount of this work. Is there an equivalent performance of work by the observer on the train? Explain.

7. Write the Galilean transformation equations for the case of arbitrary relative velocity of the frames. (*Hint.* Let **v** have components v_x, v_y, and v_z.)

8. Show that the electromagnetic wave equation

$$\frac{\partial^2 \phi}{\partial x^2} + \frac{\partial^2 \phi}{\partial y^2} + \frac{\partial^2 \phi}{\partial z^2} - \frac{1}{c^2} \frac{\partial^2 \phi}{\partial t^2} = 0,$$

does not retain its form (i.e., is not invariant) under the Galilean transformation equations (Eqs. 1-1). (*Hint.* use the chain rule in which if $x = f(x', y', z', t'.)$ Then

$$\frac{\partial f}{\partial x} = \frac{\partial f}{\partial x'} \frac{\partial x'}{\partial x} + \frac{\partial f}{\partial y'} \frac{\partial y'}{\partial x} + \frac{\partial f}{\partial z'} \frac{\partial z'}{\partial x} + \frac{\partial f}{\partial t'} \frac{\partial t'}{\partial x}).$$

9. A pilot is supposed to fly due east from A to B and then back again to A due west. The velocity of the plane in air is u' and the velocity of the air with respect to the ground is v. The distance between A and B is l and the plane's air speed u' is constant. (*a*) If $v = 0$ (still air), show that the time for the round trip is $t_0 = 2l/u'$. (*b*) Suppose that the air velocity is due east (or west). Show that the time for a round trip is then

$$t_E = \frac{t_0}{1 - v^2/(u')^2}.$$

(*c*) Suppose that the air velocity is due north (or south). Show that the time for a round trip is then

$$t_N = \frac{t_0}{\sqrt{1 - v^2/(u')^2}}.$$

(*d*) In parts (*b*) and (*c*) we must assume that $v < u'$. Why? (*e*) Draw an analogy to the Michelson-Morley experiment.

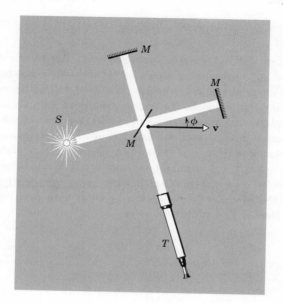

Fig. **1-11.**

10. In the description of the Michelson-Morley experiment, it was assumed that one of the arms of the interferometer was aligned along the direction of the earth's motion while the second was perpendicular to this direction. Suppose, instead, that one arm makes an angle of ϕ with the direction of motion (see Fig. 1-11). Repeat the analysis in the text for this more general case and show that, under the Lorentz-Fitzgerald contraction hypothesis, no fringe shift would be expected when the apparatus is rotated through 90°; that is, the time difference between the two beams is the same before and after rotation. (*Hint.* Remember, only the component of length in the direction of motion through the ether is affected).

11. Derive Eq. 1-10.

12. Show that, to first order in v/c, Eq. 1-11 becomes $\tan \alpha = (v/c) \sin \theta$ when the rays from a star make an arbitrary angle θ with the plane of the earth's orbit, rather than an angle $\theta = 90°$ as assumed for simplicity in the text. (That is, **v** and **c** are no longer at right angles.) Does this change the conclusions drawn there?

13. (*a*) In the Fizeau experiment (Fig. 1-10) identify the frames S and S' and the relative velocity **v** which correspond to Fig. 1-1. (*b*) Show that in the Fresnel drag formula (Eq. 1-12) $v \rightarrow v_w$ for very large values of n. How would you interpret this? (*c*) Under what circumstances will the Fresnel drag coefficient be zero? To what does this correspond physically?

14. Consider one star in a binary system moving in uniform circular motion with speed v. Consider two positions: (I) the star is moving *away* from the earth along the line connecting them, and (II) the star is moving *toward* the earth along the line connecting them (see Fig. 1-12). Let the period of the star's motion be T and its distance from earth be l. Assume l is large enough that positions I and II are a half-orbit apart. (*a*) Show that the star would appear to go from position (I) to position (II) in a time $T/2 - 2lv/(c^2 - v^2)$ and from position (II) to position (I) in a time $T/2 + 2lv/(c^2 - v^2)$, assuming that the <u>emission theories</u> are correct. (*b*) Show that the star would appear to be at both positions I and II at the same time if $T/2 = 2lv/(c^2 - v^2)$.

Fig. **1-12.**

15. A bullet from a rifle travels 1100 ft in its first second of motion. On a calm day the rifle is fired from a train along the tracks. A man stands 1100 ft away from the rifle at that instant, in the line of fire. Does the bullet or the sound of the firing reach the man first if the train (*a*) is at rest, (*b*) is moving away from the man, or (*c*) is moving toward the man? (*d*) Is the first sentence of this problem ambiguous? Explain. (*e*) State the relevance of this problem to emission theories.

References

1. See the film "The Ultimate Speed" by William Bertozzi (produced by Educational Services, Inc., Watertown, Mass.) and a complete description of it by W. Bertozzi in *Am. J. Phys.*, **32**, 551–555 (1964).
2. W. K. H. Panofsky and Melba Phillips, *Classical Electricity and Magnetism*, (Addison-Wesley, Reading, Mass., 1955) Chapter 14.
3. F. T. Trouton and H. R. Noble, *Phil. Trans. Roy. Soc.*, A **202**, 165 (1903); *Proc. Roy. Soc.* (*London*), **72**, 132 (1903). A concise account is given in W. G. V. Rosser, *An Introduction to the Theory of Relativity* (Butterworths, London, 1964), pp. 64–65. This text is an outstanding general reference.
4. A. A. Michelson, *Am. J. Sci.*, **122**, 120 (1881). A. A. Michelson and E. W. Morley, *Am. J. Sci.*, **134**, 333 (1887).
5. J. P. Cedarholm, G. L. Bland, B. L. Havens, and C. H. Townes, "New Experimental Tests of Special Relativity," *Phys. Rev. Letters*, **1**, 342–343 (1958).

6. R. J. Kennedy and E. M. Thorndike, *Phys. Rev.*, **42**, 400 (1932).
7. See Albert Stewart, "The Discovery of Stellar Aberration," *Scientific American*, p. 100 (March 1964) for an interesting and detailed description of Bradley's work.
8. The original source emission theory is that of W. Ritz, *Ann. Chim. et Phys.*, **13**, 145 (1908). Discussions of various emission theories can be found in R. C. Tolman, *Phys. Rev.*, **31**, 26 (1910); J. J. Thomson, *Phil. Mag.*, **19**, 301 (1910; and Stewart, *Phys. Rev.*, **32**, 418 (1911).
9. W. De Sitter, *Proc. Amsterdam Acad.*, **15**, 1297 (1913), and **16**, 395 (1913).
10. "Evidence Against Emission Theories," J. G. Fox, *Am. J. Phys.*, **33**, 1 (1965).
11. D. Sadeh, *Phys. Rev. Letters*, **10**, 271 (1963) (a measurement of the speed of electromagnetic radiation from the annihilation of rapidly moving positrons); "Test of the Second Postulate of Special Relativity in the GeV Region" by T. Alväger, F. J. M. Farley, J. Kjellman, and I. Wallin, *Phys. Letters*, **12**, 260 (1964).
12. R. Tomaschek, *Ann. Phys. (Leipzig)*, **73**, 105 (1924). D. C. Miller, *Proc. Nat. Acad. Sci.*, **2**, 311 (1925).
13. A. Einstein, "On the Electrodynamics of Moving Bodies," *Ann. Physik*, **17**, 891 (1905). For a translated extract see "Great Experiments in Physics," edited by Morris H. Shamos (Holt Dryden, New York, 1959), p. 318.
14. M. Born, *Naturwissenschaften*, **7**, 136 (1919).
15. H. Bondi, *Endeavour*, **20**, 121 (1961).
16. "Einstein and Some Civilized Discontents," by Martin J. Klein, *Am. J. Phys.*, **18**, 38 (1965).
17. Barbara Lovett Cline, *The Questioners* (Crowell, New York, 1965). See in this connection, Chapters 5 and 12.
18. P. A. Schlipp (ed.), *Albert Einstein: Philosopher-Scientist* (Harper Torchbooks, New York, 1959), a two-volume work.
19. Elma Ehrlich Levinger, *Albert Einstein* (Julian Messner, New York, 1949).
20. Peter Michelmore, *Einstein, Profile of the Man* (Dodd, Mead and Co., New York, 1962). In paperback, Apollo Editions, A-63.
21. William Cahn, *Einstein, A Pictorial Biography* (The Citadel Press, New York, 1955). In paperback, 1960.
22. A. Einstein, *Ann. Physik*, **17**, 132 (1905).
23. A. Einstein, *Ann. Physik*, **17**, 549 (1905).
24. R. S. Shankland, "Conversations with Albert Einstein," *Am. J. Phys.*, **31**, 47 (1963).
25. R. S. Shankland, "Michelson-Morley Experiment," *Am. J. Phys.*, **32**, 16 (1964).
26. Gerald Holton, "On the Origins of the Special Theory of Relativity," *Am. J. Phys.*, **28**, 627 (1960).

Chapter Two

Relativistic Kinematics

2.1 *The Relativity of Simultaneity*

In *Conversations with Albert Einstein*, R. S. Shankland [1] writes "I asked Professor Einstein how long he had worked on the Special Theory of Relativity before 1905. He told me that he had started at age 16 and worked for ten years; first as a student when, of course, he could spend only part-time on it, but the problem was always with him. He abandoned many fruitless attempts, 'until at last it came to me that time was suspect!' " What was it about time that Einstein questioned? It was the assumption, often made unconsciously and certainly not stressed, that there exists a universal time which is the same for all observers. Indeed, it was only to bring out this assumption explicitly that we included the equation $t = t'$ in the Galilean transformation equations (Eq. 1-1). In pre-relativistic discussions, the assumption was there implicitly by the absence of a transformation equation for t in the Galilean equations. That the same time scale applied to all inertial frames of reference was a basic premise of Newtonian mechanics.*

In order to set up a universal time scale, we must be able to give meaning, independent of a frame of reference, to statements such as "Events A and B occurred at the same time." Einstein pointed out that when we say that a train arrives at 7 o'clock this means that the exact pointing of the clock hand to 7 and the arrival of the train at the clock were simultaneous. We certainly shall not have a universal time scale if different inertial observers disagree as to whether two events are simultaneous. Let us first try to set up an unambiguous time scale in a single frame of

---

*In the *Principia* Newton wrote "Absolute, true and mathematical time, of itself, and from its own nature, flows equably without relation to anything external." Although classical philosophers accepted the universality of the time scale, many criticized this particular statement of Newton's. They found it unnecessary to hypothesize that moments of time can exist independent of events. Time is regarded as derived from events and not vice versa. Leibniz, for example, opposed Newton's view of absolute time, the difference between his view and Newton's being aptly summarized by the statement that according to Newton the universe *has* a clock whereas according to Leibniz it *is* a clock. See Ref. 2 for a fascinating account of the philosophy of time and Ref. 3 for a discussion of the Newtonian and Leibniz views.

reference; then we can set up time scales in exactly the same way in all inertial frames and compare what different observers have to say about the sequence of two events, A and B.

Suppose that the events occur at the same place in one particular frame of reference. We can have a clock at that place which registers the time of occurrence of each event. If the reading is the same for each event, we can logically regard the events as simultaneous. But what if the two events occur at different locations? Imagine now that there is a clock at the positions of each event—the clock at A being of the same nature as that at B, of course. These clocks can record the time of occurrence of the events but, before we can compare their readings, we must be sure that they are synchronized.

Some "obvious" methods of synchronizing clocks turn out to be erroneous. For example, we can set the two clocks so that they always read the same time *as seen by* observer A. This means that whenever A looks at the B clock it reads the same to him as his clock. The defect here is that if observer B uses the same criterion (that is, that the clocks are synchronized if they always read the same time to *him*), he will find that the clocks are *not* synchronized if A says that they *are*. For this method neglects the fact that it takes time for light to travel from B to A and vice versa. The student should be able to show that, if the distance between the clocks is L, one observer will see the other clock lag his by $2L/c$ when the other observer claims that they are synchronous. We certainly cannot have observers in the same reference frame disagree on whether clocks are synchronized or not, so we reject this method.

An apparent way out of this difficulty is simply to set the two clocks to read the same time and then move them to the positions where the events occur. (In principle, we need clocks everywhere in our reference frame to record the time of occurrence of events, but once we know how to synchronize two clocks we can, one by one, synchronize all the clocks.) The difficulty here is that we do not know ahead of time, and therefore cannot assume, that the motion of the clocks (which may have different velocities, accelerations, and path lengths in being moved into position) will not affect their readings or time-keeping ability. Even in classical physics, the motion can affect the rate at which clocks run.

Hence, the logical thing to do is to put our clocks into position and synchronize them by means of signals. If we had a method of transmitting signals with infinite speed, there would be no complications. The signals would go from clock A to clock B to clock C, and so on, in zero time. We could use such a signal to set all clocks at the same time reading. But no signal known has this property. All known signals require a finite time to travel some distance, the time increasing with the distance traveled. The best signal to choose would be one whose speed depends on as few factors as possible. We choose electromagnetic waves because they do not require a material medium for transmission and their speed in vacuum does not depend on their wavelength, amplitude, or direction of propagation. Furthermore, their propagation speed is the highest known and—most important for finding a universal method of synchronization—experiment shows their speed to be the same for all inertial observers.

Now we must account for the finite time of transmission of the signal and our clocks can be synchronized. To do this let us imagine an observer with a light source that can be turned on and off (e.g., a flash bulb) at each clock, A and B. Let the measured distance between the clocks (and observers) be L. The agreed-upon procedure for synchronization then is that A will turn on his light source when his clock reads $t = 0$ and observer B will set his clock to $t = L/c$ the instant he receives the signal. This accounts for the transmission time and synchronizes the clocks in a consistent way. For example, if B turns on his light source at some later time t by his clock, the signal will arrive at A at a time $t + L/c$, which is just what A's clock will read when A receives the signal.

A method equivalent to the above is to put a light source at the exact midpoint of the straight line connecting A and B and inform each observer to put his clock at $t = 0$ when the turned-on light signal reaches him. The light will take an equal amount of time to reach A and B from the midpoint, so that this procedure does indeed synchronize the clocks.

Now that we have a procedure for synchronizing clocks in one reference frame, we can judge the time order of events in that frame. The time of an event is measured by the clock whose location coincides with that of the event. Events occurring at two different places in that frame must be called *simultaneous* when the clocks at the respective places record the same time for them. Suppose that one inertial observer does find that two separated events are simultaneous. Will these same events be measured as simultaneous by an observer on another inertial frame which is moving with speed v with respect to the first? (Remember, each observer uses an identical procedure to synchronize the clocks in his

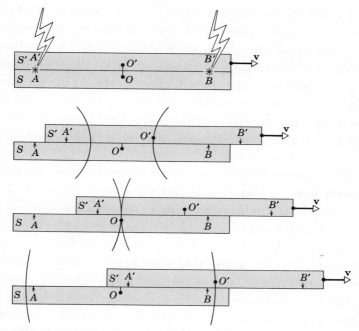

Fig. 2-1. The point of view of the *S*-frame, the *S'*-frame moving to the right. A light wave leaves *A*, *A'* and *B*, *B'* in (*a*). Successive drawings correspond to the assumption that event *AA'* and event *BB'* are simultaneous in the *S*-frame. In (*b*) one wavefront reaches *O'*. In (*c*) both wavefronts reach *O*. In (*d*) the other wavefront reaches *O'*.

reference frame.) If not, simultaneity is not independent of the frame of reference used to describe events. Instead of being absolute, simultaneity would be a relative concept. Indeed, this is exactly what we find to be true, in direct contradiction to the classical assumption.

To understand this, let us consider an example. Let there be two inertial reference frames *S'* and *S* having a relative velocity. Each frame has its own meter sticks and synchronized clocks. The observers note that two lightning bolts strike each, hitting and leaving permanent marks in the frames.* Assume that afterwards, by measurements, each inertial observer finds that he was located exactly at the midpoint of the marks which were left on his reference frame. In Fig. 2-1*a*, these marks are left at *A*, *B* on the *S*-frame and at *A'*, and *B'* on the *S'* frame, the observers

---

*The essential point is to have light sources that leave marks. Exploding sticks of dynamite would do as well, for example.

being at 0 and $0'$. Because each observer knows he was at the midpoint of the mark left by these events, he will conclude that they were simultaneous if the light signals from them arrive simultaneously at his clock (see the definitions of simultaneity given earlier). If, on the other hand, one signal arrives before the other, he will conclude that one event preceded the other. Since each observer has a synchronized set of clocks, he can conclude either that the clocks at the marks read the same time when the marks were made (simultaneous case) or that they read different times (non-simultaneous case).

Many different possibilities exist in principle as to what the measurements might show. Let us suppose, for the sake of argument, that the S-observer finds that the lightning bolts struck simultaneously. Will the S'-observer also find these events to be simultaneous? In Figs. 2-1b to 2-1d we take the point of view of the S-observer and see the S'-frame moving, say, to the right. At the instant the lightning struck at A and A', these two points coincide, and at the instant the lightning struck at B and B' those two points coincide. The S-observer found these two events to occur at the same instant, so that at that instant 0 and $0'$ must coincide also for him. However, *the light signals from the events take a finite time to reach 0 and during this time $0'$ travels to the right* (Figs. 2-1b to 2-1d). Hence, the signal from event BB' arrives at $0'$ (Fig. 2-1b) before it gets to 0 (Fig. 2-1c), whereas the signal from event AA' arrives at 0 (Fig. 2-1c) before it gets to $0'$ (Fig. 2-1d). Consistent with our starting assumption, the S-observer finds the events to be simultaneous (both signals arrive at 0 at the same instant). The S'-observer, however, finds that event BB' precedes event AA' in time; they are *not* simultaneous to him. Therefore, two separated events which are simultaneous with respect to one frame of reference are not necessarily simultaneous with respect to another frame.

Now we could have supposed, just as well, that the lightning bolts struck so that the S'-observer found them to be simultaneous. In that case the light signals reach $0'$ simultaneously, rather than 0. We show this in Fig. 2-2 where now we take the point of view of S'. The S-frame moves to the left relative to the S'-observer. But, in this case, the signals do not reach 0 simultaneously; the signal from event AA' reaches 0 before that from event BB'. Here the S'-observer finds the events to be simultaneous but the S-observer finds that event AA' precedes event BB'.

Hence, *neither* frame is preferred and the situation is perfectly recip-

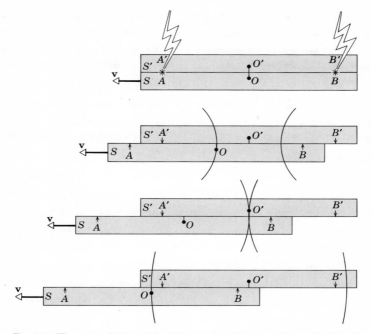

Fig. 2-2. The point of view of the S'-frame, the S-frame moving to the left. A light wave leaves A, A' and B, B' in (a). Successive drawings correspond to the assumption that event AA' and event BB' are simultaneous in S'-frame. In (b) one wavefront reaches O. In (c) both wavefronts reach O'. In (d) the other wavefront reaches O.

rocal. Simultaneity is genuinely a relative concept, not an absolute one.* Indeed, the two figures become indistinguishable if you turn one of them upside down. Neither observer can assert absolutely that he is at rest. Instead, each observer correctly states only that the other one is moving relative to him and that the signals travel with finite speed c relative to him. It should be clear that if we had an infinitely fast signal, then simultaneity *would* be an absolute concept; for the frames would not move at all relative to one another in the (zero) time it would take the signal to reach the observers.

Some other conclusions suggest themselves from the relativity of simultaneity. To measure the length of an object means to locate its end

---

*In these arguments, we have shown that *if* one observer finds the events to be simultaneous, *then* the other one will find them not to be simultaneous. Of course, it could also happen that neither observer finds the events to be simultaneous but then they would disagree either on the time order of the events or on the time interval elapsing between the events, or both (see Appendix A).

points simultaneously. Because simultaneity is a relative concept, length measurements will also depend on the reference frame and be relative. Furthermore, we find that the rates at which clocks run also depend on the reference frame. This can be illustrated as follows. Consider two clocks, one on a train and one on the ground, and assume that at the moment they pass one another (i.e., the instant that they are coincident) they read the same time (i.e., the hands of the clocks are in identical positions). Now, if the clocks continue to agree, we can say that they go at the same rate. But, when they are a great distance apart, we know from the preceding discussion that their hands cannot have identical positions simultaneously as measured both by the ground observer and the train observer. Hence, time interval measurements are also relative, that is, they depend on the reference frame of the observer. As a result of the relativity of length and time interval measurements it is perhaps possible to reconcile ourselves to the experimental fact that observers who are moving relative to each other measure the speed of light to be the same (see Question 20). In succeeding sections, we shall look more carefully into these matters.

2.2 *Derivation of the Lorentz Transformation Equations*

We have seen that the Galilean transformation equations must be replaced by new ones consistent with experiment. Here we shall derive these new equations, using the postulates of special relativity theory. To show the consistency of the theory with the discussion of the previous section, we shall then derive all the special features of the new transformation equations again from the more physical approach of the measurement processes discussed there.

We observe an event in one inertial reference frame S and characterize its location and time by specifying the coordinates x, y, z, t of the event. In a second inertial frame S', this *same event* is recorded as the space-time coordinates x', y', z', t'. We now seek the functional relationships $x' = x'(x,y,z,t)$, $y' = y'(x,y,z,t)$, $z' = z'(x,y,z,t)$, and $t' = t'(x,y,z,t)$. That is, we want the equations of transformation which relate one observer's space-time coordinates of an event with the other observer's coordinates of the same event.

We shall use the fundamental postulates of relativity theory and, in addition, the assumption that space and time are homogeneous. This homogeneity assumption (which can be paraphrased by saying that all points in space and time are equivalent) means, for example, that the results of a measurement of a length or time interval of a specific event should not depend on where or when the interval happens to be in our reference frame. We shall illustrate its application shortly.

We can simplify the algebra by choosing the relative velocity of the S and S' frames to be along a common x-x' axis and by keeping corresponding planes parallel (see Fig. 1-1). This does not impose any fundamental restrictions on our results for space is isotropic—that is, has the same properties in all directions. Also, at the instant the origins 0 and $0'$ coincide, we let the clocks there read $t = 0$ and $t' = 0$, respectively. Now, as explained below, the homogeneity assumption requires that transformation equations must be linear (i.e., they involve only the first power in the variables), so that the most general form they can take (see Question 5) is

$$
\begin{aligned}
x' &= a_{11}x + a_{12}y + a_{13}z + a_{14}t \\
y' &= a_{21}x + a_{22}y + a_{23}z + a_{24}t \\
z' &= a_{31}x + a_{32}y + a_{33}z + a_{34}t \\
t' &= a_{41}x + a_{42}y + a_{43}z + a_{44}t.
\end{aligned}
\tag{2-1}
$$

Here, the subscripted coefficients are constants that we must determine to obtain the exact transformation equations. Notice that we do not exclude the possible dependence of space and time coordinates upon one another.

If the equations were not linear, we would violate the homogeneity assumption. For example, suppose that x' depended on the square of x, that is, as $x' = a_{11}x^2$. Then the distance between two points in the primed frame would be related to the location of these points in the unprimed frame by $x_2' - x_1' = a_{11}(x_2^2 - x_1^2)$. Suppose now that a rod of unit length in S had its end points at $x_2 = 2$ and $x_1 = 1$; then $x_2' - x_1' = 3a_{11}$. If, instead, the same rod happens to be located at $x_2 = 5$ and $x_1 = 4$, we would obtain $x_2' - x_1' = 9a_{11}$. That is, the measured length of the rod would depend on where it is in space. Likewise, we can reject any dependence on t that is not linear, for the time interval of an event should not depend on the numerical setting of the hands of the observer's clock. The relationships must be linear then in order not to give the choice of origin of our space-time coordinates (or some other point) a physical preference over all other points.

Now, regarding these sixteen coefficients, it is expected that their values will depend on the relative velocity v of the two inertial frames. For example, if $v = 0$, then the two frames coincide at all times and we expect $a_{11} = a_{22} = a_{33} = a_{44} = 1$, all other coefficients being zero. More generally, if v is small compared to c, the coefficients should lead to the (classical) Galilean transformation equations. We seek to find the coefficients for *any* value of v, that is, as functions of v.

How then do we determine the values of these sixteen coefficients? Basically, we use the postulates of relativity, namely (1) The Principle of Relativity—that no preferred inertial system exists, the laws of physics being the same in all inertial systems—and (2) The Principle of the Constancy of the Speed of Light—that the speed of light in free space has the same value c in all inertial systems. Let us proceed.

The x-axis coincides continuously with the x'-axis. This will be so only if for $y = 0$, $z = 0$ (which characterizes points on the x-axis) it always follows that $y' = 0$, $z' = 0$ (which characterizes points on the x'-axis). Hence, the transformation formulas for y and z must be of the form

$$y' = a_{22}y + a_{23}z \quad \text{and} \quad z' = a_{32}y + a_{33}z$$

That is, the coefficients a_{21}, a_{24}, a_{31}, and a_{34} must be zero. Likewise, the x-y plane (which is characterized by $z = 0$) should transform over to the x'-y' plane (which is characterized by $z' = 0$); similarly, for the x-z and x'-z' planes, $y = 0$ should give $y' = 0$. Hence, it follows that a_{23} and a_{32} are zero so that

$$y' = a_{22}y \quad \text{and} \quad z' = a_{33}z.$$

These remaining constant coefficients, a_{22} and a_{33}, can be evaluated using the relativity postulate. We illustrate for a_{22}. Suppose that we have a rod lying along the y-axis, measured by S to be of unit length. According to the S' observer, the rod's length will be a_{22}, (i.e., $y' = a_{22} \times 1$). Now, suppose that the very same rod is brought to rest along the y' axis of the S'-frame. The primed observer must measure the same length (unity) for this rod when it is at rest in his frame as the unprimed observer measures when the rod is at rest with respect to him; otherwise there would be an asymmetry in the frames. In this case, however, the S-observer would measure the rod's length to be $1/a_{22}$ [i.e., $y = (1/a_{22})y' = (1/a_{22}) \times 1$]. Now, because of the reciprocal nature of these length measurements, the first postulate requires that these measurements be identical, for otherwise the frames would not be equivalent physically. Hence, we must have $a_{22} = 1/a_{22}$ or $a_{22} = 1$. The argument is identical in determining that $a_{33} = 1$. Therefore, our two middle transformation equations become

$$y' = y \quad \text{and} \quad z' = z. \tag{2-2}$$

There remain transformation equations for x' and t', namely,

$$x' = a_{11}x + a_{12}y + a_{13}z + a_{14}t$$
and
$$t' = a_{41}x + a_{42}y + a_{43}z + a_{44}t.$$

Let us look first at the t'-equation. For reasons of symmetry, we assume that t' does not depend on y and z. Otherwise, clocks placed symmetrically in the y-z plane (such as at $+y$, $-y$ or $+z$, $-z$) about the x-axis would appear to disagree as observed from S', which would contradict the isotropy of space. Hence, $a_{42} = a_{43} = 0$. As for the x'-equation, we know that a point having $x' = 0$ appears to move in the direction of the positive x-axis with speed v, so that the statement $x' = 0$ must be identical to the statement $x = vt$. Therefore, we expect $x' = a_{11}(x - vt)$ to be the correct transformation equation. (That is, $x = vt$ always gives $x' = 0$ in this equation.) Hence, $x' = a_{11} x - a_{11} vt = a_{11} x + a_{14} t$. This gives us $a_{14} = -va_{11}$, and our four equations have now been reduced to

$$\begin{aligned} x' &= a_{11}(x - vt) \\ y' &= y \\ z' &= z \\ t' &= a_{41}x + a_{44}t. \end{aligned} \tag{2-3}$$

There remains the task of determining the three coefficients a_{11}, a_{41}, and a_{44}. To do this, we use the principle of the constancy of the velocity of light. Let us assume that at the time $t = 0$ a spherical electromagnetic wave leaves the origin of S, which coincides with the origin of S' at that moment. The wave propagates with a speed c in all directions in each inertial frame. Its progress, then, is described by the equation of sphere whose radius expands with time at a rate c in terms of either the primed or unprimed set of coordinates. That is,

$$x^2 + y^2 + z^2 = c^2t^2 \tag{2-4}$$
or
$$x'^2 + y'^2 + z'^2 = c^2t'^2. \tag{2-5}$$

If now we substitute into Eq. 2-5 the transformation equations (Eqs. 2-3), we get

$$a_{11}^2(x - vt)^2 + y^2 + z^2 = c^2(a_{41}x + a_{44}t)^2.$$

Rearranging the terms gives us

$$(a_{11}^2 - c^2 a_{41}^2)x^2 + y^2 + z^2 - 2(va_{11}^2 + c^2 a_{41}a_{44})xt$$
$$= (c^2 a_{44}^2 - v^2 a_{11}^2)t^2.$$

In order for this expression to agree with Eq. 2-4, which represents the same thing, we must have

$$c^2 a_{44}^2 - v^2 a_{11}^2 = c^2$$
$$a_{11}^2 - c^2 a_{41}^2 = 1$$
$$va_{11}^2 + c^2 a_{41}a_{44} = 0.$$

Here we have three equations in three unknowns, whose solution (as the student can verify by substitution into the three equations above) is

$$a_{44} = 1/\sqrt{1 - v^2/c^2}$$
$$a_{11} = 1/\sqrt{1 - v^2/c^2} \tag{2-6}$$

and
$$a_{41} = -\frac{v}{c^2}/\sqrt{1 - v^2/c^2}.$$

By substituting these values into Eqs. 2-3, we obtain, finally, the new sought-after transformation equations,

$$x' = \frac{x - vt}{\sqrt{1 - v^2/c^2}}$$

$$y' = y$$
$$z' = z \tag{2-7}$$

$$t' = \frac{t - (v/c^2)x}{\sqrt{1 - v^2/c^2}},$$

the so-called* *Lorentz transformation equations.*

Before probing the meaning of these equations, we should put them to two necessary tests. First, if we were to exchange our frames of reference or—what amounts to the same thing—consider the given space-time coordinates of the event to be those observed in S' rather than in

---

*Poincaré originally gave this name to the equations. Lorentz, in his classical theory of electrons, had proposed them before Einstein did. However, Lorentz took v to be the speed relative to an absolute ether frame and gave a different interpretation to the equations.

S, the only change allowed by the relativity principle is the physical one of a change in relative velocity from v to $-v$. That is, from S' the S-frame moves to the left whereas from S the S'-frame moves to the right. When we solve Eqs. 2-7 for x, y, z, and t in terms of the primed coordinates (see Problem 3), we obtain

$$x = \frac{x' + vt'}{\sqrt{1 - v^2/c^2}},$$

$$y = y',$$

$$z = z', \tag{2-8}$$

$$t = \frac{t' + (v/c^2)x'}{\sqrt{1 - v^2/c^2}}$$

which are identical in form with Eqs. 2-7 except that, as required, v changes to $-v$.

Another requirement is that for speeds small compared to c, that is, for $v/c \ll 1$, the Lorentz equations should reduce to the (approximately) correct Galilean transformation equations. This is the case, for when $v/c \ll 1$, Eqs. 2-7 become*

$$x' = x - vt$$
$$y' = y$$
$$z' = z \tag{2-9}$$
$$t' = t$$

which are the classical Galilean transformation equations.

In Table 2-1 we summarize the Lorentz transformation equations.

TABLE **2-1**   THE LORENTZ TRANSFORMATION EQUATIONS

$x' = \dfrac{x - vt}{\sqrt{1 - v^2/c^2}}$	$x = \dfrac{x' + vt'}{\sqrt{1 - v^2/c^2}}$
$y' = y$	$y = y'$
$z' = z$	$z = z'$
$t' = \dfrac{t - (v/c^2)x}{\sqrt{1 - v^2/c^2}}$	$t = \dfrac{t' + (v/c^2)x'}{\sqrt{1 - v^2/c^2}}$

*In the time equation, $t' = (t - vx/c^2)/\sqrt{1 - v^2/c^2}$, consider the motion of the origin O', for example, given by $x = vt$. Then

$$t' = (t - v^2t/c^2)/\sqrt{1 - v^2/c^2} = t\sqrt{1 - v^2/c^2}.$$

As $v/c \to 0$, $t' \to t$.

2.3   *Some Consequences of the Lorentz Transformation Equations*

The Lorentz transformation equations (Eqs. 2-7 and 2-8), derived rather formally in the last section from the relativity postulates, have some interesting consequences for length and time measurements. We shall look at them briefly in this section. In the next section we shall present a more physical interpretation of these equations and their consequences, relating them directly to the operations of physical measurement. Throughout the chapter we shall cite experiments that confirm these consequences.

One consequence is this: *a body's length is measured to be greatest when it is at rest relative to the observer. When it moves with a velocity v relative to the observer its measured length is contracted in the direction of its motion by the factor $\sqrt{1 - v^2/c^2}$, whereas its dimensions perpendicular to the direction of motion are unaffected.* To prove the italicized statement, imagine a rod lying at rest along the x'-axis of the S'-frame. Its end points are measured to be at x_2' and x_1', so that its rest length is $x_2' - x_1'$. What is the rod's length as measured by the S-frame observer, for whom the rod moves with the relative speed v? For convenience, we shall let $v/c = \beta$, as before. From the first Lorentz equation we have

$$x_2' = \frac{x_2 - vt_2}{\sqrt{1 - \beta^2}} \qquad x_1' = \frac{x_1 - vt_1}{\sqrt{1 - \beta^2}}$$

so that
$$x_2' - x_1' = \frac{(x_2 - x_1) - v(t_2 - t_1)}{\sqrt{1 - \beta^2}}.$$

Now the length of the rod in the S-frame is simply the distance between the end points, x_2 and x_1, of the moving rod measured at the same instant in that frame. Hence, with $t_2 = t_1$, we obtain

$$x_2' - x_1' = \frac{x_2 - x_1}{\sqrt{1 - \beta^2}}$$

or
$$x_2 - x_1 = (x_2' - x_1')\sqrt{1 - \beta^2} \tag{2-10}$$

so that the measured length of the moving rod, $x_2 - x_1$, is contracted by the factor $\sqrt{1 - \beta^2}$ from its rest length, $x_2' - x_1'$. As for the dimensions of the rod along y and z, perpendicular to the relative motion, it follows at once from the transformation equations $y' = y$ and $z' = z$ that these are measured to be the same by both observers.

A second consequence is this: *A clock is measured to go at its fastest rate when it is at rest relative to the observer. When it moves with a velocity v relative to the observer, its rate is measured to have slowed down by a factor* $\sqrt{1 - v^2/c^2}$. To prove these italicized statements, consider a clock to be at rest at the position x' in the S'-frame. It may simplify matters to picture the hand of this clock going around and to let unit time be the time it takes the hand of the clock to go around once. Hence, the events we observe (the two successive coincidences of the hand of the clock with a given marker on the face of the clock) span the time interval t' to $t' + 1$ in the primed coordinates. The S-frame observer records these events as occurring at times

$$t_1 = \frac{t' + (v/c^2)x'}{\sqrt{1 - \beta^2}} \qquad \text{and} \qquad t_2 = \frac{(t' + 1) + (v/c^2)x'}{\sqrt{1 - \beta^2}}.$$

The clock in the S'-frame is at a fixed position x', but the time t_1 and t_2 are read from two different clocks in the S-frame, namely the stationary S-clock that happens to be coincident with the moving clock at the beginning of the interval, and the stationary S-clock coincident with the moving clock at the end of the interval. These clocks are synchronized, however, so that the time interval they record for the event is simply

$$t_2 - t_1 = \frac{1}{\sqrt{1 - \beta^2}}.$$

Clearly, if, instead of unit time, the S'-clock recorded a time interval $t_2' - t_1'$, the S-clock would have recorded the corresponding interval

$$t_2 - t_1 = \frac{t_2' - t_1'}{\sqrt{1 - \beta^2}}. \tag{2-11}$$

Hence, unit time measured on the S'-clock is recorded as a *longer* time on the S-clocks. From the point of view of observer S, the moving S'-clock appears slowed down, that is, it appears to run at a rate which is slow by the factor $\sqrt{1 - \beta^2}$. This result applies to all S'-clocks observed from S, for the location x' in our proof was arbitrary.

It is common in relativity to speak of the frame in which the observed body is at rest as the *proper frame*. The length of a rod in such a frame is then called the *proper length*. Likewise, the *proper time interval* is the time interval recorded by a clock attached to the observed body. The proper time interval can be thought of equivalently as the time interval between two events occurring at the same place in the S'-frame or the time interval measured by a single clock at one place. A nonproper (or improper) time interval would be a time interval measured by two different clocks at two different places. Thus, we see from the previous discussion that if $d\tau$ represents a proper time interval, then the expression

$$dt = \frac{d\tau}{\sqrt{1 - \beta^2}} \qquad (2\text{-}12)$$

relates the nonproper interval dt to the proper interval $d\tau$. Later we shall define other proper quantities, such as proper mass, and shall find that they represent invariant quantities in relativity theory.

A third consequence of the Lorentz transformation equations is this: Although clocks in a moving frame all appear to go at the same slow rate when observed from a stationary frame with respect to which the clocks move, the *moving clocks appear to differ from one another in their readings by a phase constant which depends on their location*, that is, *they appear to be unsynchronized*. This becomes evident at once from the transformation equation

$$t = \frac{t' + (v/c^2)x'}{\sqrt{1 - \beta^2}}.$$

For consider an instant of time in the S-frame, that is, a given value of t. Then, to satisfy this equation, $t' + (v/c^2)x'$ must have a definite fixed value. This means the greater is x' (i.e., the farther away an S'-clock is stationed on the x'-axis) the smaller is t' (i.e., the further behind in time its reading appears to be). Hence, the moving clocks appear to be out of phase, or synchronization, with one another. We shall see in the next section that this is just another manifestation of the fact that two events that occur simultaneously in the S-frame are not, in general, measured to be simultaneous in the S'-frame, and vice versa.

All the results of this section are reciprocal. That is, no matter which frame we take as the proper frame, the observer in the other frame measures a contracted length and dilated (expanded) time interval and finds the moving clocks to be out of synchronization.

◆ *Example* 1. The factor $\sqrt{1 - \beta^2}$ occurs in Eq. 2-10 and the factor $\gamma = 1/\sqrt{1 - \beta^2}$ in Eq. 2-12. Because they arise frequently in relativity, it is helpful to be able to estimate their values as a function of β. Compute $\sqrt{1 - \beta^2}$ and $\gamma = 1/\sqrt{1 - \beta^2}$ for $\beta = v/c = 0.100, 0.300, 0.600, 0.800, 0.900, 0.950,$

and 0.990, and plot them as functions of β.
We find

$\beta =$	0.100	0.300	0.600	0.800	0.900	0.950	0.990
$\sqrt{1-\beta^2} =$	0.995	0.954	0.800	0.600	0.436	0.312	0.141
$1/\sqrt{1-\beta^2} =$	1.005	1.048	1.250	1.667	2.294	3.205	7.092

These factors are plotted as a function of β in Fig. 2-3.

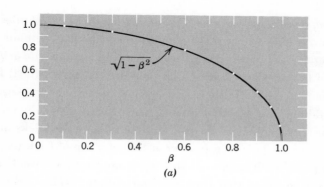

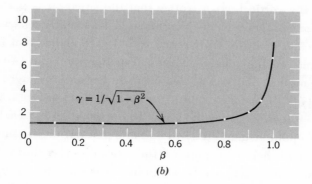

Fig. 2-3. (a) A plot of $\sqrt{1-\beta^2}$ as a function of β. (b) A plot of $\gamma = 1/\sqrt{1-\beta^2}$ as a function of β.

2.4 *A More Physical Look at the Main Features of the Lorentz Transformation Equations*

The main distinguishing features of the Lorentz transformation equations are these: (A) Lengths perpendicular to the relative motion are measured to be the same in both frames; (B) the time interval indicated on a clock is measured to be longer by an observer for whom the clock is moving than by one at rest with respect to the clock; (C) lengths parallel to the relative motion are measured to be contracted compared to the rest lengths by the observer for whom the measured bodies are moving; and (D) two clocks, which are synchronized and separated in one inertial frame, are observed to be out of synchronism from another inertial frame. Here we rederive these features one at a time by thought experiments which focus on the measuring process.

(A) *Comparison of Lengths Perpendicular to the Relative Motion.* Imagine two frames whose relative motion is v along a common x-x' axis. In each frame an observer has a stick extending up from the origin along his vertical (y and y') axis, which he measures to have a (rest) length of exactly one meter, say. As these observers approach and pass each other, we wish to determine whether or not, when the origins coincide, the top ends of the sticks coincide. We can arrange to have the sticks mark each other permanently by a thin pointer at the very top of each (e.g., a razor blade or a paintbrush bristle) as they pass one another. (We displace the sticks very slightly so that they will not collide, always keeping them parallel to the vertical axis.) Notice that the situation is perfectly symmetrical. Each observer claims that his stick is a meter long, each sees the other approach with the same speed v, and each claims that his stick is perpendicular to the relative motion. Furthermore, the two observers must agree on the result of the measurement because they agree upon the simultaneity of the measurements (the measurement occurs at the instant the origins coincide). After the sticks have passed, either each observer will find his pointer marked by the other's pointer, or else one observer will find a mark below his pointer, the other observer finding no mark. That is, either the sticks are found to have the same length by both observers, or else there is an absolute result, agreed upon by both observers, that one and the same stick is shorter than the other. That each observer finds the other stick to be the *same* length as his follows at once from the contradiction any other result would indicate with the relativity principle. Suppose, for example, that observer S finds that the S'-stick has left a mark (below his pointer) on his stick. He concludes that the S'-stick is shorter than his. This is an absolute result, for the S' observer will find no mark on his stick and will conclude also that his stick is shorter. If, instead, the mark was left on the S'-stick, then each observer would conclude that the S-stick is the shorter one. In either case, this would give us a physical basis for preferring one frame over another, for although all the conditions are symmetrical, the results would be unsymmetrical—a result that contradicts the principle of relativity. That is, the laws of physics would not be the same in each inertial frame. We would have a property for detecting absolute motion, in this case; a shrinking stick would mean absolute motion in one direction and a stretching stick would mean absolute motion in the other direction. Hence, to conform to the relativity postulate, we conclude that the length of a body (or space interval) transverse to the relative motion is measured to be the same by all inertial observers.

(B) *Comparison of Time-Interval Measurements.* A simple experiment which reveals in a direct way the quantitative relation connecting the time interval between two events as measured from two different inertial frames is the following. Imagine a passenger sitting on a train that moves with uniform velocity v with respect to the ground. The experiment will consist of turning on a flashlight aimed at a mirror directly above on the ceiling and measuring the time it takes the light to travel up and be reflected back down to its starting point. The situation is illustrated in Fig. 2-4. The passenger, who has a wrist watch, say, sees the light ray follow a strictly vertical path (Fig. 2-4a) from A to B to C and times the event by his clock (watch). This is a proper time interval, measured by a single clock at one place, the departure and arrival of the light ray occurring at the same place in the passenger's (S') frame. Another observer, fixed to the ground (S) frame, sees the train and passenger move to the right during this interval. He will measure the time interval from the readings on two stationary clocks, one at the position the experiment began (turning-on of flashlight) and a second at the position the experiment ended (arrival of light to flashlight). Hence, he compares the reading of one moving clock (the passenger's watch) to the readings on two stationary clocks. For the S-observer, the light ray follows the oblique path shown in Fig. 2-4c. Thus, the observer on the ground measures the light to travel a greater distance than does the passenger (we have already seen that the transverse distance is the same for each observer). Because the speed of light is the same in both frames, the ground observer sees more time elapse between the departure and the return of the ray of

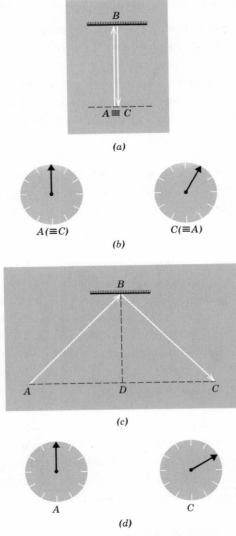

Fig. 2-4. (a) The path of a light ray as seen by a passenger in the S' frame. B is a mirror on the ceiling, A and C are the *same* point, namely, the bulb of the flashlight, in this frame. (b) The readings on the passenger's clock at the start and end of the event, showing the time interval on *one moving clock* (S' frame). (c) The path of a light ray as seen by a ground observer (S-frame). A and C are the *different locations* of the flashlight bulb at the start and the end of the event, as the train moves to the right with speed v, in this frame. (d) Readings on the *two stationary* (synchronized) *clocks* located at the start (A) of the event and the end (C) of the event (S-frame).

light than does the passenger. He concludes that the passenger's clock runs slow (see Fig. 2-4b and 2-4d). The quantitative result follows at once from the Pythagorean theorem, for

$$\Delta t' = \frac{2BD}{c} \qquad \Delta t = \frac{AB + BC}{c};$$

but

$$(BD)^2 = (AB)^2 - (AD)^2 = (BC)^2 - (DC)^2$$

so that

$$\frac{\Delta t'}{\Delta t} = \frac{2BD}{AB + BC} = \frac{2\sqrt{(AB)^2 - (AD)^2}}{2AB}$$
$$= \sqrt{1 - \left(\frac{AD}{AB}\right)^2} = \sqrt{1 - \frac{v^2}{c^2}}. \tag{2-13}$$

Here AD is the horizontal distance travelled at speed v during the time the light travelled with speed c along the hypotenuse. This result is identical to Eqs. 2-11 and 2-12, derived earlier in a more formal way.

(C) *Comparison of Lengths Parallel to the Relative Motion.* The simplest deduction of the length contraction uses the time dilation result just obtained and shows directly that length contraction is a necessary consequence of time dilation. Imagine, for example, that two different inertial observers, one sitting on a train moving through a station with uniform velocity v and the other at rest in the station, want to measure the length of the station's platform. The ground observer measures the length to be L and claims that the passenger covered this distance in a time L/v. This time, Δt, is a nonproper time, for the events observed (passenger passes back end of platform, passenger passes front end of platform) occur at two different places in the ground (S) frame and are timed by two different clocks. The passenger, however, observes the platform approach and recede and finds the two events to occur at the same place in his (S') frame. That is, his clock (wrist watch, say) is located at each event as it occurs. He measures a proper-time interval $\Delta t'$, which, as we have just seen (Eq. 2-13), is related to Δt by $\Delta t' = \Delta t \sqrt{1 - v^2/c^2}$. But $\Delta t = L/v$ so that $\Delta t' = L\sqrt{1 - v^2/c^2}/v$. The passenger claims that the platform moves with the same speed v relative to him so that he would measure the distance from back to front of the platform at $v\Delta t'$. Hence, the length of the platform to him is $L' = v\Delta t' =$

$L\sqrt{1 - v^2/c^2}$. This is the length-contraction result, namely, that a body of rest length L is measured to have a length $L\sqrt{1 - v^2/c^2}$ parallel to the relative motion in a frame in which the body moves with speed v.

Another deduction of the length contraction, although somewhat more involved, is directly related to an interpretation of the Michelson-Morley experiment. Consider a rod at rest in the S' frame and call its (rest) length there L'. (Notice that in this example the rod is at rest in S' whereas, in the previous example, the platform was at rest in S. Since in relativity the laws must be independent of the reference frame used, we should still find the same physical result—that is, the observer who sees the rod move should get a shorter length than the rest length. We shall see that the S-observer measures the shorter length in this example, consistent with the relativity principle.) We put a flashbulb at one end of the rod and a mirror at the other end (see Fig. 2-5a). The S'-observer measures the time it takes a light flash to go down and be reflected back to the bulb. This time interval, $\Delta t' = 2L'/c$, is a proper one for it is measured by a single clock at one point. How is this same sequence of events seen from the S-frame? (We can regard the S-frame as the historical ether frame through which the Michelson interferometer, the S'-frame, moves with speed v.) During the time the light pulse goes down and back, the rod moves to the right (Fig. 2-5b). Let us calculate the time (Δt_1) the pulse

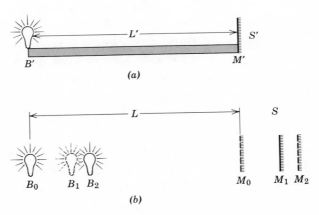

Fig. 2-5. (a) A rod is at rest in the S' frame. A bulb B' is at one end and a mirror M' at the other end of a rod of length L'. (b) Successive positions of the bulb and mirror in the S-frame as the light pulse leaves B_0 and is reflected from M_1 back to B_2 during the motion of the rod of length L to the right with speed v.

takes to reach the mirror. The light pulse must travel not only the distance L (the length of the rod in S) but also the distance $v\,\Delta t_1$ that the mirror has moved to the right during this time. Since the velocity of light is also c in this frame, we have $\Delta t_1 = (L + v\,\Delta t_1)/c$ or $\Delta t_1 = L/(c - v)$. Now, let us calculate the time Δt_2 it takes the pulse to return from the mirror to the bulb. In this case the light pulse travels less than the distance L by the amount the bulb has moved to the right during this time. Thus, $\Delta t_2 = (L - v\,\Delta t_2)/c$ or $\Delta t_2 = L/(c + v)$. The total time down and back, measured by S, is therefore

$$\Delta t = \Delta t_1 + \Delta t_2 = \frac{L}{c - v} + \frac{L}{c + v} = \frac{2cL}{c^2 - v^2} = \frac{(2L/c)}{(1 - v^2/c^2)}.$$

This time interval is a nonproper one for it is measured by two clocks at two different places in S (at B_0 and B_2). The relation between the proper and nonproper time interval of the same two events (the sending and receiving of the light flash) is given by Eq. 2-13, $\Delta t' = \Delta t\sqrt{1 - v^2/c^2}$. If we substitute for $\Delta t'$ its value $2L'/c$ and for Δt its value

$$\frac{2L/c}{1 - v^2/c^2},$$

we obtain

$$\frac{2L'}{c} = \frac{2L}{c}\frac{\sqrt{1 - v^2/c^2}}{(1 - v^2/c^2)},$$

from which it follows that

$$L = L'\sqrt{1 - v^2/c^2}. \tag{2-14}$$

The rod of rest length L' is found to have a length $L'\sqrt{1 - v^2/c^2}$ parallel to the relative motion in a frame in which the rod moves with speed v.

(D) *The Phase Difference in the Synchronization of Clocks.* The student will recall that the Lorentz transformation equation for the time (see Eqs. 2-7 and 2-8) can be written as

$$t = \frac{t' + (v/c^2)x'}{\sqrt{1 - v^2/c^2}}.$$

Here we wish to give a physical interpretation of the vx'/c^2 term, which we call the *phase difference*. We shall synchronize two clocks in one

frame and examine what an observer in another frame concludes about
the process.

Imagine that we have two clocks, A and B, at rest in the S'-frame.
Their separation is L' in this frame. We set off a flashbulb, which is at
the exact midpoint, and instruct observers at the clocks to set them to
read $t' = 0$ when the light reaches them (see Fig. 2-6a). This is an agreed-
upon procedure for synchronizing two separated clocks (see Section 2-1).
We now look at this synchronization process as seen by an observer in
the S-frame, for whom the clocks A and B move to the right (see Fig.
2-6b) with speed v.

To the S-observer, the separation of the clocks will be $L'\sqrt{1 - v^2/c^2}$.
He observes the following sequence of events. The flash goes off and
leaves the midpoint traveling in all directions with a speed c. As the
wavefront expands at the rate c, the clocks move to the right at the rate

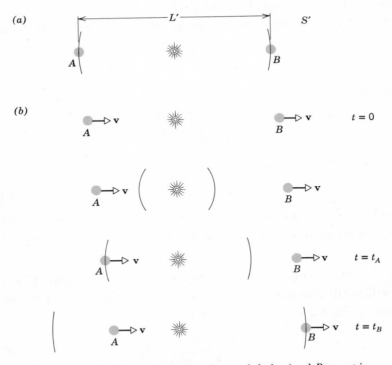

Fig. 2-6. (a) A flash sent from the midpoint of clocks A and B, at rest in
the S'-frame a distance L' apart, arrives simultaneously at A and B. (b) The
sequence of events as seen from the S-frame, in which the clocks are a distance L apart and move to the right with speed v.

v. Clock *A* intercepts the flash first, before *B*, and the *A* observer sets his clock at $t' = 0$ (third picture in sequence). Hence, as far as the *S*-observer is concerned, *A* sets his clock to zero time *before B* does and the setting of the primed clocks does not appear simultaneous to the unprimed observer. Here again we see the relativity of simultaneity; that is, the clocks in the primed frame are *not* synchronized according to the unprimed observer, who uses exactly the same procedure to synchronize his clocks.

By how much do the *S'*-clocks differ in their readings according to the *S*-observer? Let $t = 0$ be the time *S* sees the flash go off. Then, when the light pulse meets clock *A*, at $t = t_A$, we have

$$ct_A = (L'/2) \sqrt{1 - v^2/c^2} - vt_A.$$

That is, the distance the pulse travels to meet *A* is less than their initial separation by the distance *A* travels to the right during this time. When the light pulse later meets clock *B* (fourth picture in sequence), at $t = t_B$, we have $ct_B = (L'/2) \sqrt{1 - v^2/c^2} + vt_B$. The distance the pulse travels to meet *B* is greater than their initial separation by the distance *B* travels to the right during this time. As measured by the clocks in *S*, therefore, the time interval between the setting of the primed clocks is

$$\Delta t = t_B - t_A = \frac{L' \sqrt{1 - v^2/c^2}/2}{c - v} - \frac{L' \sqrt{1 - v^2/c^2}/2}{c + v}$$

or

$$\Delta t = \frac{L'v \sqrt{1 - v^2/c^2}}{c^2 - v^2}.$$

During this interval, however, *S* observes clock *A* to run slow by the factor $\sqrt{1 - v^2/c^2}$ (for "moving clocks run slow") so that to observer *S* it will read

$$\Delta t' = \Delta t \sqrt{1 - v^2/c^2} = \frac{L'v(1 - v^2/c^2)}{c^2 - v^2} = \frac{L'v}{c^2}$$

when clock *B* is set to read $t' = 0$.

The result is that the *S*-observer finds the *S'* clocks to be out of synchronization, with clock *A* reading *ahead* in time by an amount $L'v/c^2$. The greater the separation L' of the clocks in the primed frame, the further behind in time is the reading of the *B* clock as observed at a given instant from the unprimed frame. This is in exact agreement with the Lorentz transformation equation for the time.

Hence, all the features of the Lorentz transformation equations, which we derived in a formal way directly from the postulates of relativity in Section 2-2, can be derived more physically from the measurement processes which were, of course, chosen originally to be consistent with those postulates.

▶ *Example* 2. Why is the fact that simultaneity is not an absolute concept an unexpected result? It is because the speed of light has such a large value compared to ordinary speeds. Consider these two cases, which are symmetrical in terms of an interchange of the space and time coordinates. *Case 1: S′* observes that two events occur at the same place but are separated in time; S will then declare that the two events occur in different places. *Case 2: S′* observes that two events occur at the same time but are separated in space; S will then declare that the two events occur at different times.

Case 1 is readily acceptable on the basis of daily experience. If a man (S′) on a moving train lights two cigarettes, one ten minutes after the other, then these events occur at the same place on *his* reference frame (the train). A ground observer (S), however, would assert that these same events occur at different places in *his* reference system (the ground). Case 2, although true, cannot be easily supported on the basis of daily experience. Suppose that S′, seated at the center of a moving railroad car, observes that two men, one at each end of the car, light cigarettes simultaneously. The ground observer S, watching the railroad car go by, would assert (if he could make precise enough measurements) that the man in the back of the car lit his cigarette a little before the man in the front of the car lit his. The fact that the speed of light is so high compared to the speeds of familiar large objects makes Case 2 less intuitively reasonable than Case 1, as we now show.

(*a*) In Case 1, assume that the time separation in S′ is 10 minutes; what is the distance separation observed by S? (*b*) In Case 2, assume that the distance separation in S′ is 25 meters; what is the time separation observed by S? Take $v = 20.0$ m/sec which corresponds to 45 mi/hr or $\beta = v/c = 6.6 \times 10^{-8}$.

(*a*) From Eqs. 2-8 we have

$$x_2 - x_1 = \frac{x_2' - x_1'}{\sqrt{1 - \beta^2}} + \frac{v(t_2' - t_1')}{\sqrt{1 - \beta^2}}.$$

We are given that $x_2' = x_1'$ and $t_2' - t_1' = 10$ minutes, so that

$$x_2 - x_1 = \frac{(20.0 \text{ m/sec})(10 \text{ min})}{\sqrt{1 - (6.6 \times 10^{-8})^2}} = 12000 \text{ m} = 12 \text{ km}.$$

This result is readily accepted. Because the denominator above is unity for all practical purposes, the result is even numerically what we would expect from the Galilean equations.

(b) From Eqs. 2-8 we have

$$t_2 - t_1 = \frac{t_2' - t_1'}{\sqrt{1 - \beta^2}} + \frac{(v/c^2)(x_2' - x_1')}{\sqrt{1 - \beta^2}}.$$

We are given that $t_2' = t_1'$ and that $x_2' - x_1' = 25$ m, so that

$$t_2 - t_1 = \frac{[(20 \text{ m/sec})/(3.0 \times 10^8 \text{ m/sec})^2](25 \text{ m})}{\sqrt{1 - (6.6 \times 10^{-8})^2}} = 5.6 \times 10^{-15} \text{ sec}.$$

The result is *not* zero, a value that would have been expected by classical physics, but the time interval is so short that it would be very hard to show experimentally that it really was not zero.

If we compare the expressions for $x_2 - x_1$ and for $t_2 - t_1$ above, we see that, whereas v appears as a factor in the second term of the former, v/c^2 appears in the latter. Thus the relatively high value of c puts Case 1 within the bounds of familiar experience but puts Case 2 out of these bounds.

In the following example we consider the realm wherein relativistic effects are easily observable.

Example 3. Among the particles of high-energy physics are charged pions, particles of mass between that of the electron and the proton and of positive or negative electronic charge. They can be produced by bombarding a suitable target in an accelerator with high-energy protons, the pions leaving the target with speeds close to that of light. It is found that the pions are radioactive and, when they are brought to rest, their half-life is measured to be 1.77×10^{-8} secs. That is, half of the number present at any time have decayed 1.77×10^{-8} sec later. A collimated pion beam, leaving the accelerator target at a speed of $0.99c$, is found to drop to half its original intensity 39 m from the target.

(a) Are these results consistent?

If we take the half-life to be 1.77×10^{-8} sec and the speed to be 2.97×10^8 m/sec ($=0.99c$), the distance traveled over which half the pions in the beam should decay is

$$d = vt = 2.97 \times 10^8 \text{ m/sec} \times 1.77 \times 10^{-8} \text{ sec} = 5.3 \text{ m}.$$

This appears to contradict the direct measurement of 39 m.

(b) Show how the time dilation accounts for the measurements.

If the relativistic effects did not exist, then the half-life would be measured to be the same for pions at rest and pions in motion (an assumption we made in part a above). In relativity, however, the nonproper and proper half-lives are related by

$$\Delta t = \frac{\Delta \tau}{\sqrt{1 - v^2/c^2}}.$$

The proper time in this case is 1.77×10^{-8} sec, the time interval measured by a clock attached to the pion, that is, at one place in the rest frame of the pion. In the laboratory frame, however, the pions are moving at high speeds and the time interval there (a nonproper one) will be measured to be larger (moving clocks appear to run slow). The nonproper half-life, measured by two different clocks in the laboratory frame, would then be

$$\Delta t = \frac{1.77 \times 10^{-8} \text{ sec}}{\sqrt{1 - (0.99)^2}} = 1.3 \times 10^{-7} \text{ sec}.$$

This is the half-life appropriate to the laboratory reference frame. Pions that live this long, traveling at a speed $0.99c$, would cover a distance

$$d = 0.99c \times \Delta t = 2.97 \times 10^{+8} \text{ m/sec} \times 1.3 \times 10^{-7} \text{ sec} = 39 \text{ m},$$

exactly as measured in the laboratory.

(c) Show how the length contraction accounts for the measurements.

In part *a* we used a length measurement (39 m) appropriate to the laboratory frame and a time measurement (1.77×10^{-8} sec) appropriate to the pion frame and incorrectly combined them. In part *b* we used the length (39 m) and time (1.3×10^{-7} sec) measurements appropriate to the laboratory frame. Here we use length and time measurements appropriate to the pion frame.

We already know the half-life in the pion frame, that is, the proper time 1.77×10^{-8} sec. What is the distance covered by the pion beam during which its intensity falls to half its original value? If we were sitting on the pion, the laboratory distance of 39 m would appear much shorter to us because the laboratory moves at a speed $0.99c$ relative to us (the pion). In fact, we would measure the distance

$$d' = d\sqrt{1 - v^2/c^2} = 39\sqrt{1 - (0.99)^2} \text{ m}.$$

The time elapsed in covering this distance is $d'/0.99c$ or

$$\Delta \tau = \frac{39 \text{ m} \sqrt{1 - (0.99)^2}}{0.99c} = 1.77 \times 10^{-8} \text{ sec},$$

exactly the measured half-life in the pion frame.

Thus, depending on which frame we choose to make measurements in, this example illustrates the physical reality of either the time-dilation or the length-contraction predictions of relativity. Each pion carries its own clock, which determines the proper time τ of decay, but the decay time observed by a laboratory observer is much greater. Or, expressed equivalently, the moving pion sees the laboratory distances contracted and in its proper decay time can cover laboratory distances greater than those measured in its own frame.

Notice that in this region of $v \approx c$ the relativistic effects are large. There can be no doubt whether in our example, the distance is 39 m or 5.3 m. If the proper time were applicable to the laboratory frame, the time $(1.3 \times 10^{-7}$ sec) to travel 39 m would correspond to over seven half-lives (i.e., 1.3×10^{-7} sec$/1.8 \times 10^{-8}$ sec $\cong 7$). Instead of the beam being reduced to half its original intensity, it would be reduced to $(1/2)^7$ or $1/128$ its original intensity in travelling 39 m. Such differences are very easily detectable.

This example is by no means an isolated result (see, e.g., Problems 27 to 30 and Ref. 4). All the kinematic (and dynamic) measurements in high-energy physics are consistent with the time-dilation and length-contraction results. The experiments and the accelerators themselves are designed to take relativistic effects into account. Indeed, relativity is a routine part of the everyday world of high-speed physics and engineering.

Example 4. We could define the length of a moving rod as the product of its velocity by the time interval between the instant that one end point of the rod passes a fixed marker and the instant that the other end point passes the same marker. Show that this definition also leads to the length contraction result of Eq. 2-10.

Let the rod be at rest in the primed frame. Then

$$x_2' = \frac{x_2 - vt_2}{\sqrt{1 - \beta^2}} \qquad \text{and} \qquad x_1' = \frac{x_1 - vt_1}{\sqrt{1 - \beta^2}}$$

where x_2' and x_1' are the end points of the rod whose proper length is $x_2' - x_1'$. The positions of the end points in the unprimed frame are x_2 and x_1 measured at times t_2 and t_1, respectively. However, because the marker is fixed, $x_2 = x_1$; that is, we stay at the same x-position in the S-frame and watch the rod go by. Hence,

$$x_2 = x_1$$

so that

$$x_2'\sqrt{1 - \beta^2} + vt_2 = x_1'\sqrt{1 - \beta^2} + vt_1$$

or

$$t_1 - t_2 = \frac{(x_2' - x_1')\sqrt{1 - \beta^2}}{v}.$$

The defined length of the rod is $v(t_1 - t_2)$. From the above, it follows that

$$v(t_1 - t_2) = (x_2' - x_1')\sqrt{1 - \beta^2}$$

which is the contraction of the proper length, $x_2' - x_1'$, given by Eq. 2-10. ◀

2.5 *The Observer in Relativity*

There are many shorthand expressions in relativity which can easily be misunderstood by the uninitiated. Thus the phrase "moving clocks run slow" means that a clock moving at a constant velocity relative to an inertial frame containing synchronized clocks will be found to run slow *when timed by those clocks*. We compare *one moving clock* with *two synchronized stationary clocks.* Those who assume that the phrase means anything else often encounter difficulties.

Similarly, we often refer to "an observer." The meaning of this term also is quite definite, but it can be misinterpreted. *An observer is really an infinite set of recording clocks distributed throughout space, at rest and synchronized with respect to one another.* The space-time coordinates of an event (x,y,z,t) are recorded by the clock at the location (x,y,z) of the event at the time (t) it occurs. Measurements thus recorded throughout space-time (we might call them local measurements) are then available to be picked up and analyzed by an experimenter. Thus, the observer can also be thought of as the experimenter who collects the measurements made in this way. Each inertial frame is imagined to have such a set of recording clocks, or such an observer. The relations between the space-time coordinates of a physical event measured by one observer (S) and the space-time coordinates of the *same* physical event measured by another observer (S') are the equations of transformation.

A misconception of the term "observer" arises from confusing "measuring" with "seeing." For example, it had been commonly assumed for some time that the relativistic length contraction would cause rapidly moving objects to appear to the eye to be shortened in the direction of motion. The location of all points of the object measured at the same time would give the "true" picture according to our use of the term "observer" in relativity. But, in the words of V. F. Weisskopf [5]:

"When we see or photograph an object, we record light quanta emitted by the object when they arrive simultaneously at the retina or at the photographic film. This implies that these light quanta have *not* been emitted simultaneously by all points of the object. The points further away from the observer have emitted their part of the picture earlier than the closer points. Hence, if the object is in motion, the eye or the photograph gets a distorted picture of the object, since the object has been at different locations when different parts of it have emitted the light seen in the picture."

To make a comparison with the relativistic predictions, therefore, we must first allow for the time of flight of the light quanta from the different parts of the object. Without this correction, we see a distortion due to *both* the optical *and* the relativistic effects. In this sense, the Lorentz contraction *is* visible, particularly for views taken at right angles to the motion of rapidly moving large objects [see Ref. 6]. But the term "observer" does *not* mean "viewer" in relativity and we shall continue to use it only in the sense of "measurer" described above.

2.6 The Relativistic Addition of Velocities

In classical physics, if we have a train moving with a velocity **v** with respect to ground and a passenger on the train moves with a velocity **u**′ with respect to the train, then the passenger's velocity relative to the ground **u** is just the vector sum of the two velocities (see Eq. 1-5), that is,

$$\mathbf{u} = \mathbf{u}' + \mathbf{v}. \tag{2-15}$$

This is simply the classical, or Galilean, velocity addition theorem. How do velocities add in special relativity theory?

Consider, for the moment, the special case wherein all velocities are along the common x–x' direction of two inertial frames S and S'. Let S be the ground frame and S' the frame of the train, whose speed relative to the ground is v (see Fig. 2-7). The passenger's speed in the S'-frame is u', and his position on the train as time goes on can be described by $x' = u't'$. What is the speed of the passenger observed from the ground? Using the Lorentz transformation equations (Eqs. 2-7), we have

$$x' = \frac{x - vt}{\sqrt{1 - v^2/c^2}} = u't' \qquad \text{and} \qquad t' = \frac{t - (v/c^2)x}{\sqrt{1 - v^2/c^2}}.$$

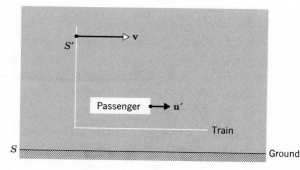

Fig. 2-7. A schematic view of the system used in deriving the equations for the relativistic addition of velocities.

Combining these yields

$$x - vt = u'\left(t - \frac{v}{c^2} x\right),$$

which can be written as

$$x = \frac{(u' + v)}{(1 + u'v/c^2)} t. \tag{2-16}$$

If we call the passenger's speed relative to ground u, then his ground location as time goes on is given by $x = ut$. Comparing this to Eq. 2-16, we obtain

$$u = \frac{u' + v}{1 + u'v/c^2} \tag{2-17}$$

This is the *relativistic*, or Einstein *velocity addition theorem.*

If u' and v are very small compared to c, Eq. 2-17 reduces to the classical result, Eq. 2-15, $u = u' + v$, for then the second term in the denominator of Eq. 2-17 is negligible compared to one. On the other hand, if $u' = c$, it always follows that $u = c$ no matter what the value of v. Of course, $u' = c$ means that our "passenger" is a light pulse and we know that an assumption used to derive the transformation formulas was exactly this result; that is, that all observers measure the same speed c for light. Formally, we get, with $u' = c$,

$$u = \frac{c + v}{1 + cv/c^2} = \frac{c + v}{c(c + v)} c^2 = c.$$

Hence, any velocity (less than c) relativistically added to c gives a resultant c. In this sense, c plays the same role in relativity that an infinite velocity plays in the classical case.

The Einstein velocity addition theorem can be used to explain the observed result of the experiments designed to test the various emission theories of Chapter One. The basic result of these experiments is that the velocity of light is independent of the velocity of the source (see Section 1-8). We have seen that this is a basic postulate of relativity so that we are not surprised that relativity yields agreement with these experiments. If, however, we merely looked at the formulas of relativity, unaware of their physical origin, we could obtain this specific result from the velocity addition theorem directly. For, let the source be the S' frame. In that frame the pulse (or wave) of light has a speed c in vacuum according to the emission theories. Then, the pulse (or wave) speed measured by the S-observer, for whom the source moves, is given by Eq. 2-18, and is also c. That is, $u_x = c$ when $u_x{'} = c$, as shown above.

It follows also from Eq. 2-17 that the addition of two velocities, each smaller than c, cannot exceed the velocity of light.

▶ *Example* 5. In Example 2 of Chapter One, we found that when two electrons leave a radioactive sample in opposite directions, each having a speed $0.67c$ with respect to the sample, the speed of one electron relative to the other is $1.34c$ according to classical physics. What is the relativistic result?

We may regard one electron as the S-frame, the sample as the S'-frame, and the other electron as the object whose speed in the S-frame we seek (see Fig. 1-3). Then

$$u' = 0.67c \qquad v = 0.67c$$

and $\qquad u = \dfrac{u' + v}{1 + u'v/c^2} = \dfrac{(0.67 + 0.67)c}{1 + (0.67)^2} = \dfrac{1.34}{1.45}c = 0.92c.$

The speed of one electron relative to the other is less than c.

Does the relativistic velocity addition theorem alter the result of Example 1 of Chapter One? Explain.

▶ *Example* 6. Show that the Einstein velocity addition theorem leads to the observed Fresnel drag coefficient of Eq. 1-11.

In this case, v_w is the velocity of water with respect to the apparatus and c/n is the velocity of light relative to the water. That is, in our formula we have

$$u' = \frac{c}{n} \qquad \text{and} \qquad v = v_w.$$

Then, the velocity of light relative to the apparatus is

$$u = \frac{c/n + v_w}{1 + v_w/nc}$$

and for v_w/c small (in the experiments $v_w/c = 2.3 \times 10^{-8}$) we can neglect terms of second order in v_w/c, so that

$$u \cong \left(\frac{c}{n} + v_w\right)\left(1 - \frac{v_w}{nc}\right) \cong \frac{c}{n} + v_w\left(1 - \frac{1}{n^2}\right).$$

This is exactly Eq. 1-11, the observed first-order effect. Notice that there is no need to assume any "drag" mechanism, or to invent theories on the interaction between matter and the "ether." The result is an inevitable consequence of the velocity addition theorem and illustrates the powerful simplicity of relativity. ◀

It is interesting and instructive to note that there *are* speeds in excess of *c*. Although matter or energy (i.e., signals) cannot have speeds greater than *c*, certain kinematical processes *can* have super-light speeds (see Ref. 7 and Question 26). For example, the succession of points of intersection of the blades of a giant scissors, as the scissors is rapidly closed, may be generated at a speed greater than *c*. Here geometrical points are involved, the motion being an illusion, whereas the material objects involved (atoms in the scissors blades, e.g.) always move at speeds less than *c*. Other similar examples are the succession of points on a fluorescent screen as an electron beam sweeps across the screen, or the light of a searchlight beam sweeping across the cloud cover in the sky. The electrons, or the light photons, which carry the energy, move at speeds not exceeding *c*.

Thus far, we have considered only the transformation of velocities parallel to the direction of relative motion of the two frames of reference (the *x–x'* direction). To signify this, we should put *x* subscripts on *u* and *u'* in Eq. 2-17, obtaining

$$u_x = \frac{u_x' + v}{1 + u_x'(v/c^2)} \tag{2-18}$$

For velocities that are perpendicular to the direction of relative motion, the result is more involved. Imagine than an object moves parallel to the *y'*-axis in *S'*. Let it be observed to be at y_1' and y_2' at the times t_1' and t_2', respectively, so that its velocity in *S'* is $u_y' = \Delta y'/\Delta t' = (y_2' - y_1')/(t_2' - t_1')$. To find its velocity in *S*, we use the Lorentz transformation equations and obtain

$$y_2' - y_1' = y_2 - y_1$$

$$t_2' - t_1' = \frac{t_2 - t_1 - (x_2 - x_1)v/c^2}{\sqrt{1 - v^2/c^2}} = \frac{\Delta t - \Delta x(v/c^2)}{\sqrt{1 - v^2/c^2}}$$

so that

$$\frac{\Delta y'}{\Delta t'} = \frac{\Delta y \sqrt{1 - v^2/c^2}}{\Delta t - \Delta x(v/c^2)} = \frac{(\Delta y/\Delta t)\sqrt{1 - v^2/c^2}}{1 - \left(\dfrac{\Delta x}{\Delta t}\right)v/c^2}.$$

Now $\Delta y/\Delta t$ is u_y and $\Delta x/\Delta t$ is u_x so that

$$u_y' = \frac{u_y \sqrt{1 - v^2/c^2}}{1 - u_x(v/c^2)}.$$

For comparison with Eq. 2-18, we can write the corresponding inverse transformation. We merely change v to $-v$ and interchange primed and unprimed quantities, obtaining

$$u_y = \frac{u_y' \sqrt{1 - v^2/c^2}}{1 + u_x'(v/c^2)}. \tag{2-19}$$

The student can derive the result also by seeking $\Delta y/\Delta t$ directly, instead of $\Delta y'/\Delta t'$ as is done above (see Problem 31). In exactly the same way, we also find

$$u_z = \frac{u_z' \sqrt{1 - v^2/c^2}}{1 + u_x'(v/c^2)}. \tag{2-20}$$

In Table 2-2 we summarize the relativistic velocity transformation equations. We shall have occasion to use these results, and to interpret them further, in later sections. For the moment, however, let us note certain aspects of the transverse velocity transformations. The perpendicular, or transverse, components (i.e., u_y and u_z) of the velocity of an object as seen in the S-frame are related both to the transverse components (i.e., u_y' and u_z') and to the parallel component (i.e., u_x') of the velocity of the object in the S'-frame. The result is not simple because neither observer is a proper one. If we choose a frame in which $u_x' = 0$, however, then the transverse results become $u_z = u_z' \sqrt{1 - v^2/c^2}$ and $u_y = u_y' \sqrt{1 - v^2/c^2}$. But no length contraction is involved for transverse space intervals, so what is the origin of the $\sqrt{1 - v^2/c^2}$ factor? We need only point out that velocity, being a ratio of length interval to time interval, involves the time coordinate too, so that time dilation is involved. Indeed, this special case of the transverse velocity transformation is a direct time-dilation effect.

TABLE **2-2**   THE RELATIVISTIC VELOCITY TRANSFORMATION EQUATIONS

$u_x' = \dfrac{u_x - v}{1 - u_x v/c^2}$	$u_x = \dfrac{u_x' + v}{1 + u_x' v/c^2}$
$u_y' = \dfrac{u_y \sqrt{1 - v^2/c^2}}{1 - u_x v/c^2}$	$u_y = \dfrac{u_y' \sqrt{1 - v^2/c^2}}{1 + u_x' v/c^2}$
$u_z' = \dfrac{u_z \sqrt{1 - v^2/c^2}}{1 - u_x v/c^2}$	$u_z = \dfrac{u_z' \sqrt{1 - v^2/c^2}}{1 + u_x' v/c^2}$

We can obtain the relativistic *acceleration* transformation equations, also, by time differentiation of the velocity transformation equations (see Problem 42). With $a_x = du_x/dt$ and $a_x{}' = du_x{}'/dt'$ as the x and x' components of the acceleration, we obtain

$$a_x{}' = a_x \frac{(1 - v^2/c^2)^{3/2}}{(1 - u_x v/c^2)^3},$$

for example, with similar (more involved) equations for $a_y{}'$, $a_z{}'$, and a_y, a_z. The principal features to note are that (1) the acceleration of a particle depends upon the inertial reference frame in which it is measured (unlike the Galilean result wherein $a_x{}' = a_x$), and (2) the relativistic result reduces to the classical result when u and v are small compared to c ($a_x{}' \to a_x$ as u_x/c and $v/c \to 0$). For emphasis we repeat that, although in special relativity the frames are inertial (unaccelerated), the objects whose motions we study may be accelerating with respect to such frames.

2.7   *Aberration and Doppler Effect in Relativity*

Up to now we have shown how relativity can account for the experimental results of various light-propagation experiments listed in Table 1-2 (e.g., the Fresnel drag coefficient and the Michelson-Morley result) and at the same time how it predicts new results also confirmed by experiment (time dilation in pion or meson decay, also in Table 1-2). Here we deduce the aberration result. In doing this, we shall also come upon another new result predicted by relativity and confirmed by experiment, namely a transverse Doppler effect.

Consider a train of plane monochromatic light waves of unit amplitude emitted from a source at the origin of the S'-frame, as shown in Fig. 2-8. The rays, or wave normals, are chosen to be in (or parallel to) the x'-y' plane, making an angle θ' with the x'-axis. An equation describing the propagation would be of the form

$$\cos 2\pi \left[\frac{x' \cos \theta' + y' \sin \theta'}{\lambda'} - \nu' t' \right], \tag{2-21}$$

for this is a single periodic function, amplitude unity, representing a wave moving with velocity $\lambda' \nu'$ ($= c$) in the θ'-direction. Notice, for example, that for $\theta' = 0$ it reduces to $\cos 2\pi[x'/\lambda' - \nu' t']$ and for $\theta' = \pi/2$ it reduces to $\cos 2\pi[y'/\lambda' - \nu' t']$, well-known expressions for propa-

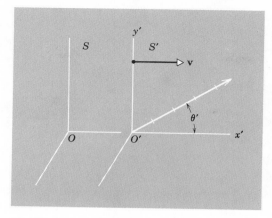

Fig. 2-8. A ray, or wave normal, of plane monochromatic light waves is emitted from the origin of the S' frame. The bars signify wavefronts separated by one wavelength from adjacent wavefronts. The direction of propagation makes an angle θ' with the x'-axis, the rays being parallel to the x'-y' plane.

gation along the positive-x' and positive-y' directions, respectively, of waves of frequency ν' and wavelength λ'. The alternate forms, cos $(2\pi/\lambda')[x' - \lambda'\nu't']$ and cos $(2\pi/\lambda')[y' - \lambda'\nu't']$ show that the wave speed is $\lambda'\nu'$ which, for electromagnetic waves, is equal to c.

In the S-frame these wavefronts will still be planes, for the Lorentz transformation is linear and a plane transforms into a plane. Hence, in the unprimed, or S, frame the equation describing the propagation will have the same form:

$$\cos 2\pi \left[\frac{x \cos \theta + y \sin \theta}{\lambda} - \nu t \right] \qquad (2\text{-}22)$$

Here, λ and ν are the wavelength and frequency, respectively, measured in the S-frame, and θ is the angle a ray makes with the x-axis. We know, if Eqs. 2-21 and 2-22 are to represent electromagnetic waves, that $\lambda\nu = c$, just as $\lambda'\nu' = c$, for c is the velocity of electromagnetic waves, the same for each observer.

Now let us apply the Lorentz transformation equations directly to Eq. 2-21, putting

$$x' = \frac{x - vt}{\sqrt{1 - \beta^2}} \qquad \text{and} \qquad t' = \frac{t - (v/c^2)x}{\sqrt{1 - \beta^2}}.$$

We obtain

$$\cos 2\pi\left[\frac{1}{\lambda'}\frac{(x-vt)}{\sqrt{1-\beta^2}}\cos\theta' + \frac{y\sin\theta'}{\lambda'} - \nu'\frac{[t-(v/c^2)x]}{\sqrt{1-\beta^2}}\right]$$

or, on rearranging terms,

$$\cos 2\pi\left[\frac{\cos\theta'+\beta}{\lambda'\sqrt{1-\beta^2}}x + \frac{\sin\theta'}{\lambda'}y - \frac{(\beta\cos\theta'+1)\nu'}{\sqrt{1-\beta^2}}t\right]$$

As expected, this has the form of a plane wave in the S-frame and must be identical to Eq. 2-22, which represents the same thing. Hence, the coefficient of x, y, and t in each equation must be equated, giving us

$$\frac{\cos\theta}{\lambda} = \frac{\cos\theta'+\beta}{\lambda'\sqrt{1-\beta^2}} \qquad (2\text{-}23)$$

$$\frac{\sin\theta}{\lambda} = \frac{\sin\theta'}{\lambda'} \qquad (2\text{-}24)$$

$$\nu = \frac{\nu'(1+\beta\cos\theta')}{\sqrt{1-\beta^2}} \qquad (2\text{-}25)$$

We also have the relation

$$\lambda\nu = \lambda'\nu' = c, \qquad (2\text{-}26)$$

a condition we knew in advance.

In the procedure that we have adopted here, we start with a light wave in S' for which we know λ', ν', and θ' and we wish to find what the corresponding quantities λ, ν, and θ are in the S-frame. That is, we have three unknowns but we have four equations (Eqs. 2-23 to 2-26) from which to determine the unknowns. The unknowns have been overdetermined, which means simply that the equations are not all independent. If we eliminate one equation, for instance, by dividing one by another (i.e., we combine two equations), we shall obtain three independent relations. It is simplest to divide Eq. 2-24 by Eq. 2-23; this gives us

$$\tan\theta = \frac{\sin\theta'\sqrt{1-\beta^2}}{\cos\theta'+\beta} \qquad (2\text{-}27a)$$

which is *the relativistic equation for the aberration of light*. It relates the directions of propagation, θ and θ', as seen from two different inertial frames. The inverse transformation can be written at once as

$$\tan \theta' = \frac{\sin \theta \sqrt{1 - \beta^2}}{\cos \theta - \beta} \tag{2-27b}$$

wherein β of Eq. 2-27a becomes $-\beta$ and we interchange primed and unprimed quantities. Experiments in high-energy physics involving photon emission confirm the relativistic formula exactly.

▶ *Example* 7. Show that the exact relativistic aberration formula, Eq. 2-27a, can be derived from the velocity transformation equations, Eqs. 2-18 and 2-19.

Let a source S' (an atom, for example), which is moving along the x-axis at a speed v, emit light at an angle θ' to the x'-axis of its own rest frame (see Fig. 2-8, e.g.). In the S-frame the emitting angle is θ.

The speed of light in the θ'-direction is c so that the component of velocity along the x'-direction is $u_{x}' = \cos \theta'$ and that along the y'-direction is $u_{y}' = c \sin \theta'$.

Using the velocity addition formulas, we obtain

$$u_x = \frac{u_{x}' + v}{1 + u_{x}'v/c^2} = \frac{c \cos \theta' + v}{1 + (v \cos \theta')/c}$$

and

$$u_y = \frac{u_{y}' \sqrt{1 - \beta^2}}{1 + u_{x}'v/c^2} = \frac{c \sin \theta' \sqrt{1 - \beta^2}}{1 + (v \cos \theta')/c}.$$

Now, $\tan \theta = c \sin \theta / c \cos \theta = u_y/u_x$ so that, with u_x and u_y as found above,

$$\tan \theta = \frac{u_y}{u_x} = \frac{c \sin \theta' \sqrt{1 - \beta^2}}{c \cos \theta' + v} = \frac{\sin \theta' \sqrt{1 - \beta^2}}{\cos \theta' + \beta}$$

which is the relativistic aberration formula, Eq. 2-27a.

Example 8. Show that the observed first-order aberration effect, which corresponds to the classical picture, is a special case of the exact relativistic formula.

Consider the case of a star directly overhead in the S-frame. One receives plane waves whose direction of propagation is along the negative y direction. Hence, $\theta = 3\pi/2$. In S', the propagation direction is θ', given by Eq. 2-27b with $\theta = 3\pi/2$. That is,

$$\tan \theta' = \frac{\sin (3\pi/2) \sqrt{1 - \beta^2}}{\cos (3\pi/2) - \beta} = \frac{-\sqrt{1 - \beta^2}}{-\beta}. \quad ◀$$

When v is very small compared to c ($v \ll c$), then v/c, or β, is very small compared to one. Thus, β^2 will be negligible compared to one; neglecting terms in the second order then, we can write

$$\tan \theta' = \frac{-\sqrt{1 - \beta^2}}{-\beta} \cong \frac{-1}{-\beta} = \frac{1}{\beta} = \frac{c}{v}.$$

This result is in perfect agreement with the observed first-order aberration effect, corresponding to the classical interpretation of the situation, as shown in Fig. 2-9. In Fig. 2-9a we show the propagation direction of the starlight in S and in S' and in Fig. 2-9b the orientation of the telescopes in S and S' which observe the star.

▶ *Example 8.* Max Born, in *Einstein's Theory of Relativity* [8], says in this connection:

"This result is particularly remarkable because all the other theories have considerable difficulty in explaining aberration. From the Galilean transformation one obtains no deflection at all of the wave plane and the wave direction, and to explain aberration one has to introduce the concept 'ray,' which in moving systems need not coincide with the direction of propagation. In Einstein's theory this difficulty disappears. In every inertial system S the direction of the ray (that is, the direction along which the energy is transported) coincides with the perpendicular to the wave planes, and the aberration results, in the same way as the Doppler effect and Fresnel's convection coefficient, from the concept of a wave with the help of the Lorentz transformation. This method of deriving the fundamental laws of the optics of

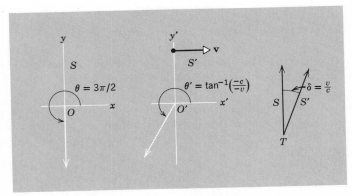

Fig. 2-9. (a) In S, the direction of propagation from the source is along $-y$, $\theta = 3\pi/2$. In S', the same ray makes an angle with $-y'$-axes. (b) The line of sight of the telescope in S is vertical and in S' is inclined forward by an angle $\delta = v/c$, in order to see the source.

moving bodies shows very strikingly that Einstein's theory of relativity is superior to all other theories." ◀

The third of our four equations above (Eqs. 2-23 to 2-26) gives us directly the one remaining phenomenon we promised to discuss; that is, *the relativistic equation for the Doppler effect,*

$$\nu = \frac{\nu'(1 + \beta \cos \theta')}{\sqrt{1 - \beta^2}} \qquad (2\text{-}25a)$$

which we can also write inversely as

$$\nu' = \frac{\nu(1 - \beta \cos \theta)}{\sqrt{1 - \beta^2}}. \qquad (2\text{-}25b)$$

Let us first check that the relativistic formula reduces to the classical one. That is, for $v \ll c$ we can neglect terms higher than first order in v/c, or β, and the first-order result should be the classical one. From Eq. 2-25b, we get (using the binomial theorem expansion through first-order terms)

$$\nu = \frac{\nu' \sqrt{1 - \beta^2}}{1 - \beta \cos \theta} \cong \frac{\nu'}{1 - \beta \cos \theta} \cong \nu'(1 + \beta \cos \theta)$$

which is the classical result. This becomes clear on consideration of the more familiar special cases. For, with $\theta = 0$, which corresponds to observer S seeing the source move toward him or his moving toward the source, we obtain

$$\nu = \nu'(1 + \beta) = \nu'\left(1 + \frac{v}{c}\right)$$

which shows that the observed frequency ν is greater than the proper frequency ν'. With $\theta = 180°$, which corresponds to observer S seeing the source move away from him or his moving away from the source, we obtain

$$\nu = \nu'(1 - \beta) = \nu'\left(1 - \frac{v}{c}\right)$$

which shows that the observed frequency ν is less than the proper frequency ν'. Finally, for $\theta = 90°$, wherein the line of sight is perpendicular to the relative motion, there is no Doppler effect classically; that is, $\nu = \nu'$. All these first-order results are classical effects.

Now, if v is *not* small compared to c, we should obtain relativistic (second-order) effects. It is convenient to think of these effects separately as a longitudinal one and a transverse one. Thus, for the *longitudinal Doppler effect in relativity*, we use Eq. 2-25b and set $\theta = 0$ or $\theta = 180°$. That is, in $\nu = (\nu' \sqrt{1 - \beta^2})/(1 - \beta \cos \theta)$, with $\theta = 0$ (source and observer move *toward* one another) we obtain

$$\nu = \nu' \sqrt{\frac{1 + \beta}{1 - \beta}} = \nu' \sqrt{\frac{c + v}{c - v}}; \qquad (2\text{-}28)$$

and with $\theta = 180°$ (source and observer move *away* from one another) we obtain

$$\nu = \nu' \sqrt{\frac{1 - \beta}{1 + \beta}} = \nu' \sqrt{\frac{c - v}{c + v}} \qquad (2\text{-}29)$$

These results, were first confirmed experimentally in 1938 by Ives and Stilwell, who (following a suggestion first made by Einstein in 1907) used a beam of excited hydrogen atoms of well-defined speed and direction as the source of radiation [9, 10]. The experiment was repeated in 1961 with higher accuracy by Mandelberg and Witten [11], again confirming the relativistic effect.

More striking, however, is the fact that the relativistic formula predicts a *transverse Doppler effect*, an effect that is *purely relativistic*, for there is no transverse Doppler effect in classical physics at all. This prediction follows from Eq. 2-25b, $\nu = (\nu' \sqrt{1 - \beta^2})/(1 - \beta \cos \theta)$, when we set $\theta = 90°$, obtaining

$$\nu = \nu' \sqrt{1 - \beta^2}. \qquad (2\text{-}30)$$

If our line of sight is $90°$ to the relative motion, then we should observe a frequency ν which is *lower* than the proper frequency ν' of the source which is sweeping by us. Ives and Stilwell [9] in 1938 and 1941, and Otting [12] in 1939 confirmed the existence of this transverse Doppler effect, and more recently Kundig [13] obtained excellent quantitative data confirming the relativistic formula to within the experimental error of 1.1 percent.

It is instructive to note that the transverse Doppler effect has a simple time-dilation interpretation. The moving source is really a moving clock, beating out electromagnetic oscillations. We have seen that moving clocks appear to run slow. Hence, we see a given number of oscillations in a time that is longer than the proper time. Or, equivalently, we see a smaller number of oscillations in our unit time than is seen in the unit time of the proper frame. Therefore, we observe a lower frequency than the proper frequency. The transverse Doppler effect is another physical example confirming the relativistic time dilation.

In both the Doppler effect and aberration, the theory of relativity introduces an intrinsic simplification over the classical interpretation of these effects in that the two separate cases which are different in classical theory (namely, source at rest-moving observer and observer at rest-moving source) are identical in relativity. This, too, is in accord with observation. Notice, also, that a single derivation yields at once three effects, namely aberration, longitudinal Doppler effect, and transverse Doppler effect. Perhaps it should be remarked, however, that there are certain properties of the electromagnetic wave which *cannot* be derived merely by considering the phase term, as we have done. In order to determine things such as the degree of polarization, the distribution with direction of the power flow, and the momentum content, we need to know the transformation properties of the electromagnetic fields themselves (Chapter Four).

2.8   *The Common Sense of Special Relativity*

We are now at a point where a retrospective view can be helpful. Later we shall see more predictions of special relativity which are confirmed by experiment, in direct contradiction to classical views. And throughout atomic, nuclear, high-energy, and solid-state physics, relativity is used in an almost commonplace way as the correct description of the real microscopic world. Furthermore, relativity is a consistent theory, as we have shown already in many ways and shall continue to show later. However, because our everyday macroscopic world is classical to a good approximation and students have not yet lived with or used relativity enough to become sufficiently familiar with it, there may remain misconceptions about the theory which are worth discussing now.

(A) *The Limiting Speed c of Signals.* We have seen that, if it were possible to transmit signals with infinite speed, we could establish in an absolute way whether or not two events are simultaneous. The relativity of simultaneity depended on the existence of a finite speed of transmission of signals. Now we probably would grant that it is unrealistic to expect that any physical action could be transmitted with infinite speed. It does indeed seem fanciful that we could initiate a signal that would travel to all parts of our universe in zero time. It is really the classical physics (which at bottom makes such an assumption) that is fictitious (science fiction) and not the relativistic physics, which postulates a limiting speed. Furthermore, when experiments are carried out, the relativity of time measurements is confirmed. Nature does indeed show that relativity is a practical theory of measurement and not a philosophically idealistic one, as is the classical theory.

We can look at this in another way. From the fact that experiment denies the absolute nature of time, we can conclude that signals cannot be transmitted with infinite speed. Hence, there must be a certain finite speed that cannot be exceeded and which we call the limiting speed. The principle of relativity shows at once that this limiting speed is the speed of light, since the result that no speed can exceed a given limit is certainly a law of physics and, according to the principle of relativity, the laws of physics are the same for all inertial observers. Therefore this given limit, the limiting speed, must be exactly the same in all inertial reference frames. We have seen, from experiment, that the speed of light has exactly this property.

Viewed in this way, the speed of electromagnetic waves in vacuum assumes a role wider than the travel rate of a particular physical entity. It becomes instead a limiting speed for the motion of anything in nature.

(B) *Absolutism and Relativity.* The theory of relativity could have been called, instead, the theory of absolutism with some justification.

The fact that the observers who are in relative motion assign different numbers to length and time intervals between the pair of events, rather than finding these numbers to be absolutes, upsets the classical mind. This is so in spite of the fact that even in classical physics the measured values of the momentum or kinetic energy of a particle, for example, also are different for two observers who are in relative motion. What is troublesome, apparently, is the philosophic notion that length and time in the abstract are absolute quantities and the belief that relativity contradicts this notion. Now, without going into such a philosophic byway, it is important to note that relativity simply says that the *measured* length or time interval between a pair of events is affected by the relative *motion* of the events and measurer. Relativity is a theory of measurement, and motion affects measurement. Let us look at various aspects of this.

That relative motion should affect measurements is almost a "common-sense" idea—classical physics is full of such examples, including the aberration and Doppler effects already discussed. Furthermore, to explain such phenomena in relativity, we need not talk about the structure of matter or the idea of an ether in order to find changes in length and duration due to motion. Instead, the results follow directly *from the measurement process itself.* Indeed, we find that the phenomena are *reciprocal.* That is, just as A's clock seems to B to run slow, so does B's clock seem to run slow to A; just as A's meter stick seems to B to have contracted in the direction of motion, so likewise B's meter stick seems to A to have contracted in exactly the same way.

Moreover, there *are* absolute lengths and times in relativity. The *rest length* of a rod is an absolute quantity, the same for all inertial observers: If a given rod is measured by different inertial observers by bringing the rod to rest in their respective frames, each will measure the same length. Similarly for clocks, the *proper time* (which might better have been called "local time") is an invariant quantity:* the frequency of oscillation of an ammonia molecule, for instance, would be measured to be the same by different inertial observers who bring the molecule to rest in their respective frames.

Where relativity theory is clearly "more absolute" than classical physics is in the relativity principle itself: the *laws of physics* are absolute. We have seen that the Galilean transformations and classical notions contradicted the invariance of electromagnetic (and optical) laws, for example. Surely, giving up the absoluteness of the laws of physics, as classical notions of time and length demand, would leave us with an arbitrary and complex physical world. By comparison, relativity is absolute and simple.

(C) *The "Reality" of the Length Contraction.* Is the length contraction "real" or apparent? We might answer this by posing a similar question. Is the frequency, or wavelength, shift in the Doppler effect real or appar-

---

*In terms of simultaneity, we can say that the time order of two events *at the same place* can be absolutely determined. It is in the case that two events are separated in space that simultaneity is a relative concept.

ent? Certainly the proper frequency (i.e., the rest frequency) of the source is measured to be the same by all observers who bring the source to rest before taking the measurement. Likewise, the proper length is invariant. When the source and observer are in relative motion, the observer definitely measures a frequency (or wavelength) shift. Likewise, the moving rod is definitely measured to be contracted. The effects are real in the same sense that the measurements are real. We do not claim that the proper frequency has changed because of our measured shift. Nor do we claim that the proper length has changed because of our measured contraction. The effects are apparent (i.e., caused by the motion) in the same sense that proper quantities have not changed.

We do not speak about theories of matter to explain the contraction but, instead, we invoke the measurement process itself. For example, we do not assert, as Lorentz sought to prove, that motion produces a physical contraction through an effect on the elastic forces in the electronic or atomic constitution of matter (motion is *relative*, not absolute), but instead we remember the fish story. If a fish is swimming in water and his length is the distance between his tail and his nose, measured simultaneously, observers who disagree on whether measurements are simultaneous or not will certainly disagree on the measured length. Hence, length contraction is due to the relativity of simultaneity.

Since length measurements involve a comparison of two lengths (moving rod and measuring rod, e.g.) we can see that the Lorentz length contraction is really not a property of a single rod by itself but instead is a relation between two such rods in relative motion. The relation is both observable and reciprocal.

(D) *Rigid Bodies and Unit Length.* In classical physics, the notion of an ideal rigid body was often used as the basis for length (i.e., space) measurements. In principle, a rigid rod of unit length is used to lay out a distance scale. Even in relativity we can imagine a standard rod defining a unit distance, this same rod being brought to rest in each observer's frame to lay out space-coordinate units. However, the concept of an ideal rigid body is untenable in relativity, for such a body would be capable of transmitting signals instantaneously; a disturbance at one end would be propagated with infinite velocity through the body, in contradiction to the relativistic principle that there is a finite upper limit to the speed of transmission of a signal.

Conceptually, then, we must give up the notion of an ideal rigid body. This causes no problems for, at bottom, time measurements are primary and space measurements secondary. We know that this is so in relativity (the simultaneity concept is used in the definition of length) but it is less well recognized that a similar situation exists in classical physics.

For example, we do not use the rigid-body concept in making distance measurements on the astronomical scale. Instead we use the "radar" method. We measure the round-trip time for electromagnetic waves and derive distance from a product of the velocity c and the time interval. Even the units, such as light-years, suggest this procedure. An analagous "sonar" technique is used by animals (e.g., bats and fish) for distance measurement. And on the atomic and subatomic scale we do not invoke rigid bodies for distance measurements either. We again use the properties of electromagnetic waves and not of rigid bodies. Indeed, the very quantity that is today taken as the unit of length is the wavelength of light of a given frequency ν, the wavelength being the distance c/ν traveled in one period at a speed c. In atomic theory, the frequencies are the standard or characteristic quantities, so that the time standards are primary and lengths are determined from them by the use of c.

It is fitting, in emphasizing the common sense of relativity, to conclude with this quotation from Bondi [14] on the presentation of relativity theory:

"At first, relativity was considered shocking, anti-establishment and highly mysterious, and all presentations intended for the population at large were meant to emphasize these shocking and mysterious aspects, which is hardly conducive to easy teaching and good understanding. They tended to emphasize the revolutionary aspects of the theory whereas, surely, it would be good teaching to emphasize the continuity with earlier thought. . . .

"It is first necessary to bring home to the student very clearly the Newtonian attitude. Newton's first law of dynamics leads directly to the notion of an *inertial observer*, defined as an observer who finds the law of inertia to be correct . . . . The utter equivalence of inertial observers to each other for the purpose of Newton's first law is a direct and logical consequence of this law. The equivalence with regard to the second law is not a logical necessity but a very plausible extension, and with this plausible extension we arrive at Newton's principle of relativity: *that all inertial observers are equivalent as far as dynamical experiments go.* It will be obvious that the restriction to dynamical experiments is due simply to this principle of relativity having been derived from the laws of dynamics. . . .

"The next step . . . is to point out how absurd it would be if dynamics were in any sense separated from the rest of physics. There is no experiment in physics that involves dynamics alone and nothing else. . . . Hence, Newton's principle of relativity is empty because it refers only to a class of experiment that does not exist—the purely dynamical experiment. The choice is therefore presented of either throwing out this principle or removing its restriction to dynamical experiments. The first alternative does not lead us any further, and clearly disregards something of significance in our experience. The second alternative immediately gives us Einstein's principle of relativity: *that all inertial observers are equivalent.* It presents this principle, not as a logical deduction, but as a reasonable guess, a fertile guess from which observable consequences may be derived so that this particular hypothesis can be subjected to experimental testing. Thus, the principle of relativity is seen, not as a revolutionary new step, but as a natural, indeed an almost obvious, completion of Newton's work."

Questions

1. Distinguish between sound and light as to their value as synchronizing signals. Is there a lack of analogy?

2. If the limiting speed of signals in classical physics were c rather than infinity, would simultaneity be an absolute concept or a relative concept in classical physics?

3. Give an example from classical physics in which the motion of a clock affects its rate, that is, the way it runs. (The magnitude of the effect may depend on the detailed nature of the clock.)

4. Explain how the result of the Michelson-Morley experiment was put into our definition (procedure) of simultaneity (for synchronizing clocks).

5. The transformation equations (with the sixteen coefficients) would still be linear if we added a different constant term to each of them. We implicitly took all these constants to be zero. What is the meaning of this choice? (*Hint.* Consider the choice of origins.)

6. According to Eqs. 2-4 and 2-5, each inertial observer finds the center of the spherical electromagnetic wave to be at his own origin at all times, even when the origins do not coincide. How is this result related to our procedure for synchronizing clocks?

7. How can we justify excluding the negative roots in solving for the coefficients a_{11} and a_{44} in Section 2-2?

8. What assumptions, other than the relativity principle and the constancy of c, were made in deducing the Lorentz transformation equations?

9. In our deduction of the length contraction, we arrive at the same result that was proposed by Lorentz. Why then did we reject the Lorentz length contraction hypothesis; that is, in what way do our assumptions differ from those of Lorentz?

10. Two observers, one at rest in S and one at rest in S', each carry a meter stick oriented parallel to their relative motion. *Each* observer finds on measurement that the *other* observer's meter stick is shorter than his meter stick. Explain this apparent paradox. (*Hint.* Compare the following situation. Harry waves good-bye to Walter, in the rear of a station wagon driving away from Harry. Harry says that Walter gets smaller. Walter says that Harry gets smaller. Are they measuring the same thing?)

11. Although in relativity (where motion is relative and not absolute) we find that "moving clocks run slow," this effect has nothing to do with motion altering the way a clock works. What does it have to do with?

12. In time dilation, what is dilated? Would "time retardation" be a better term?

13. Comment on the statement of G. J. Whitrow [2]: "Just as observers in different places have different spatial perspectives of the universe, so observers with different velocities have different temporal perspectives."

14. We have always set the clocks at the origins of two inertial frames to read zero when they are coincident. If these clocks are synchronized to a time other than zero, can we use the Lorentz transformations as before? Explain (see Problem 5).

15. Is it true that two events which occur at the same place and at the same time for one observer will be simultaneous for all observers? Explain.

16. If an event A *precedes* an event B at the *same* point in one frame of reference, will A precede B in all other inertial reference frames? Will they occur at the same point in any other inertial frame? Will the time interval between the events be the same in any other inertial frame? Explain. (See Topical Appendix A.)

17. If two events are simultaneous but separated in space in frame S, will they be simultaneous in any other frame S'? Will their space separation be the same in any other frame? Explain. (See Topical Appendix A.)

18. We saw that two moving clocks appear to be out of synchronization by an amount $L'v/c^2$. Does the sign of the effect change, if we reverse the direction of motion of the clocks? (Sending v to $-v$ is equivalent to changing the observer from S to S'.) Explain physically.

19. Recalling that each observer finds the other observer's length scale to contract and the time scale to dilate, explain how it happens that they disagree on the sign of phase-difference effect?

20. If we assume the existence of an ether and the correctness of the Lorentz transformation equations, we can show that all inertial observers measure the same speed c for light regardless of their speed through the ether (see, e.g., Chapter VIII of Ref. 15). Make this plausible. (*Hint.* In addition to time dilation and length contraction we need to account for the phase difference in the synchronization of clocks.)

21. Show, from the velocity addition theorem of relativity, how we can account for the result of the Michelson-Morley experiment and the double-star observations.

22. Equation 2-17 for the relativistic addition of parallel velocities holds whether u' and v are positive or negative, although our examples considered only positive quantities. Modify an example to include a negative value for u' or v and show that the physical conclusions are unchanged.

23. Compare the results obtained for length- and time-interval measurements by observers in frames whose relative velocity is c. In what sense, from this point of view, does c become a limiting velocity?

24. In Example 6, what would happen if $v_w = -c/n$?

25. Consider a spherical light wavefront spreading out from a source. As seen by the source, what is the difference in velocity of portions of the wavefront traveling in opposite directions? What is the relative velocity of one portion of the wavefront with respect to the other portion?

26. The sweep rate of the tail of a comet can exceed the speed of light. Explain this phenomenon and show that there is no contradiction with relativity.

27. Starting from Max Born's quotation in Section 2-7, make an argument showing that relativity is consistent with the existence of photons.

28. Imagine a source of light emitting radiation (photons) uniformly in all directions in S'. In S, the radiation will be concentrated in the forward direction for high values of v. Explain, qualitatively (see Problem 43).

29. List several experimental results not predicted or explained by classical physics which are predicted or explained by special relativity theory.

30. Is everything relative according to relativity theory or are there any invariant things permitted by the theory? That is, are there any things which appear to be the same for all observers? If so, name some of them.

31. Why *is* Einstein's theory called the theory of relativity? Would some other name characterize it better?

32. Is the classical concept of an incompressible fluid valid in relativity? Explain.

33. For a classical assembly of particles, the total angular momentum is the sum of the orbital and spin angular momenta. Can we regard the spin angular momentum as an example of a "proper" quantity in classical physics? (In the proper frame, the spin angular momentum equals the total angular momentum, the orbital part being zero.)

34. We have stressed the utility of relativity at high speeds. Relativity is also useful in cosmology, where great distances and long time intervals are involved. Show, from the form of the Lorentz transformation equations, why this is so.

Problems

1. (a) Assume, in Fig. 2-1, that S' is a train having a speed of 100 mi/hr and that it is 0.5 miles long (proper length). What is the elapsed time between the reception of the two wavefronts by $0'$? [Do this two ways: first by using the Lorentz transformation; second, by finding expressions for the time of receipt of the two signals by $0'$ and subtracting. *Hint.* Remember that you are viewing the events from the ground (S) frame.] (b) What if the train were at rest on the tracks? What if the wavefronts traveled with infinite speed?

2. Show that Eqs. 2-6 for a_{44}, a_{11}, and a_{41} are the solutions to the equations preceding them.

3. Derive Eqs. 2-8 directly from Eqs. 2-7.

4. Suppose that an event occurs in S at $x = 100$ km, $y = 10$ km, $z = 1.0$ km at $t = 5.0 \times 10^{-6}$ seconds. Let S' move relative to S at $0.92c$ along the common x-x' axis, the origins coinciding at $t' = t = 0$. What are the coordinates x', y', z', and t' of this event in S'? Check the answer by using the inverse transformation to obtain the original data.

5. Two observers in the S frame, A and B, are separated by a distance of 60 m. Let S' move at a speed $\frac{3}{5}c$ relative to S, the origins of the two systems, O' and O, being coincident at $t' = t = 3 \times 10^{-7}$ sec $(90/c)$. The S' frame has two observers, one at A' and one at a point B' such that, according to clocks in the S frame, A' is opposite A at the same time that B' is opposite B (Fig. 2-1a). (a) What is the reading on the clock of B' when B' is opposite B? Do this twice: first, use the direct Lorentz transformation to find t'; second, use the inverse Lorentz transformation but again solve for t'. Do the answers agree? (*Careful:* x and x' are related as improper and proper lengths). (b) The S' system continues moving until A' is opposite B. What is the reading on the clock of B when he is opposite A'? (c) What is the reading on the clock of A' when he is opposite B? Do this also in two ways: first, use the Lorentz transformations; second, use the concept of proper and improper time intervals. (*Note.* You may find it convenient to express time in units of $1/c$, i.e., 3×10^{-7} sec $= 90/c$ and so on.)

6. At what speed v will the Galilean and Lorentz expressions for x differ by 0.10 percent? By 1 percent? By 10 percent?

7. Prove the invariance of the electromagnetic wave equation in relativity by showing that the corresponding differential operator is an invariant. That is, show that

$$\frac{\partial^2}{\partial x^2} + \frac{\partial^2}{\partial y^2} + \frac{\partial^2}{\partial z^2} - \frac{1}{c^2}\frac{\partial^2}{\partial t^2} = \frac{\partial^2}{\partial x'^2} + \frac{\partial^2}{\partial y'^2} + \frac{\partial^2}{\partial z'^2} - \frac{1}{c^2}\frac{\partial^2}{\partial t'^2}$$

when the space-time variables are related by the Lorentz transformations (see Problem 1-8).

8. Show that the proper time, given by Eq. 2-12 as $d\tau = dt\sqrt{1 - \beta^2}$, is an invariant quantity with respect to a Lorentz transformation. [*Hint.* In $\beta^2 = v^2/c^2$, let $v^2 = (dx/dt)^2 + (dy/dt)^2 + (dz/dt)^2$.]

9. Two events, one at position x_1, y_1, z_1 and another at a different position x_2, y_2, z_2 occur at the *same time t* according to observer S. (a) Do these events appear to be simultaneous to an observer in S' who moves relative to S at speed v? (b) If not, what is the time interval he measures between occurrences of these events? (c) How is this time interval affected as $v \rightarrow 0$? As the separation between events goes to zero?

10. A cart moves on a track with a constant velocity v (See Fig. 2-10). A and B are on the ends of the cart and observers C and D are stationed along the track. We define event AC as the occurrence of A passing C, and the others similarly. (a) Of the four events BD, BC, AD, AC, which are useful for measuring the rate of a clock carried by A for observers along the track? (b) Let Δt be the time interval between these two events for observers along the track. What time interval does the moving clock show? (c) Suppose that the events BC and AD are simultaneous in the track reference frame. Are they simultaneous in the cart's reference frame? If not, which is earlier?

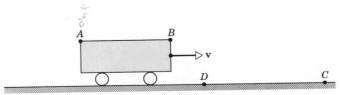

Fig. 2-10. Problems 10 and 11.

11. A cart moves on a track with constant velocity, as in Problem 10. Event *AD* is simultaneous with *BC* in the track frame. (*a*) The track observers set out to measure the length of the cart *AB*. They can do so either by using the events *BD* and *AD* and working through time measurements or by using the events *BC* and *AB*. In either case, the observers in the cart are not apt to regard these results as valid. Explain why for each case. (*b*) Suppose that the observers in the cart seek to measure the distance *DC* by making simultaneous marks on a long meter stick. Where (relative to *A* and *B*) would the observer, *E*, be situated such that *AD* is simultaneous with *EC* in the cart frame? Explain why in terms of synchronization. Can you see why there is a length contraction?

12. As seen from inertial system *S* an event occurs at point *A* on the *x*-axis and then 10^{-6} sec later an event occurs at point *B* further out on the *x*-axis. *A* and *B* are 600 m apart as seen from *S*. (*a*) Does there exist another inertial system *S'*, moving with speed less than *c* parallel to the *x*-axis, such that the two events appear simultaneous as seen from *S'*? If so, what is the magnitude and direction of the velocity of *S'* with respect to *S*? What is the separation of events *A* and *B* according to *S'*? (*b*) Repeat part *a* for the case where *A* and *B* are only 100 m apart as seen from *S*.

13. What is the proper time interval between the occurrence of two events: (*a*) if in some inertial frame the events are separated by 10^9 m and occur 5 sec apart? (*b*) If . . . 7.5×10^8 m and occur 2.5 sec apart? (*c*) If . . . 5×10^8 m and occurs 1.5 sec apart?

14. In the usual set-up of frames *S'* and *S* having relative velocity *v* along *x-x'*, the origins coinciding at $t = t' = 0$, we shall find that, at a later time, *t*, there is only one plane in *S* on which the clocks agree with those of *S'*. (*a*) Show that this plane is given by

$$x = \left(\frac{c^2}{v}\right)\left[1 - \left(1 - \frac{v^2}{c^2}\right)^{1/2}\right]t$$

and moves with velocity

$$u = \left(\frac{c^2}{v}\right)\left[1 - \left(1 - \frac{v^2}{c^2}\right)^{1/2}\right]$$

in *S*. (*b*) Show that this speed is less than *v*. (*c*) Suppose that an observer *S''* moves with the velocity *u* relative to *S*. This means that clocks opposite him in *S* and *S'* will each measure the same improper time interval for an event in which an observer in the *S''* frame carries the proper time. Using the result of (*b*) and the expression for time dilation, explain how this is possible.

15. (*a*) In Problem 14, let $v = \frac{3}{5}c$. Find *u*, the velocity of *S''* relative to *S*. Is your answer consistent with Problem 14(*b*)? (*b*) Using this value of *u* in

the velocity transformation equations, find the velocity of the frame S' relative to frame S''. Is your answer consistent with Problem 14(c)? (c) Prove that the result of (b) is a general result; that is, for any relative velocity v between frames S and S', an observer in this special frame S'' will see frame S moving with a velocity $-u$ and frame S' moving with a velocity $+u$. (d) Justify the result (c) logically using symmetry arguments and the fact that there is no preferred reference frame.

16. In our physical derivation of the length contraction (Section 2-4) we assumed that the time dilation was given. In a similar manner derive the time dilation for longitudinal light paths, assuming instead that the length contraction is given.

17. Show how the four results of the physical measurement processes of Section 2-4 can be combined to derive the Lorentz transformation equations of Section 2-2.

18. An airplane 40.0 m in length in its rest system is moving at a uniform velocity with respect to earth at a speed of 630 m/sec. (a) By what fraction of its rest length will it appear to be shortened to an observer on earth? (b) How long would it take by earth clocks for the airplane's clock to fall behind by one microsecond? (Assume that special relativity only applies).

19. The rest radius of the earth may be taken as 6400 km and its orbital speed about the sun as 30 km/sec. By how much would the earth's diameter appear to be shortened to an observer on the sun, due to the earth's orbital motion?

20. Consider a universe in which the speed of light $c = 100$ mi/hr. A Lincoln Continental traveling at a speed v relative to a fixed radar speed trap overtakes a Volkswagon traveling at the speed limit of 50 mi/hr $= c/2$. The Lincoln's speed is such that its length is measured by the fixed observer to be the same as that of the Volkswagon. By how much is the Lincoln exceeding the speed limit? The proper length of the Lincoln is twice that of the Volkswagon.

21. A 100-Mev electron, for which $\beta = 0.999975$, moves along the axis of an evacuated tube which has a length l' of 3.00 m, as measured by a laboratory observer S' with respect to whom the tube is at rest. An observer S moving with the electron would see the tube moving past at a speed v. What length would observer S measure for this tube?

22. The length of a spaceship is measured to be exactly half its proper length. (a) What is the speed of the spaceship relative to the observer's frame? (b) What is the dilation of the spaceship's unit time?

23. The radius of our galaxy is 3×10^{20} m, or about 3×10^4 light-years. (a) Can a person, in principle, travel from the center to the edge of our galaxy in a normal lifetime? Explain, using either time-dilation or length-

contraction arguments. (*b*) What constant velocity would he need to make the trip in 30 years (proper time)?

24. Two spaceships, each of proper length 100 m, pass near one another heading in opposite directions. If an astronaut at the front of one ship measures a time interval of 2.50×10^{-6} sec for the second ship to pass him, then (*a*) what is the relative velocity of the spaceships? (*b*) What time interval is measured on the first ship for the front of the second ship to pass from the front to the back of the first ship?

25. Suppose that a pole vaulter, holding a 16 ft long pole parallel to his direction of motion, runs through an 8 ft long shed which is open at each end. Is it possible to close sliding doors at each end of the shed such that the pole is entirely in the shed before it strikes the exit door? Discuss the situation from the point of view of the pole-vaulter and an observer on the shed roof [see Ref. 16].

26. A rod of rest length 1.0 m is moving longitudinally on a smooth table with a velocity $0.8c$ relative to the table. A circular hole of rest diameter 1.0 m lies in its path. (*a*) What is the diameter of the hole as seen by the rod? (*b*) What is the length of the rod as seen by the hole? (*c*) Does the rod fall into the hole (gravity acting) or not? Explain (see Refs. 17 and 18).

27. (*a*) If the average (proper) lifetime of a μ-meson is 2.3×10^{-6} sec, what average distance would it travel in vacuum before dying as measured in reference frames in which its velocity is $0.00c$, $0.60c$, $0.90c$, and $0.99c$? (*b*) Compare each of these distances with the distance the meson sees itself traveling through.

28. A π^+ meson is created in a high-energy collision of a primary cosmic-ray particle in the earth's atmosphere 200 km above sea level. It descends vertically at a speed of $0.99c$ and disintegrates, in its proper frame, 2.5×10^{-8} sec after its creation. At what altitude above sea level is it observed from earth to disintegrate?

29. The mean lifetime of μ-mesons stopped in a lead block in the laboratory is measured to be 2.3×10^{-6} sec. The mean lifetime of high-speed μ-mesons in a burst of cosmic rays observed from the earth is measured to be 1.6×10^{-5} sec. Find the speed of these cosmic-ray μ-mesons.

30. Laboratory experiments on μ-mesons at rest show that they have a (proper) average lifetime of about 2.3×10^{-6} sec. Such μ-mesons are produced high in the earth's atmosphere by cosmic-ray reactions and travel at a speed $0.99c$ relative to the earth a distance of from 4000 to 13000 m after formation before decaying. (*a*) Show that the average distance a μ-meson can travel before decaying is much less than even the shorter distance of 4000 m, if its lifetime in flight is only 2.3×10^{-6} sec. (*b*) Explain the consistency of the observations on length traveled and

lifetime by computing the lifetime of a μ-meson in flight as measured by a ground observer. (*c*) Explain the consistency by computing the length traveled as seen by an observer at rest on the meson in its flight through the atmosphere.

31. (*a*) Derive Eq. 2-18 in the same way in which Eq. 2-19 was derived. (*b*) Derive Eq. 2-19 directly, rather than by taking the inverse of $u_y{'}$.

32. In Fig. 2-11, A and B are the points of intersection of the x-axes (stationary rod) and an inclined rod (moving rod) at two different times. The inclined rod is moving in the $+y$-direction (without turning) with a speed v. (*a*) Show that the point of intersection of the rods has a speed $u = v \cot \theta$ to the left. (*b*) Let $\theta = 60°$ and $v = \frac{1}{3}c$. Show that u then exceeds c and explain why no contradiction with relativity exists.

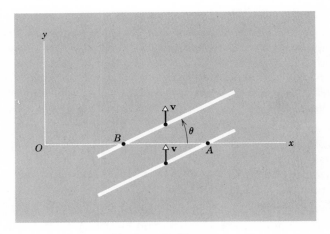

Fig. **2-11.** Problem 32

33. One cosmic-ray particle approaches the earth along its axis with a velocity $0.8c$ toward the North Pole and another with a velocity $0.6c$ toward the South Pole. What is the relative speed of approach of one particle with respect to the other? (*Hint.* It is useful to consider the earth and one of the particles as the two inertial systems.)

34. Suppose that a particle moves parallel to the x-x' axis, that $v = 25{,}000$ mi/hr and $u_x{'} = 25{,}000$ mi/hr. What percent error is made in using the Galilean rather than the Lorentz equation to calculate u_x? The speed of light is 6.7×10^8 mi/hr.

35. Consider three inertial frames of reference S, S', and S''. Let S' move with velocity v with respect to S, and let S'' move with velocity v' with respect to S'. All velocities are colinear. (*a*) Write the transformation equations relating x, y, z, t with x', y', z', t' and also those relating $x', y',$

z', t' with x'', y'', z'', t''. Combine these equations to get the relations between x, y, z, t and x'', y'', z'', t''. (*b*) Show that these relations are equivalent to a direct transformation from S to S'' in which the relative velocity v'' of S'' with respect to S is given by the relativistic addition theorem

$$v'' = \frac{v + v'}{1 + vv'/c^2}.$$

(*c*) Explain how the above analysis proves that two successive Lorentz transformations are equivalent to one direct transformation.

36. Suppose that a particle moves relative to the primed system with the velocity u' in the x'-y' plane so that its trajectory makes an angle θ' with the x'-axis. (*a*) Show that its equations of motion in S' are given by

$$x' = u't' \cos \theta' \qquad y' = u't' \sin \theta' \qquad z' = 0.$$

(*b*) In the S-frame, the corresponding velocity u and angle θ will be given by the equations

$$x = ut \cos \theta \qquad y = ut \sin \theta \qquad z = 0.$$

Justify this statement. (*c*) Show, using the Lorentz transformation equations, that the magnitude and direction of the velocity in S is given by

$$u^2 = \frac{u'^2 + v^2 + 2u'v \cos \theta' - (u'^2v^2/c^2) \sin^2 \theta'}{[1 + (u'v/c^2) \cos \theta']^2}$$

and

$$\tan \theta = \frac{u' \sin \theta' \sqrt{1 - \beta^2}}{u' \cos \theta' + v}$$

(*d*) How is this result related to the relativistic equation for the aberration of light, Eq. 2-27*a*? (*Hint.* What is u' in the case of light?) (*e*) Show that the expression for u^2 in part (*c*) is identical to that obtained by using Eqs. 2-18 and 2-19 with $u^2 = u_x^2 + u_y^2$.

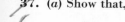

37. (*a*) Show that, with $u'^2 = u_x'^2 + u_y'^2$ and $u^2 = u_x^2 + u_y^2$, we can write

$$c^2 - u^2 = \frac{c^2(c^2 - u'^2)(c^2 - v^2)}{(c^2 + u_x'v)^2}.$$

(*b*) From this result show that if $u' < c$ and $v < c$, then u must be less than c. That is, the relativistic addition of two velocities, each less than c, is itself a velocity less than c. (*c*) From this result, show that if $u' = c$ or $v = c$, then u must equal c. That is, the relativistic addition of any velocity to the velocity of light merely gives again the velocity of light [Ref. 19].

38. Consider a radioactive nucleus moving with uniform velocity $0.05c$ relative to the laboratory. (*a*) The nucleus decays by emitting an electron with a speed $0.8c$ along the direction of motion (the common x-x'

axis). Find the velocity (magnitude and direction) of the electron in the lab frame, S. (*b*) The nucleus decays by emitting an electron with speed $0.8c$ along the positive y'-axis. Find the velocity (magnitude and direction) of the electron in the lab frame. (*c*) The nucleus decays by emitting an electron with a speed $0.8c$ along the positive y-axis (i.e., perpendicular to the original motion of the nucleus in the lab frame). Find the speed of the electron in the lab frame and the direction of emission in the original rest frame of the nucleus, S'.

39. Suppose that event A causes event B in frame S, the effect being propagated with a speed *greater than c*. Show, using the velocity addition theorem, that there exists an inertial frame S', which moves relative to S with a velocity less than c, in which the order of these events would be reversed. Hence, if concepts of cause and effect are to be preserved, it is impossible to send signals with a speed greater than that of light.

40. A stick at rest in S has a length L and is inclined at an angle θ to the x-axis (see Fig. 2-12). Find its length L' and angle of inclination θ' to the x'-axis as measured by an observer in S' moving at a speed v relative to S along the x-x' axes.

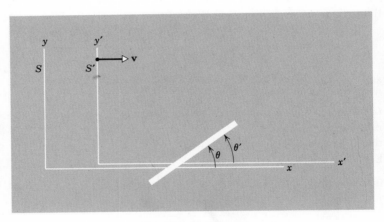

Fig. **2-12.** Problem 40

41. An object moves with speed u at an angle θ to the x-axis in system S. A second system S' moves with speed v relative to S along x. What speed u' and angle θ' will the object appear to have to an observer in S'?

42. Derive the relativistic acceleration transformation

$$a_{x}' = \frac{a_x\left(1 - \dfrac{v^2}{c^2}\right)^{3/2}}{\left(1 - \dfrac{u_x v}{c^2}\right)^3},$$

in which $a_x = du_x/dt$ and $a_{x'} = du_{x'}/dt'$. [*Hint.*

$$du_x/dt' = (du_x/dt)(dt/dt').]$$

43. Imagine a source of light emitting radiation uniformly in all directions in rest-frame S'. Find the distribution of radiation in the laboratory frame S in which the source moves at a speed $\frac{4}{5}c$. (*Hint.* Find the corresponding angle θ for $\theta' = 0, 30, 60, 90, 120, 150,$ and $180°$. A polar graph plot of the data would be helpful.) Can you guess why this phenomena is often referred to as the "headlight effect"?

44. A, on earth, signals with a flashlight every six minutes. B is on a space station that is stationary with respect to the earth. C is on a rocket traveling from A to B with a constant velocity of $0.6c$ relative to A (see Fig. 2-13). (*a*) At what intervals does B receive the signals from A? (*b*) At what intervals does C receive signals from A? (*c*) If C flashes a light using intervals equal to those he received from A, at what intervals does B receive C's flashes?

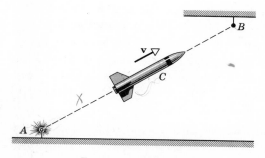

Fig. 2-13. Problem 44

45. A radar transmitter (T) is fixed to a system S_2 which is moving to the right with speed v relative to system S_1 (see Fig. 2-14). A timer in S_2, having a period τ_0 (measured in S_2) causes transmitter T to emit radar pulses, which travel at the speed of light, and are received by R, a receiver fixed to S_1. (*a*) What would be the period (τ) of the timer relative to observers A and B, spaced a distance $v\tau$ apart? (*b*) Show that the receiver R would observe the time interval between pulses arriving from S_2 not as τ or as τ_0 but as $\tau' = \tau_0\sqrt{(c + v)/(c - v)}$. (*c*) Explain why the observer at R measures a different period for the transmitter than do observers A and B who are in his own reference frame. (*Hint.* Compare the events measured by R to the events measured by A and B. What is meant by the proper time in each case?)

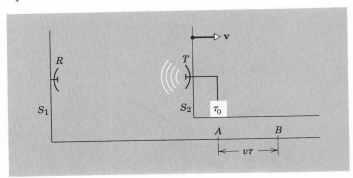

Fig. **2-14.** Problem 45

46. In the case of wave propagation in a medium, the Doppler shifts for the case of source moving through medium and observer moving through medium are different, whereas for light in vacuo the two situations are equivalent. Show that if we take the geometric mean of the two former results, we get exactly the relativistic Doppler shift (see Section 40-5, Ref. 10).

47. A rocketship is receding from the earth at a speed of $0.2c$. A light in the rocketship appears blue to passengers on the ship. What color would it appear to be to an observer on the earth?

48. Give the wavelength shifts in the relativistic longitudinal Doppler effect for the sodium D_1 line (5896 Å) for source and observer approaching at relative velocities of $0.1c$, $0.4c$, $0.8c$. Is the classical (first-order) result a good approximation?

49. Give the wavelength shift in the relativistic Doppler effect for the 6563 Å H_α line emitted by a star receding from the earth with a relative velocity $10^{-3}c$, $10^{-2}c$, and $10^{-1}c$. Is the classical (first-order) result a good approximation?

50. Give the wavelength shift, if any, in the Doppler effect for the sodium D_2 line (5890 Å) emitted from a source moving in a circle with constant speed $0.1c$ measured by an observer fixed at the center of the circle.

References

1. *Am. J. Phys.*, January 1963, p. 47.
2. G. J. Whitrow, *The Natural Philosophy of Time* Harper Torchbooks, Harper and Row, New York, 1963.
3. Herman Erlichson, "The Leibniz-Clarke Controversy: Absolute versus Relative Space and Time," *Am. J. Phys.*, **35**, 89 (1967).

4. David H. Frisch and James H. Smith, "Measurement of Relativistic Time Dilation Using μ-Mesons," *Am. J. Phys.*, **31**, 342 (1963); and the related film "Time Dilation—An Experiment with μ-Mesons," Educational Services, Inc., Watertown, Mass.

5. V. T. Weisskopf, "The Visual Appearance of Rapidly Moving Objects," *Physics Today* 13(9) (September 1960).

6. G. D. Scott and M. R. Viner, "The Geometrical Appearance of Large Objects Moving at Relativistic Speeds," *Am. J. Phys.*, **33**, 534 (1965).

7. Milton A. Rothman, "Things that go Faster than Light," *Scientific American*, **203**, 142 (July 1960).

8. Max Born, *Einstein's Theory of Relativity* Dover Publications, New York, 1962.

9. H. E. Ives and G. R. Stilwell, *J. Opt. Soc. Am.*, **28**, 215 (1938); and **31**, 369 (1941).

10. D. Halliday and R. Resnick, *Physics*, John Wiley and Sons, 1966, p. 1008.

11. Mandelberg and Witten, *J. Opt. Soc. Am.*, **52**, 529 (1962).

12. G. Otting, *Phys. Z.*, **40**, 681 (1939).

13. Walter Kündig, *Phys. Rev.*, **129**, 2371 (1963).

14. H. Bondi, "The Teaching of Special Relativity," *Physics Education*, **1**, (4), 223 (1966).

15. David Bohm, *The Special Theory of Relativity* W. A. Benjamin, New York, 1965.

16. E. M. Dewan, "Stress Effects Due to Lorentz Contraction," *Am. J. Phys.*, **31**, 383 (1963).

17. W. Rindler, "Length Contraction Paradox," *Am. J. Phys.*, **29**, 365 (1961).

18. R. Shaw, "Length Contraction Paradox" *Am. J. Phys.*, **30**, 72 (1962).

19. W. Rindler, *Special Relativity*, Interscience Publishers, New York, 1960.

Chapter Three
Relativistic Dynamics

3.1 *Mechanics and Relativity*

In Chapter One we saw that experiment forced us to the conclusion that the Galilean transformations had to be replaced and the basic laws of mechanics, which were consistent with those transformations, needed to be modified. In Chapter Two we obtained the new transformation equations, the Lorentz transformations, and examined their implications for kinematical phenomena. Now we must consider dynamic phenomena and find how to modify the laws of classical mechanics so that the new mechanics is consistent with relativity.

Basically, classical Newtonian mechanics is inconsistent with relativity because its laws are invariant under a Galilean transformation and *not* under a Lorentz transformation. This formal result is plausible, as well, from other considerations. For example, in Newtonian mechanics a force can accelerate a particle to indefinite speeds, whereas in relativity the limiting speed is *c*. Another difficulty with classical mechanics is that it permits action-at-a-distance forces while requiring action and reaction forces to be equal. Such equality of action and reaction has no meaning in relativity except for contact forces, because the simultaneity of separated events is relative.

For example, in classical mechanics, we may say that two bodies on a frictionless surface connected by a light stretched spring are subject to equal but opposite forces at the same instant. In relativity, where simultaneity of separated events is a relative concept, "the same instant" differs from one inertial observer to another. Unless the action and reaction are contact forces (so that the interacting particles are not separated) we cannot give meaning to them independent of the frame of reference used.

The electrostatic force, which seems to be an action-at-a-distance one, can be treated instead as a field phenomenon. That is, the source charge sets up a field and the test charge interacts with the field at its location. Other apparent action-at-a-distance forces can similarly be treated as field phenomena. The net effect of relativistic considerations then is simply that we abandon the action-at-a-distance view, which is easily done with little sacrifice in classical physics.

110

In seeking a new law of motion that is consistent with relativity, we therefore exclude "action-at-a-distance" forces. But we can include collision phenomena (contact forces) or field phenomena (charges in an electromagnetic field), for example, neither of which involve the action-at-a-distance concept. In either case, when we obtain a law of motion that is invariant under a Lorentz transformation, we must also insure that it reduces to the Newtonian form as $v/c \to 0$ since, in the domain where $v/c \ll 1$, Newton's laws are consistent with experiment. Thus, the relativistic law of motion will be a generalization of the classical one.

We shall proceed by studying collisions first. Here we assume that the interaction between particles takes place only during an infinitesimally short time interval in which the particles have negligible separation (i.e., the range of forces is short compared to the dimensions of the system). During the collision the particles are accelerated, but before and after the interaction there is no acceleration. The laws of conservation of momentum and energy are valid classically during this interaction. If we require that these conservation laws also be valid relativistically (i.e., invariant under a Lorentz transformation) and hence that they be general laws of physics, we must modify them from the classical form in such a way that they also reduce to the classical form as $v/c \to 0$. In this way, we shall obtain the relativistic law of motion.

We could also proceed by studying the motion of charged particles in an electromagnetic field. In a sense, relativity was constructed in such a way as to preserve the laws of electromagnetism, so that the electromagnetic forces would be expected to be invariant under a Lorentz transformation. Since all forces must have the same invariant form, this approach would also yield the relativistic law of motion. However, to proceed in this way, we first need to know how the electric and magnetic fields transform. We shall examine this later. Here we simply assert that the collision approach and the electromagnetic field approach lead to the same form of the relativistic equation of motion. Let us now arrive at this through collisions.

3.2 *The Need to Redefine Momentum*

The first thing we wish to show is that if we want to find a quantity like momentum (for which there is a conservation law in classical physics) that is also subject to a conservation law in relativity, then we cannot use the same expression for momentum as the classical one. We must, instead, redefine momentum in order that a law of conservation of momentum in collisions be invariant under a Lorentz transformation.

Let us first analyze an elastic collision between two identical bodies as seen by different inertial observers, S and S', according to Newtonian mechanics. We choose the collision (Fig. 3-1) to be highly symmetrical in S': the bodies, say A and B, have initial velocities that are equal in magnitude but opposite in direction, the total momentum being zero. That is, $\mathbf{u}_{yA}' = -\mathbf{u}_{yB}'$ and $\mathbf{u}_{xA}' = -\mathbf{u}_{xB}'$. Since the collision is elastic, the final velocities have the same magnitude as the initial velocities, the total momentum after collision remaining zero. We have $\mathbf{u}_{yA}' = -\mathbf{U}_{yA}' = \mathbf{U}_{yB}' = -\mathbf{u}_{yB}'$ and $\mathbf{u}_{xA}' = \mathbf{U}_{xA}' = \mathbf{U}_{xB}' = -\mathbf{u}_{xB}'$. That is, observer S' notes that the y'-components of velocity for the bodies simply

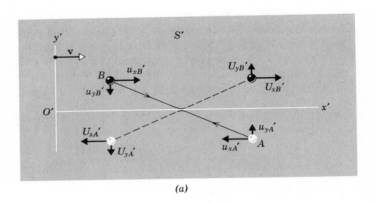

(a)

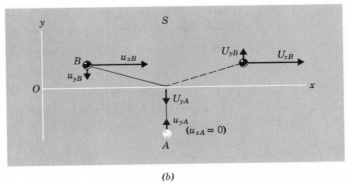

(b)

Fig. 3-1. A particular elastic collision as viewed by (a) observer S' and (b) observer S. Here, small letters (u) refer to before the collision, capital letters (U) refer to after the collision. The subscripts (A and B) denote the particle and (x and y) the component. The values in S' are primed, those in S are not.

reverse their signs during the collision, the x'-components remaining unchanged.

As seen by observer S, the reference frame S' is moving to the right with a speed v. We deliberately choose

$$\mathbf{v} = \mathbf{u}_{xB}' = -\mathbf{u}_{xA}' \tag{3-1}$$

so that the body A has no x-component of motion in frame S (see Fig. 3-1b). The y-components of velocity should be unaffected by the transformation, according to Newtonian mechanics, and momentum should still be conserved in the collision as viewed by S. That is, $\mathbf{u}_{yA} = \mathbf{u}_{yA}'$, $\mathbf{u}_{yB} = \mathbf{u}_{yB}'$, $\mathbf{u}_{yA} = -\mathbf{U}_{yA}$ and $\mathbf{u}_{yB} = -\mathbf{U}_{yB}$. The momentum lost by body A, $2mu_{yA}$, equals that gained by body B, $2mu_{yB}$, so that in magnitude

$$2mu_{yA} = 2mu_{yB} \tag{3-2}$$

and, because the bodies have identical mass m, we conclude that

$$u_{yA} = u_{yB}. \tag{3-3}$$

These are the Newtonian results.

Now, let us see whether these results are consistent with the Lorentz transformations. They are not, for they contradict the relativistic velocity transformations. If we use the equations in Table 2-2 we find that relativity requires, for body B,

$$u_{yB}' = \frac{u_{yB}\sqrt{1 - \beta^2}}{1 - u_{xB}v/c^2} \tag{3-4}$$

whereas for body A, for which $u_{xA} = 0$,

$$u_{yA}' = u_{yA}\sqrt{1 - \beta^2}. \tag{3-5}$$

Hence, the y-components of velocity *are* affected by the relativistic transformations. For one thing, they do not have the same values in one frame as in the other, but, more important, if they are equal to one another in magnitude in one frame, they are not necessarily equal to one another in the other frame. In fact, assuming as before that $u_{yB}' = u_{yA}'$, we find by combining and rearranging Eqs. 3-4 and 3-5, that

$$u_{yA} = u_{yB}\frac{1}{1 - u_{xB}v/c^2}, \tag{3-6}$$

in contradiction to the Newtonian result, Eq. 3-3. Hence, the *changes* in the y-component velocities have different magnitudes in one frame than in the other during the collision. The result is that, if we compute momentum according to the classical formulas $\mathbf{p} = m\mathbf{u}$ and $\mathbf{p}' = m\mathbf{u}'$, then when momentum is conserved in a collision in one frame it is not conserved in the other frame.

This result contradicts the basic postulate of special relativity that the laws of physics are the same in all inertial systems. If the conservation of momentum in collisions is to be a law of physics, then the classical definition of momentum cannot be correct in general. We notice that the disagreement between Eqs. 3-3 and 3-6 becomes trivial when $u_{xB} \ll c$ and $v \ll c$, so that it is at high speeds that the Newtonian formulation of the momentum conservation law breaks down. We need a generalization of the definition of momentum, therefore, that reduces to the classical result at low speeds.

In the next section, we shall show that it is possible to preserve the *form* of the classical definition of the momentum of a particle, $\mathbf{p} = m\mathbf{u}$, where $\mathbf{p}$ is the momentum, m the mass, and $\mathbf{u}$ the velocity of a particle, and also to preserve the classical law of the conservation of momentum of a system of interacting particles, providing that we modify the classical concept of mass. We need to let the mass of a particle be a function of its speed u, that is, $m = m_0/\sqrt{1 - u^2/c^2}$, where m_0 is the classical mass and m is the relativistic mass of the particle. Clearly, as u/c tends to zero, m tends to m_0. The relativistic momentum then becomes $\mathbf{p} = m\mathbf{u} = m_0\mathbf{u}/\sqrt{1 - \beta^2}$ and reduces to the classical expression $\mathbf{p} = m_0\mathbf{u}$ as $\beta \to 0$. Let us now deduce these results.

3.3 *Relativistic Momentum*

In Eq. 3-2, based on momentum conservation, we assumed that the mass m was the same for each body, and, in this way, we were led to the (incorrect) result that the y-component velocities had equal magnitude. True, the bodies were identical when placed side by side at rest. However, since the measured length of a rod and the measured rate of a clock are affected by the motion of the rod or the clock relative to the observer, it may be that the measured mass of a body also depends on its motion with respect to the observer. In that case the *form* of the Newtonian momentum still could be correct so that, for example, we could rewrite Eq. 3-2 as

$$2m_A u_{yA} = 2m_B u_{yB}. \tag{3-7}$$

The masses are now labelled as m_A and m_B, however, to suggest that they may have different values.

Bodies A and B, in Fig. 3-1b, do travel at different speeds in the S-frame and, if we accept the relativistic result (Eq. 3-6) for the speeds, we obtain

$$m_B = m_A \frac{u_{yA}}{u_{yB}} = \frac{m_A}{1 - u_{xB}v/c^2} \tag{3-8}$$

by combining Eqs. 3-6 and 3-7. Hence, the *relativistic masses*, m_A and m_B, are *not* equal if the relativistic conservation of momentum law is to have the same form as the Newtonian law. It remains to find how the relativistic mass must vary with the speed.

We can simplify Eq. 3-8 by eliminating v. Recall that $v = u_{xB}{}'$ (Eq. 3-1) and that $u_{xB}{}'$ is related to u_{xB} by the Lorentz velocity transformation (Table 2-2)

$$u_{xB}{}'(= v) = \frac{u_{xB} - v}{1 - u_{xB}v/c^2}.$$

Solving for v, we get

$$v = \frac{c^2}{u_{xB}} (1 - \sqrt{1 - (u_{xB}/c)^2}).$$

If we substitute this expression for v into Eq. 3-8 we obtain

$$m_B = \frac{m_A}{\sqrt{1 - (u_{xB}/c)^2}}.$$

We can find how the relativistic mass of either particle varies with the speed in a simple manner by considering a special case of the collision in which the y-y' velocity components are made to approach zero. Then, the particles' speeds will be identical to the magnitude of their respective x-component velocities. This is illustrated in Fig. 3-2a and 3-2b. Observer S' simply sees two bodies moving past each other making a grazing collision; observer S sees body A at rest and body B moving past it, at a speed u_{xB}, again making a grazing collision. Equation 3-9 must apply to

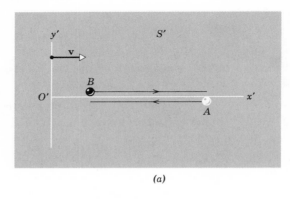

(a)

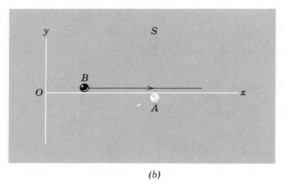

(b)

Fig. **3-2.** The same collision as in Fig. 3-1 for the limiting case in which $u_{yA}' = u_{yB}' = 0$.

this grazing collision as well as to others because we put no restriction on the value of u_y' in deriving it.

Since body A is at rest in S its mass m_A must be the ordinary Newtonian mass which we now call the *rest mass* and denote by m_0. This is the same as the mass of body B when body B is at rest, the two bodies being identical. However, in S, body B is moving with a speed u_{xB}, which we can simply call u; its mass m_B, which we can call the *relativistic mass* and denote by m, will not be m_0. From Eq. 3-9 we obtain

$$m = \frac{m_0}{\sqrt{1 - u^2/c^2}} \qquad (3\text{-}10)$$

which tells us how the relativistic mass m of a body moving at a speed u varies with u. We see at once that when $u = 0$, the body then being at rest, we obtain $m = m_0$, the rest mass. More generally, as $u/c \to 0$, we find $m \to m_0$, which is the Newtonian limit of the more general expression for the relativistic mass m.

Hence, if we want to preserve the *form* of the classical momentum conservation law while requiring that the law be relativistically invariant, we must define the mass of a moving body by Eq. 3-10. That is, momentum still has the form $m\mathbf{u}$, but mass is defined as $m = m_0/\sqrt{1 - u^2/c^2}$. Note that u is the speed of the body relative to S, which we can regard as the laboratory frame, and that u has no connection necessarily with changing reference frames. By accepting Eq. 3-10 as our definition of the mass of a moving body, we implicitly assume that the mass of a body does not depend on its acceleration relative to the reference frame, although it does depend on its speed. Mass remains a scalar quantity in the sense that its value is independent of the *direction* of the velocity of the body. The rest mass m_0 is often called the *proper mass*, for it is the mass of the body measured, like proper length and proper time, in the inertial frame in which the body is at rest.

We have presented above a derivation of an expression for relativistic momentum which obviously centers around a very special case. For example, the velocity of the particle (B) is parallel to the relative S-S' velocity and the derivation depended only upon invoking conservation of momentum in the y-direction. Such a derivation enables us to make an educated guess as to what the general result may be. We have avoided rather involved general derivations which, however, lead to exactly the same results. When the general case is done, u becomes the absolute value of the velocity of the particle; that is, $u^2 = u_x^2 + u_y^2 + u_z^2$.

To complete our particular deduction, we need to carry our argument two steps further. First, using the expression for momentum which we have tentatively derived, we can demonstrate explicitly that *if* the momentum of a system of interacting particles is conserved in one inertial frame S, *then* (using the Lorentz transformation) it is conserved in any other inertial frame S' (see Problem 43). In fact, it turns out that this form of a momentum is the only one that does have this property. Second, this momentum conservation law is an experimental fact; that is, experiment proves this relativistic law to be true. Not only have we found a definition of momentum that conserves this quantity in the theory, but the theory is in harmony with physical experiment.

Hence, to conclude, in order to make the conservation of momentum in collisions a law that is experimentally valid in all reference frames, we must define momentum, not as $m_0\mathbf{u}$, but as

$$\mathbf{p} = \frac{m_0\mathbf{u}}{\sqrt{1 - u^2/c^2}}. \tag{3-11}$$

The components of the momentum then are

$$p_x = \frac{m_0 u_x}{\sqrt{1 - u^2/c^2}} \qquad p_y = \frac{m_0 u_y}{\sqrt{1 - u^2/c^2}} \qquad p_z = \frac{m_0 u_z}{\sqrt{1 - u^2/c^2}} \tag{3-12}$$

which we write out explicitly to emphasize that the magnitude u of the total velocity appears in the denominator of each component equation.

▶ *Example* 1. For what value of u/c ($= \beta$) will the relativistic mass of a particle exceed its rest mass by a given fraction f?

From Eq. 3-10 we have

$$f = \frac{m - m_0}{m_0} = \frac{m}{m_0} - 1 = \frac{1}{\sqrt{1 - \beta^2}} - 1$$

which, solved for β, is

$$\beta = \frac{\sqrt{f(2 + f)}}{1 + f}.$$

The table below shows some computed values, which hold for all particles regardless of their rest mass.

f	β
0.001 (0.1 percent)	0.014
0.01	0.14
0.1	0.42
1 (100 percent)	0.87
10	0.994
100	0.999 ◀

3.4 *Alternative Views of Mass in Relativity*

The student, in his readings in relativity, is likely to encounter two different interpretations of the relativistic momentum. Therefore, it will avoid confusion later to present here an explanation of these different interpretations. This will show that neither treatment is wrong but that the differences are a matter of taste.

The classical momentum has components such as $p_x = m_0 \, (dx/dt)$. If, in relativity, we wish to continue to regard momentum as a product of a mass and an ordinary velocity, then we must modify the mass and write $p_x = m(dx/dt)$ where m, called the relativistic mass, is $m_0/\sqrt{1-\beta^2}$. This is the view that we presented in earlier sections.

However, we can choose to regard the mass as an invariant scalar quantity which gives the inertial property of a body. Then, in the relativistic expression for momentum, we connect the factor $1/\sqrt{1-\beta^2}$ with the ordinary velocity instead of with the mass. That is, we can write $p_x = m_0(dx/d\tau)$ in which $dx/d\tau$ is the x-component of a relativistic velocity. Here, the mass m_0 is an invariant and the proper time interval $d\tau$ is also an invariant. Such a formulation is useful because it emphasizes invariant quantities. Furthermore, it is consistent with the basic philosophy of relativity, in this sense: relativity modifies our concepts of time and space, so that kinematic quantities, such as velocity, are expected to change, whereas properties of bodies not directly relevant to time and space (such as charge and mass) should remain unaffected. If, for example, we compare the classical expression for momentum, $p_x = m_0(dx/dt)$, with this form of the relativistic expression for momentum, $p_x = m_0(dx/d\tau)$, the difference between them is seen to be caused not by any difference in the value of the mass but, instead, by the difference between proper time $d\tau$ and nonproper time dt. Indeed, it should be noted that, whether we identify the factor $1/\sqrt{1-\beta^2}$ with the mass or with the velocity, the origin of this factor in collision measurements is kinematical; that is, it is caused by the relativity of time measurements.

Nevertheless, there are advantages of a pedagogic nature to using the concept of relativistic mass. Both the momentum ($m\mathbf{u}$) and the total energy (mc^2), as we shall see later, have simple, familiar forms in terms of relativistic mass m, although (see Question 3) we cannot simply replace m_0 of every classical formula by m to obtain a correct relativistic formula. Also, as $u \to c$, $m \to \infty$ in the relativistic mass formulation and this gives a plausible explanation for the limiting speed c that a body can acquire; its inertia increases with velocity making it harder to increase the velocity further. Finally, the constancy of the proper mass of a body turns out to be confined to perfectly elastic collisions, a rare situation in practice; since proper mass can vary (a matter that we discuss later in Section 3-6), it seems less objectionable than otherwise to speak of a relativistic mass that varies with the speed. We shall continue to use the term "rest mass" for m_0, and the term "relativistic mass" for m.

3.5 *The Relativistic Force Law and the Dynamics of a Single Particle*
Newton's second law must now be generalized to

$$\mathbf{F} = \frac{d}{dt}(\mathbf{p}) = \frac{d}{dt}\left(\frac{m_0\mathbf{u}}{\sqrt{1-u^2/c^2}}\right) \tag{3-13}$$

in relativistic mechanics. When the law is written in this form we can immediately deduce the law of the conservation of relativistic momentum from it; when $\mathbf{F}$ is zero, $\mathbf{p} = m_0\mathbf{u}/\sqrt{1 - u^2/c^2}$ must be a constant. In the absence of external forces, the momentum is conserved. Furthermore, when $\mathbf{F}$ as defined by Eq. 3-13 is not zero, we can easily derive the result (see Problem 44) that if, for a system of interacting particles, the total relativistic momentum changes by an amount $\Delta\mathbf{P}$, then this change is equal to the total impulse $\int\mathbf{F}\,dt$ given to the system. Hence, the force defined by Eq. 3-13 has the general properties we seek. Notice that this new form of the law, Eq. 3-13, is *not* equivalent to writing $F = ma = (m_0/\sqrt{1 - u^2/c^2})(du/dt)$, in which we simply multiply the acceleration by the relativistic mass.

We find also that experiment agrees with Eq. 3-13. When, for example, we investigate the motion of high-speed charged particles, it is found that the equation correctly describing the motion is

$$q(\mathbf{E} + \mathbf{u} \times \mathbf{B}) = \frac{d}{dt}\left(\frac{m_0\mathbf{u}}{\sqrt{1 - u^2/c^2}}\right), \tag{3-14}$$

which agrees with Eq. 3-13. Here, $q(\mathbf{E} + \mathbf{u} \times \mathbf{B})$ is the Lorentz electromagnetic force, in which $\mathbf{E}$ is the electric field, $\mathbf{B}$ is the magnetic field, and $\mathbf{u}$ is the particle velocity, all measured in the same reference frame, and q and m_0 are constants that describe the electrical (charge) and inertial (rest mass) properties of the particle, respectively. Notice that the Lorentz force law of classical electromagnetism remains valid relativistically, as we should expect from the discussion of Chapter One.

Later we shall turn to the question of how electric and magnetic fields, and forces, transform from one Lorentz frame to another. For the moment, however, we confine ourselves to one reference frame (the laboratory frame) and develop other concepts in mechanics, such as work and energy, which follow from the relativistic expression for force (Eq. 3-13). We shall confine ourselves to the motion of a single particle. In succeeding sections we shall consider many-particle systems.

In Newtonian mechanics we defined the kinetic energy, K, of a particle to be equal to the work done by an external force in increasing the speed of the particle from zero to some value u. That is,

$$K = \int_{u=0}^{u=u} \mathbf{F} \cdot d\mathbf{l}$$

where $\mathbf{F} \cdot d\mathbf{l}$ is the work done by the force $\mathbf{F}$ in displacing the particle through $d\mathbf{l}$. For simplicity, we can limit the motion to one dimension, say x, the three-dimensional case being an easy extension (see Problem 8). Then, classically,

$$K = \int_{u=0}^{u=u} F \, dx = \int m_0\left(\frac{du}{dt}\right) dx = \int m_0 \, du \, \frac{dx}{dt} = m_0 \int_0^u u \, du = \tfrac{1}{2}m_0 u^2.$$

Here we write the particle mass as m_0 to emphasize that, in Newtonian mechanics, we do not regard the mass as varying with the speed, and we take the force to be $m_0 a = m_0(du/dt)$.

In relativistic mechanics, it proves useful to use a corresponding definition for kinetic energy in which, however, we use the relativistic equation of motion, Eq. 3-13, rather than the Newtonian one. Then, relativistically,

$$K = \int_{u=0}^{u=u} F \, dx = \int \frac{d}{dt}(mu) \, dx = \int d(mu) \frac{dx}{dt}$$

$$= \int (m \, du + u \, dm) \, u = \int_{u=0}^{u=u} (mu \, du + u^2 \, dm) \quad (3\text{-}15)$$

in which both m and u are variables. These quantities are related, furthermore, by Eq. 3-10, $m = m_0/\sqrt{1 - u^2/c^2}$, which we can rewrite as

$$m^2 c^2 - m^2 u^2 = m_0^2 c^2.$$

Taking differentials in this equation yields

$$2mc^2 \, dm - m^2 2u \, du - u^2 2m \, dm = 0,$$

which, on division by $2m$, can be written also as

$$mu \, du + u^2 \, dm = c^2 \, dm.$$

The left side of this equation is exactly the integrand of Eq. 3-15. Hence, we can write the relativistic expression for the kinetic energy of a particle as

$$K = \int_{u=0}^{u=u} c^2 \, dm = c^2 \int_{m=m_0}^{m=m} dm = mc^2 - m_0 c^2. \quad (3\text{-}16a)$$

By using Eq. 3-10, we obtain equivalently

$$K = m_0 c^2 \left[\frac{1}{\sqrt{1 - u^2/c^2}} - 1 \right]. \qquad (3\text{-}16b)$$

Also, if we take $mc^2 = E$, where E is called the *total energy* of the particle—a name whose aptness will become clear later—we can express Eqs. 3-16 compactly as

$$E = m_0 c^2 + K \qquad (3\text{-}17)$$

in which $m_0 c^2$ is called the *rest energy* of the particle. The rest energy (by definition) is the energy of the particle at rest, when $u = 0$ and $K = 0$. The total energy of the particle (Eq. 3-17) is the sum of its rest energy* and its kinetic energy.

The relativistic expression for K must reduce to the classical result, $\frac{1}{2}m_0 u^2$, when $u/c \ll 1$. Let us check this. From

$$K = m_0 c^2 [(1/\sqrt{1 - u^2/c^2}) - 1]$$
$$= m_0 c^2 \left[\left(1 - \frac{u^2}{c^2}\right)^{-1/2} - 1 \right]$$

the binomial theorem expansion in (u/c) gives

$$K = m_0 c^2 \left[1 + \frac{1}{2}\left(\frac{u}{c}\right)^2 + \frac{3}{8}\left(\frac{u}{c}\right)^4 + \cdots - 1 \right]$$
$$= \frac{1}{2}m_0 u^2,$$

in which we take only the first two terms in the expansion as significant when $u/c \ll 1$, thereby confirming the Newtonian limit of the relativistic result.

It is interesting to notice also that, as $u \rightarrow c$, in Eq. 3-16b, the kinetic energy K tends to infinity. That is, from Eq. 3-15, an infinite amount of work would need to be done on the particle to accelerate it up to the speed of light. Once again we find c playing the role of a limiting velocity. Note also from Eq. 3-16a, which permits us to write $K = (m - m_0) c^2$, that a change in the kinetic energy of a particle is related to a change in its (inertial) mass.

---

*In classical physics, the energy of a single particle is defined only to within an arbitrary constant. Relativity fixes this arbitrary constant so that the energy of a particle at rest is taken to be $E_0 = m_0 c^2$. The physical meaning of this (see Section 3-6) is that even a particle that is not in motion has a *rest* energy, given by $m_0 c^2$.

We often seek a connection between the kinetic energy K of a rapidly moving particle and its momentum p. This can be found by eliminating u between Eq. 3-16b and Eq. 3-11. The student can verify (Problem 10) that the result is

$$(K + m_0c^2)^2 = (pc)^2 + (m_0c^2)^2 \tag{3-18a}$$

which, with the total energy $E = K + m_0c^2$, can also be written as

$$E^2 = (pc)^2 + (m_0c^2)^2. \tag{3-18b}$$

The right triangle of Fig. 3-3 is a useful mnemonic device for remembering Eqs. 3-18.

The relationship between K and p (Eq. 3-18a) should reduce to the Newtonian expression $p = \sqrt{2m_0K}$ for $u/c \ll 1$. To see that it does, let us expand Eq. 3-18a, obtaining

$$K^2 + 2Km_0c^2 = p^2c^2.$$

When $u/c \ll 1$, the kinetic energy, K, of a moving particle will always be much less than its rest energy, m_0c^2 (see Problem 7). Under these circumstances, the first term on the left above (K^2) can be neglected in comparison with the second term ($2K\,m_0c^2$), and the equation becomes $p = \sqrt{2m_0K}$, as required.

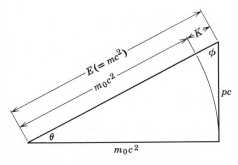

Fig. 3-3. A mnemonic device, using a right triangle and the Pythagorean relation, to help in remembering the relations between total energy E, rest energy m_0c^2, and momentum p. The relation is $E^2 = (pc)^2 + (m_0c^2)^2$. Shown also is the relation, $E = m_0c^2 + K$, between total energy, rest energy and kinetic energy K. The student can show that $\sin\theta = \beta$ and $\sin\phi = \sqrt{1 - \beta^2}$, where $\beta = u/c$.

The relativistic expression, Eq. 3-18*b*, often written as

$$E = c\sqrt{p^2 + m_0^2 c^2}, \tag{3-19}$$

is useful in high-energy physics to calculate the total energy of a particle when its momentum is given, or vice versa. By differentiating Eq. 3-19 with respect to *p*, we can obtain another useful relation.

$$\frac{dE}{dp} = \frac{pc}{\sqrt{m_0^2 c^2 + p^2}} = \frac{pc^2}{c\sqrt{m_0^2 c^2 + p^2}} = \frac{pc^2}{E}.$$

But with $E = mc^2$ and $\mathbf{p} = m\mathbf{u}$ this reduces to

$$\frac{dE}{dp} = u. \tag{3-20}$$

As a final consideration in the relativistic dynamics of a single particle, we look at the acceleration of a particle under the influence of a force. In general, the force is given by $\mathbf{F} = d\mathbf{p}/dt = \dfrac{d}{dt}(m\mathbf{u})$ or

$$\mathbf{F} = m\frac{d\mathbf{u}}{dt} + \mathbf{u}\frac{dm}{dt}. \tag{3-21}$$

We know that $m = E/c^2$ so that

$$\frac{dm}{dt} = \frac{1}{c^2}\frac{dE}{dt} = \frac{1}{c^2}\frac{d}{dt}(K + m_0 c^2) = \frac{1}{c^2}\frac{dK}{dt}.$$

But

$$\frac{dK}{dt} = \frac{(\mathbf{F} \cdot d\mathbf{l})}{dt} = \mathbf{F} \cdot \frac{d\mathbf{l}}{dt} = \mathbf{F} \cdot \mathbf{u}$$

so that

$$\frac{dm}{dt} = \frac{1}{c^2}\mathbf{F} \cdot \mathbf{u}.$$

We can now substitute this into Eq. 3-21 and obtain

$$\mathbf{F} = m\frac{d\mathbf{u}}{dt} + \frac{\mathbf{u}(\mathbf{F} \cdot \mathbf{u})}{c^2}.$$

The acceleration **a** is defined by $\mathbf{a} = d\mathbf{u}/dt$ so that the general expression for acceleration is

$$\mathbf{a} = \frac{d\mathbf{u}}{dt} = \frac{\mathbf{F}}{m} - \frac{\mathbf{u}}{mc^2}(\mathbf{F} \cdot \mathbf{u}). \tag{3-22}$$

What this equation tells us at once is that, in general, the acceleration **a** is *not* parallel to the force in relativity, since the last term above is in the direction of the velocity **u**.

There are two simple but useful cases, however, in which the accelera-tion *is* parallel to the force. One case is that in which the force **F** is paral-lel to the velocity **u**, so that **a** is parallel both to **u** and **F**. Here the particle moves in a straight line, such as when a charged particle starts from rest in a uniform electric field. Since **a**, **F**, and **u** are all parallel, we can write Eq. 3-21 *in this special case* as $\mathbf{F} = m(du/dt) + u(dm/dt)$; and, by sub-stituting $m = m_0/\sqrt{1 - u^2/c^2}$, we shall find (see Problem 11) that $\mathbf{F} = m_0 a/(1 - u^2/c^2)^{3/2}$. To fix in our mind that this result applies when **F** and **a** are *parallel to the velocity* **u**, we shall write it as

$$F_{\parallel} = \frac{m_0}{(1 - u^2/c^2)^{3/2}}\, a_{\parallel}.$$

The quantity $m_0/(1 - u^2/c^2)^{3/2}$ is sometimes called the "longitudinal mass."

Another case in which **a** is parallel to **F** is that in which the force **F** is perpendicular to the velocity **u**, for then $\mathbf{F} \cdot \mathbf{u} = 0$ and Eq. 3-22 be-comes $\mathbf{a} = \mathbf{F}/m = \mathbf{F}\sqrt{1 - u^2/c^2}/m_0$. The force on a charged particle moving with velocity **u** in a magnetic field **B** (i.e., $\mathbf{F} = q\mathbf{u} \times \mathbf{B}$), exem-plifies this case. Here, to fix in our mind that this result applies when **F** and **a** are *perpendicular to the velocity* **u**, we shall write it as

$$F_{\perp} = \frac{m_0}{\sqrt{1 - u^2/c^2}}\, a_{\perp},$$

suggesting the name "transverse mass" for the quantity $m_0/\sqrt{1 - u^2/c^2}$.

◆ *Example* 2. (*a*) What is the kinetic energy acquired by a particle of charge q starting from rest in a uniform electric field when it falls through an electro-static potential difference of V_0 volts? The work done on the charge q by the electric field **E** in a displacement $d\mathbf{l}$ is

$$dW = q\mathbf{E} \cdot d\mathbf{l}.$$

Let the uniform field be in the x-direction so that $\mathbf{E} \cdot d\mathbf{l} = E_x\, dx$ and

$$W = \int qE_x\, dx.$$

Now $E_x = -(dV/dx)$, where V is the electrostatic potential, so that

$$W = -\int q\frac{dV}{dx}dx = -q\int dV = -q(V_f - V_i)$$
$$= q(V_i - V_f) = qV_0$$

where V_0 is the difference between the initial potential V_i and the final potential V_f. The kinetic energy acquired by the charge is equal to the work done on it by the field so that

$$K = qV_0. \tag{3-23}$$

Notice that we have implicitly assumed that the charge q of the particle is a constant, independent of the particle's motion.

(b) Assume the particle to be an electron and the potential difference to be 10^4 volts. Find the kinetic energy of the electron, its speed, and its mass at the end of the acceleration.

The charge on the electron is $e = -1.602 \times 10^{-19}$ coulomb. The potential difference is now a rise, $V_i - V_f = -10^4$ volts, a negative charge accelerating in a direction opposite to **E**. Hence, the kinetic energy acquired is

$$K = qV_0 = (-1.602 \times 10^{-19})(-10^4) \text{ joules} = 1.602 \times 10^{-15} \text{ joules.}$$

From Eq. 3-16, $K = mc^2 - m_0c^2$, we obtain

$$\frac{K}{c^2} = (m - m_0)$$

or

$$(1.602 \times 10^{-15} \text{ joules}/8.99 \times 10^{16} \, m^2/\text{sec}^2) = m - m_0 = 1.78 \times 10^{-32} \text{ kg}$$

and, with $m_0 = 9.109 \times 10^{-31}$ kg, we find the mass of the moving electron to be

$$m = (9.109 + 0.178) \times 10^{-31} \text{ kg} = 9.287 \times 10^{-31} \text{ kg.}$$

Notice that $m/m_0 = 1.02$, so that the mass increase due to the motion is about 2 percent of the rest mass.

From Eq. 3-10, $m = m_0/\sqrt{1 - u^2/c^2}$, we have

$$\frac{u^2}{c^2} = \left[1 - \left(\frac{m_0}{m}\right)^2\right] = \left[1 - \left(\frac{9.109}{9.287}\right)^2\right] = 0.038$$

or $u = 0.195c = 5.85 \times 10^7$ m/sec.

The electron acquires a speed of about one-fifth the speed of light.

These are the relativistic predictions. We shall see below that they are confirmed by direct experiment.

omit   *Example* 3. (a) Show that, in a region in which there is a uniform magnetic field, a charged particle entering at right angles to the field moves in a circle whose radius is proportional to the particle's momentum.

Call the charge of the particle q and its rest mass m_0. Let its velocity be **u**. The force on the particle is then

$$\mathbf{F} = q\mathbf{u} \times \mathbf{B}$$

which is at right angles both to **u** and to **B**, the magnetic field. Hence, from

Eq. 3-22, the acceleration,

$$\mathbf{a} = \frac{\mathbf{F}}{m} = \frac{q}{m}\mathbf{u} \times \mathbf{B},$$

is in the same direction as the force. Because the acceleration is always at right angles to the particle's velocity $\mathbf{u}$, the speed of the particle is constant and the particle moves in a circle. Let the radius of the circle be r, so that the centripetal acceleration is u^2/r. We equate this to the acceleration obtained from above, $a = quB/m$, and find

$$\frac{quB}{m} = \frac{u^2}{r}$$

or

$$r = \frac{mu}{qB} = \frac{p}{qB}. \tag{3-24}$$

Hence, the radius is proportional to the momentum $p(= mu)$.

Notice that both the equation for the acceleration and the equation for the radius (Eq. 3-24) are identical in form to the classical results, but that the rest mass m_0 of the classical formula is replaced by the relativistic mass $m = m_0/\sqrt{1 - u^2/c^2}$.

How would the motion change if the initial velocity of the charged particle had a component parallel to the magnetic field?

(*b*) Compute the radius, both classically and relativistically, of a 10 Mev electron moving at right angles to a uniform magnetic field of strength 2.0 webers/m^2.

Classically, we have $r = m_0 u/qB$. The classical relation between kinetic energy and momentum is $p = \sqrt{2m_0 K}$ so that

$$p = \sqrt{2m_0 K}$$
$$= \sqrt{2 \times 9.1 \times 10^{-31} \text{ kg} \times 10 \text{ Mev} \times 1.6 \times 10^{-13} \text{ joule/Mev}}$$
$$= 17 \times 10^{-22} \text{ kg m/sec.}$$

Then

$$r = \frac{m_0 u}{qB} = \frac{p}{qB} = \frac{17 \times 10^{-22}}{1.6 \times 10^{-19} \times 2.0} \text{meter}$$
$$= 5.3 \times 10^{-3} \text{ meter} = 0.53 \text{ cm.}$$

Relativistically, we have $r = mu/qB$. The relativistic relation between kinetic energy and momentum (Eq. 3-18a) may be written as

$$p = \frac{1}{c}\sqrt{(K + m_0 c^2)^2 - (m_0 c^2)^2}.$$

Here, the rest energy of an electron, $m_0 c^2$, equals 0.51 Mev, so that

$$p = \frac{1}{3 \times 10^8}\sqrt{(10 + 0.51)^2 - (0.51)^2}\frac{\text{Mev-sec}}{\text{meter}}\ (1.16 \times 10^{-13} \text{ joule/Mev})$$
$$= 5.6 \times 10^{-21} \text{ kg} - \text{m/sec.}$$

Then

$$r = \frac{mu}{qB} = \frac{p}{qB} = \frac{5.6 \times 10^{-21}}{1.6 \times 10^{-19} \times 2.0} \text{ meter}$$
$$= 1.8 \times 10^{-2} \text{ meter} = 1.8 \text{ cm.}$$

Experiment bears out the relativistic result (see below). ◀

The first experiments in relativistic dynamics, by Bucherer [1], made use of Eq. 3-24. Electrons (from the β-decay of radioactive particles) enter a velocity selector, which determines the speed of those that emerge, and then enter a uniform magnetic field, where the radius of their circular path can be measured. Bucherer's results are shown in Table 3-1.

TABLE **3-1**   BUCHERER'S RESULTS

u/c	$e/m(= u/rB)$ in coul/kg	$\dfrac{e}{m_0}\left(= \dfrac{e}{m\sqrt{1 - u^2/c^2}}\right)$ in coul/kg
(Measured)	(Measured)	(Computed)
0.3173	1.661×10^{11}	1.752×10^{11}
0.3787	1.630×10^{11}	1.761×10^{11}
0.4281	1.590×10^{11}	1.760×10^{11}
0.5154	1.511×10^{11}	1.763×10^{11}
0.6870	1.283×10^{11}	1.767×10^{11}

The first column gives the measured speeds in terms of the fraction of the speed of light. The second column gives the ratio e/m computed from the measured quantities in Eq. 3-24 as $e/m = u/rB$. It is clear that the value of e/m varies with the speed of the electrons. The third column gives the calculated values of $e/m\sqrt{1 - u^2/c^2} = e/m_0$, which are seen to be constant. The results are consistent with the relativistic relation

$$r = \frac{m_0 u}{qB\sqrt{1 - u^2/c^2}}$$

rather than the classical relation $r = m_0 u/qB$ and can be interpreted as confirming Eq. 3-10, $m = m_0/\sqrt{1 - u^2/c^2}$, for the variation of mass with speed.* Many similar experiments have since been performed,

---

*These results verify not only that relativity predicts the correct functional form for $m(u)$ but also that the value of the limiting speed (c) is 3×10^{10} cm/sec.

greatly extending the range of u/c and always resulting in confirmation of the relativistic results (see Fig. 3-4).

The student may properly ask why, in measuring a variation of e/m with speed, we attribute the variation solely to the mass rather than to the charge, for instance, or some other more complicated effect. We might have concluded, for example, that $e = e_0 \sqrt{1 - u^2/c^2}$. Actually, we have implicitly assumed above that the charge on the electron is independent of its speed. This assumption is a direct consequence of relativistic electrodynamics, wherein the charge of a particle is not changed by its motion. That is, charge is an invariant quantity in relativity. This is plausible, as a little thought shows, for otherwise the neutral character of an atom, say, would be upset merely by the motion of the electrons in it. As a clincher, of course, we turn to experiment which not only verifies relativity theory as a whole but also confirms directly this specific result of the constancy of e (see Refs. 2 and 3 for an analysis of such an experiment).

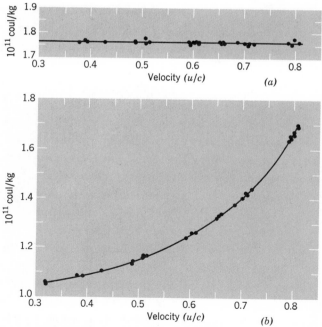

Fig. 3-4. Experimental verification of the relativistic mass formula. Experimental points are shown for u/c ranging from 0.32 to 0.82. (a) The ratio $e/m_0 = e/m \sqrt{1 - u^2/c^2}$. (b) The ratio $m/m_0 = 1/\sqrt{1 - u^2/c^2}$.

The relations used in Example 2, above, are tested directly in a recent experiment by Bertozzi [4]. Electrons are accelerated to high speed in the electric field of a linear accelerator and emerge into a vacuum chamber. Their speed can be measured by determining the time of flight in passing two targets of known separation. As we vary the voltage of the accelerator, we can plot the values of eV, the kinetic energy of the emerging electrons, versus the measured speed u. In the experiment, an independent check was made to confirm the relation $K = eV$. This is accomplished by stopping the electrons in a collector, where the kinetic energy of the absorbed electrons is converted into heat energy which raises the temperature of the collector, and determining the energy released per electron by calorimetry. It is found that the average kinetic energy per electron before impact, measured in this way, agrees with the kinetic energy obtained from eV.

In Fig. 3-5, we show a plot of the results. Here, on the ordinate, is plotted u^2 versus $2K/m_0$, on the absicca. At low energies, the experimental results (solid curve) agree with the classical prediction (dashed curve), $K = \frac{1}{2}m_0 u^2$ (i.e., $2K/m_0 = u^2$). However, as the energy rises, we find that $2K/m_0 > u^2$. In fact, the measured values of u were always less than c, regardless of how high the energy became, so that the experimental curve approaches but never reaches the dotted line corresponding

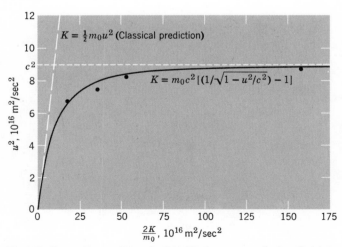

Fig. 3-5. Bertozzi's experimental points (dots) are seen to fit the relativistic expression (solid line) rather than the classical expression (dashed line) for kinetic energy K versus u^2.

to $u = c$. We see that to attain a given speed we need more kinetic energy than is classically predicted and that, by extrapolation, we would need an infinite energy to accelerate the electron to the speed of light. The experimental curve fits the relativistic prediction of Eq. 3-17,

$$K = m_0 c^2 \left(\frac{1}{\sqrt{1 - u^2/c^2}} - 1 \right),$$

and can be regarded as another confirmation of the relativistic mass formula of Eq. 3-10, $m = m_0 \sqrt{1 - u^2/c^2}$.

The student should note carefully that the relativistic formula for kinetic energy is *not* $\frac{1}{2}mu^2$; this shows the danger, mentioned earlier, in assuming that we can simply substitute the relativistic mass for the rest mass in generalizing a classical formula to a relativistic one. This is not so for the kinetic energy.

3.6 *The Equivalence of Mass and Energy* look at

In Section 3-3 we examined an elastic collision, that is, a collision in which the kinetic energy of the bodies remained constant. Now let us consider an inelastic collision. In particular, consider two identical bodies of rest mass m_0, each with kinetic energy K as seen by a particular observer S', which collide and stick together forming a single body of rest mass M_0. The situation before and after the collision in the S'-frame is shown in Fig. 3-6: here, before collision, bodies A and B each have a speed u', with velocities oppositely directed and along the x'-axis; the combined body C, formed by the collision, is at rest in S', as required by conservation of momentum. In another reference frame S, moving with respect to S' with a speed $v(= u')$ to the left along the common x-x' axis, the combined body C will have a velocity of magnitude v directed to the right along x. Body A will be stationary before collision in this frame and body B will have a speed u_B. The situation in the S-frame is shown in Fig. 3-7.

The velocity u_B in the S-frame can be obtained from the relativistic velocity transformation equation, Eq. 2-18, as

$$u_B = \frac{u' + v}{1 + u'v/c^2} = \frac{u' + u'}{1 + u'^2/c^2} = 2u'/(1 + u'^2/c^2).$$

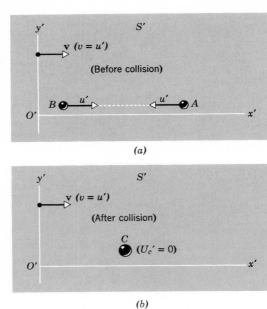

Fig. **3-6.** A particular inelastic collision as viewed by observer S', (a) before the collision, and (b) after the collision.

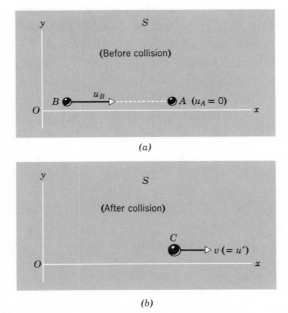

Fig. **3-7.** The same collision as in Fig. 3-6 as viewed by observer S, (a) before the collision, and (b) after the collision.

The relativistic mass of B in the S-frame is

$$m_B = \frac{m_0}{\sqrt{1 - u_B^2/c^2}} = \frac{m_0(1 + u'^2/c^2)}{(1 - u'^2/c^2)},$$

as the student should verify. In S, the combined mass C travels at a speed $v(= u')$ after collision, since it was stationary in S'. Hence, applying conservation of relativistic momentum in the x-direction in this frame (the y-component of momentum is automatically conserved), we have

$$\text{(before)} = \text{(after)}$$

$$\frac{m_0}{\sqrt{1 - u_B^2/c^2}}\, u_B + 0 = \frac{M_0}{\sqrt{1 - v^2/c^2}}\, v.$$

With $v = u'$ and u_B as given above, this becomes

$$\frac{m_0(1 + u'^2/c^2)}{(1 - u'^2/c^2)} \cdot \frac{2u'}{(1 + u'^2/c^2)} = \frac{M_0 u'}{\sqrt{1 - u'^2/c^2}}$$

whence

$$M_0 = \frac{2m_0}{\sqrt{1 - u'^2/c^2}}. \tag{3-25}$$

The rest mass of the combined body is *not* the sum of the rest masses of the original bodies ($2m_0$) but is *greater* by an amount

$$M_0 - 2m_0 = 2m_0\left(\frac{1}{\sqrt{1 - u'^2/c^2}} - 1\right). \tag{3-26a}$$

Before the collision, the bodies had kinetic energy in S' equal to

$$K_A + K_B = 2K = 2m_0c^2\left(\frac{1}{\sqrt{1 - u'^2/c^2}} - 1\right) \tag{3-26b}$$

but all the kinetic energy disappeared on collision. In its place, after the collision, there appears some form of internal energy, such as heat energy or excitation energy. We now see that this extra internal energy results in the rest mass (inertia) of the combined body being greater than the total rest mass (inertia) of the two separate bodies. Thus, rest mass is equivalent to energy (rest-mass energy) and must be included in applying the conservation of energy principle. This result follows from the Lorentz transformation and the conservation of momentum principle which were used in arriving at it.

From Eqs. 3-26a and 3-26b we see that $K_A + K_B = (M_0 - 2m_0)c^2$, which shows directly, in this case, that the energy associated with the increase in rest mass after the collision, $\Delta m_0 c^2$, equals the kinetic energy present before the collision. We can say, then, that although in an inelastic collision kinetic energy alone is not conserved, *total energy* is conserved. The total energy includes rest-mass energy plus kinetic energy. Furthermore, the conservation of total energy is equivalent to the conservation of relativistic mass. We prove this below, after which we shall draw some important conclusions.

▶ *Example* 4. (*a*) Show that, in both frames S and S', the total energy is conserved in the completely inelastic collision of Figs. 3-6 and 3-7.

Consider first the S'-frame (Fig. 3-6).

Before the collision the total energy is

$$2(m_0 c^2 + K) = 2m_0 c^2 / \sqrt{1 - u'^2/c^2}.$$

After the collision the total energy is

$$M_0 c^2 = \left(\frac{2m_0}{\sqrt{1 - u'^2/c^2}} \right) c^2 = 2m_0 c^2 / \sqrt{1 - u'^2/c^2}.$$

Hence, the total energy is conserved in the collision in frame S'.

Now consider the S-frame (Fig. 3-7).

Before the collision, the total energy is

$$m_0 c^2 + (m_0 c^2 + K_B) = 2m_0 c^2 + m_0 c^2 \left[\frac{1}{\sqrt{1 - u_B^2/c^2}} - 1 \right]$$

$$= 2m_0 c^2 + m_0 c^2 \left[\frac{2u'^2/c^2}{1 - u'^2/c^2} \right] = \frac{2m_0 c^2}{(1 - u'^2/c^2)}.$$

After the collision, the total energy is

$$M_0 c^2 + K_c = \frac{2m_0}{\sqrt{1 - u'^2/c^2}} c^2 + \frac{2m_0}{\sqrt{1 - u'^2/c^2}} c^2 \left[\frac{1}{\sqrt{1 - v^2/c^2}} - 1 \right],$$

which, with $v = u'$, becomes

$$\frac{2m_0}{\sqrt{1 - u'^2/c^2}} c^2 + \frac{2m_0}{\sqrt{1 - u'^2/c^2}} c^2 \left[\frac{1}{\sqrt{1 - u'^2/c^2}} - 1 \right] = \frac{2m_0 c^2}{(1 - u'^2/c^2)}.$$

Hence, the total energy is conserved in the collision in frame S.

(*b*) Show that the relativistic mass is also conserved in each frame.

Consider first the S'-frame (Fig. 3-6).

Before the collision the relativistic mass is

$$\frac{m_0}{\sqrt{1 - u'^2/c^2}} + \frac{m_0}{\sqrt{1 - u'^2/c^2}} = \frac{2m_0}{\sqrt{1 - u'^2/c^2}}.$$

After the collision the relativistic mass is the same as the rest mass, for $U_C' = 0$; that is,

$$M_0/\sqrt{1 - U_C'^2/c^2} = \left(\frac{2m_0}{1 - u'^2/c^2}\right)/\sqrt{1 - 0} = \frac{2m_0}{\sqrt{1 - u'^2/c^2}}.$$

Hence, the relativistic mass is conserved in the collision in frame S'. Now consider the S-frame (Fig. 3-7).
Before the collision the relativistic mass is

$$m_0 + \frac{m_0}{\sqrt{1 - u_B^2/c^2}} = m_0 + m_0 \frac{(1 + u'^2/c^2)}{(1 - u'^2/c^2)} = \frac{2m_0}{(1 - u'^2/c^2)}$$

After the collision the relativistic mass is

$$M_0/\sqrt{1 - v^2/c^2} = \left(\frac{2m_0}{\sqrt{1 - u'^2/c^2}}\right)/\sqrt{1 - u'^2/c^2} = \frac{2m_0}{(1 - u'^2/c^2)}.$$

Hence, the relativistic mass is conserved in the collision in frame S. ◀

We have seen that the conservation of total energy is equivalent to the conservation of (relativistic) mass. That is, the invariance of energy implies the invariance of (relativistic) mass. Mass and energy are equivalent; they form a single invariant that we can call mass-energy. Simply by multiplying the mass equations above by the universal constant c^2, we obtain numerically the corresponding energy equations. The relation

$$E = mc^2 \tag{3-27}$$

expresses the fact that mass-energy can be expressed in energy units (E) or equivalently in mass units ($m = E/c^2$). In fact, it has become common practice to refer to masses in terms of electron volts, such as saying that the rest mass of an electron is 0.51 Mev, for convenience in energy calculations.* Likewise, particles of zero rest mass (such as photons, see below) may be assigned an effective mass equivalent to their energy. Indeed, the mass that we associate with various forms of energy really has all the properties that we have given to mass heretofore, properties such as inertia, weight, contribution to the location of the center of mass of a system, and so forth. We shall exhibit some of these properties later in the chapter (see also Ref. 5).

---

*It should be emphasized that mass is not numerically equal to energy, for their units are different. However, they are physically equivalent quantities which correspond to one another. It is somewhat like the correspondence between the height of a mercury column and the air pressure.

Equation 3-27, $E = mc^2$, is, of course, one of the famous equations of physics. It has been confirmed by numerous practical applications and theoretical consequences. Einstein, who derived the result originally in another context, made the bold hypothesis that it was universally applicable. He considered it to be the most significant consequence of his special theory of relativity.

If we look back now at our single-particle equations (Section 3-4), we see that they are consistent with the conclusions we draw from two-body collisions. There we defined the total energy of a particle as mc^2 and gave it the symbol E. Then we used the relation $E = mc^2$ (below Eq. 3-21) and found that $dm/dt = (1/c^2)(dK/dt)$. This can be expressed also as

$$\frac{dK}{dt} = c^2\frac{dm}{dt} \tag{3-28}$$

which states that a change in the kinetic energy of a particle causes a proportionate change in its (relativistic) mass. That is, mass and energy are equivalent, their units* differing by a factor c^2.

If the kinetic energy of a body is regarded as a form of external energy, then the rest-mass energy may be regarded as the internal energy of the body. This internal energy consists, in part, of such things as molecular motion, which changes when heat energy is absorbed or given up by the body, or intermolecular potential energy, which changes when chemical reactions (such as dissociation or recombination) take place. Or the internal energy can take the form of atomic potential energy, which can change when an atom absorbs radiation and becomes excited or emits radiation and is deexcited, or nuclear potential energy, which can be changed by nuclear reactions. The largest contribution to the internal energy is, however, the total rest-mass energy contributed by the "fundamental" particles, which is regarded as the primary source of internal energy. This too, may change, as, for example, in electron-positron creation and annihilation (see Problems 31, 37, and 38). The rest mass (or proper mass) of a body, therefore, is not a constant, in general. Of course, if there are no changes in the internal energy of a body (or if we consider

---

*A convenient identity (see Problem 28) is $c^2 = (3 \times 10^8 \text{ m/sec})^2 = 931 \text{ Mev/a.m.u.}$

a closed system through which energy is not transferred) then we may regard the rest mass of the body (or of the system) as constant.

This view of the internal energy of a particle as equivalent to rest mass suggests an extension to a collection of particles. We sometimes regard an atom as a particle and assign it a rest mass, for example, although we know that the atom consists of many particles with various forms of internal energy. Likewise, we can assign a rest mass to any collection of particles in relative motion, in a frame in which the center-of-mass is at rest (i.e., in which the resultant momentum is zero). The rest mass of the system as a whole would include the contributions of the internal energy of the system to the inertia.

Returning our attention now to collisions or interactions between bodies, we have seen that regardless of the nature of the collision the total energy is conserved and that the conservation of total energy is equivalent to the conservation of (relativistic) mass. In classical physics we had two separate conservation principles: (1) the conservation of (classical) mass, as in chemical reactions, and (2) the conservation of energy. In relativity, these merge into one conservation principle, that of conservation of mass-energy. The two classical laws may be viewed as special cases which would be expected to agree with experiment only if energy transfers into or out of the system are so small compared to the system's rest mass that the corresponding fractional change in rest mass of the system is too small to be measured.

▶ *Example 5.* One atomic mass unit (1 a.m.u.) is equal to 1.66×10^{-27} kg (approximately). The rest mass of the proton (the nucleus of a hydrogen atom) is 1.00731 a.m.u. and that of the neutron (a neutral particle and a constituent of all nuclei except hydrogen) is 1.00867 a.m.u. A deuteron (the nucleus of heavy hydrogen) is known to consist of a neutron and a proton. The rest mass of the deuteron is found to be 2.01360 a.m.u. Hence, the rest mass of the deuteron is *less than* the combined rest masses of neutron and proton by

$$\Delta m_0 = [(1.00731 + 1.00867) - 2.01360] \text{ a.m.u.} = 0.00238 \text{ a.m.u.},$$

which is equivalent, in energy units, to

$$\Delta m_0 c^2 = (0.00238 \times 1.66 \times 10^{-27} \text{ kg})(3.00 \times 10^8 \text{ m/sec})^2$$
$$= 3.57 \times 10^{-13} \text{ joules} = 2.22 \times 10^6 \text{ ev}$$
$$= 2.22 \text{ Mev.}$$

When a neutron and a proton at rest combine to form a deuteron, this exact amount of energy is given off in the form of electromagnetic (gamma) radiation. If the deuteron is to be broken up into a proton and a neutron, this same amount of energy must be *added* to the deuteron. This energy, 2.22 Mev, is therefore called the *binding energy* of the deuteron.

Notice that

$$\frac{\Delta m_0}{M_0} = \frac{0.00238}{2.01360} = 1.18 \times 10^{-3} = 0.12 \text{ percent.}$$

This fractional rest-mass change is characteristic of the magnitudes that are found in nuclear reactions.

Example 6. The binding energy of a hydrogen atom is 13.58 ev. That is, the energy one must add to a hydrogen atom to break it up into its constituent parts, a proton and an electron, is 13.58 ev. The rest mass of a hydrogen atom, M_0, is 1.00797 a.m.u. The change in rest mass, Δm_0, when a hydrogen atom is ionized is

$$13.58 \text{ ev} = \frac{13.58 \text{ ev}}{931 \times 16^6 \text{ ev/a.m.u.}} = 1.46 \times 10^{-8} \text{ a.m.u.}$$

so that

$$\frac{\Delta m_0}{M_0} = \frac{1.46 \times 10^{-8}}{1.008} = 1.45 \times 10^{-8} = 1.45 \times 10^{-6} \text{ percent.}$$

Such a fractional change in rest mass is actually smaller than the experimental error in measuring the ratio of the masses of proton and electron, so that in practice we could not detect the change. Thus, in chemical reactions, we could not have detected changes in rest mass and the classical principle of conservation of (rest) mass is practically correct.

Example 7. Consider the following thought experiment. A rectangular tube of mass M and length L is at rest in a frame S. A pulse of electromagnetic radiation of energy E is emitted at one end of the tube and subsequently absorbed at the other end. Show that the inertia associated with this radiation is $m = E/c^2$.

The situation is depicted in Fig. 3-8. The pulse of electromagnetic radiation is emitted to the right. From Maxwell's electromagnetic theory a momentum $p = E/c$ is associated with this radiation, so that, to conserve momentum, the tube recoils to the left at a speed v. If m represents the mass to be associated with the radiant energy, then the mass of the recoiling tube is $M - m$ and the conservation of momentum in S requires

$$(M - m)v = \frac{E}{c}.$$

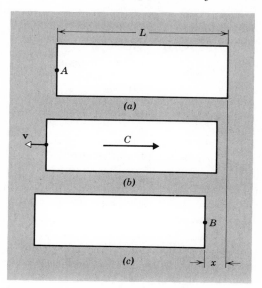

Fig. 3-8. (a) A rectangular tube of length L and mass M at rest in frame S. (b) A pulse of radiation is emitted at A to the right and the tube recoils with speed v to the left. (c) The radiation is absorbed at B, in the right end of the tube, bringing the tube to rest after it has moved a recoil distance x.

The time of flight of the pulse of radiation, whose speed is c, is $t = (L - x)/c$, which is the same as the time of recoil of the tube $t = x/v$, where x is the distance of the recoil. Combining these, we get

$$\frac{v}{c} = \frac{x}{L - x}.$$

Since the forces are all internal, the center of mass of the system does not change during the process of emission and absorption. If m is the effective mass transferred by the radiation, the center of mass will not change if $Mx = mL$ (the student should be able to show this), or

$$m = \frac{Mx}{L}.$$

We combine the above equations and solve for m as follows. Using

$$\frac{x}{L - x} = \frac{E/c^2}{M - m}$$

we find

$$x = \frac{EL/(M-m)c^2}{1 + E/c^2(M-m)} = \frac{EL/c^2}{(M-m) + E/c^2}$$

Then, inserting $m = x(M/L)$, we find

$$m = \frac{ME/c^2}{(M-m) + E/c^2}.$$

whose solution is $m = E/c^2$.

If we think more deeply about the thought experiment, we shall conclude that this analysis of it violates the spirit of relativity. How does the right end of the tube get the "message" to start moving to the left after the left end recoils? To "beat" the emitted pulse of radiation, this message must travel faster than light. If the tube moved as a rigid body, the message would travel with infinite speed. Certainly the whole tube does not recoil rigidly, so what is the meaning of v?

What happens, in fact, is that the "recoil signal" travels as an elastic wave along the walls of the tube, with the speed of sound, and arrives at the right end after the pulse of radiation does. But, by then, the pulse has been absorbed and another signal travels back as an elastic wave to the front end. Hence, the tube vibrates and is not rigid at all. A correct analysis of this situation, although obviously involved, leads to the same basic result obtained in the example. ◀

Einstein deduced the result of Example 7 in another way. Let the tube be at rest in the laboratory, but let it contain radiant (electromagnetic) energy of amount E in thermodynamic equilibrium with the walls. Now, radiant energy exerts a pressure on the walls of the tube and, in this particular case (equilibrium), the total force on one wall annuls that on the opposite wall. If, however, the tube is accelerated in a forward direction by an applied force, the radiation reflected off the rear wall during this acceleration will change its momentum more than that reflected off the front. The result is that the radiation exerts a net force on the tube, resisting its acceleration and contributing to the inertia of the tube exactly as much as a mass $m = E/c^2$ would.*

In a paper [6] entitled "Does the Inertia of a Body Depend upon its Energy Content," Einstein writes:

"If a body gives off the energy E in the form of radiation, its mass diminishes by E/c^2. The fact that the energy withdrawn from the body becomes energy of radiation evidently makes no difference, so that we

---

*See Example 9 and Ref. 7 for still another derivation of $E = mc^2$.

are led to the more general conclusion that the mass of a body is a measure of its energy content. . . . It is not impossible that with bodies whose energy-content is variable to a high degree (e.g., with radium salts) the theory may be successfully put to the test. If the theory corresponds to the facts, radiation conveys inertia between the emitting and absorbing bodies."

Experiment has abundantly confirmed Einstein's theory.

Today, we call such a pulse of radiation a photon and may regard it as a particle of zero rest mass. The relation $p = E/c$, taken from classical electromagnetism, is consistent with the result of special relativity for particles of "zero rest mass" since, from Eq. 3-19, $E = c\sqrt{p^2 + m_0 c^2}$, we find that $p = E/c$ when $m_0 = 0$. This is consistent also with the fact that photons travel with the speed of light since, from the relation $E = mc^2 = m_0 c^2 / \sqrt{1 - u^2/c^2}$, the energy E would go to zero as $m_0 \to 0$ for $u < c$. In order to keep E finite (neither zero nor infinite) as $m_0 \to 0$, we must let $u \to c$. Strictly speaking, however, the term zero rest mass is a bit misleading because it is impossible to find a reference frame in which photons (or anything that travels at the speed of light) are at rest (see Question 12). However, if m_0 is determined from energy and momentum measurements as $m_0 = \sqrt{(E/c^2)^2 - (p/c)^2}$, then $m_0 = 0$ when (as for a photon*) $p = E/c$.

The result, that a particle of zero rest mass can have a finite energy and momentum and that such particles must move at the speed of light, is also consistent with the meaning we have given to rest mass as internal energy. For if rest mass is internal energy, existing when a body is at rest, then a "body" without mass has no internal energy. Its energy is all external, involving motion through space. Now, if such a body moved at a speed less than c in one reference frame, we could always find another reference frame in which it *is* at rest. But if it moves at a speed c in one reference frame, it will move at this same speed c in all reference frames. It is consistent with the Lorentz transformation then that a body of zero rest mass should move at the speed of light and be nowhere at rest.

---

*For students who are unfamiliar with the relation $p = E/c$, found in electromagnetism, the argument can be run in reverse. Start with the relativistic relation $E = m_0 c^2 / \sqrt{1 - u^2/c^2}$. This implies that E approaches infinity if $u = c$, unless $m_0 = 0$. Therefore photons, which by definition have $u = c$, must have $m_0 = 0$. Then from $E = c[p^2 + m_0^2 c^2]^{1/2}$ it follows that photons must satisfy the relation $p = E/c$. That this same result is found independently in classical electromagnetism illustrates the consistency between relativity and classical electromagnetism.

▶ *Example* 8. The earth receives radiant energy from the sun at the rate of 1.34×10^3 watts/m². At what rate is the sun losing rest mass due to its radiation? The sun's rest mass is now about 2.0×10^{30} kg.

If we assume that the sun radiates isotropically, then the total solar-radiation rate equals the radiant energy passing per unit time through a sphere having the radius r of the mean earth-sun separation, 1.49×10^{11} m, or

$$[1.34 \times 10^3 \text{ watts/meter}^2][4\pi (1.49 \times 10^{11} \text{ meters})^2] = 3.92 \times 10^{26} \text{ watts.}$$

Since mass/time equals (energy/time)/(energy/mass), we find, from

$$c^2 = E/m = 8.99 \times 10^{16} \text{ joules/kg,}$$

that

$$\frac{3.92 \times 10^{26} \text{ joules/sec}}{8.99 \times 10^{16} \text{ joules/kg}} = 4.36 \times 10^9 \text{ kg/sec}$$

is the rate of loss of solar rest mass.

At this rate, the fractional decrease of solar rest mass is

$$\frac{4.36 \times 10^9 \text{ kg/sec} \times 3.14 \times 10^7 \text{ sec/yr}}{2.0 \times 10^{30} \text{ kg}} = 6.8 \times 10^{-14}/\text{yr.}$$

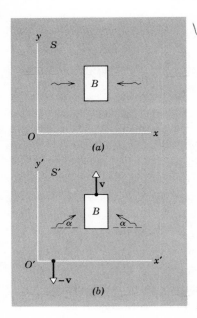

Fig. 3-9. (a) Body B is at rest in S. Two pulses of radiation are incident upon it in the directions shown by the arrows. (b) In S', which moves relative to S with speed v in the negative y-direction, body B moves at speed v along +y' and the pulses are directed up at an angle α from the x'-axis, as shown by the arrows.

▶ *Example* 9. We present here an "elementary derivation of the equivalence of mass and energy" attributable to Einstein [7].

Consider a body B at rest in frame S (Fig. 3-9a). Two pulses of radiation, each of energy $E/2$, are incident on B, one pulse moving in the $+x$-direction, the other in the $-x$-direction. These pulses are absorbed by B, whose energy therefore increases by an amount E; from symmetry considerations, B must stay at rest in S. Now consider the same process relative to S', which moves with a constant speed v relative to S in the negative y-direction. Here (Fig. 3-9b) B moves in the positive y'-direction with speed v. The pulses of radiation are here directed upward in part, making an angle α with the x'-axis. The velocity of B remains unchanged in S' after absorption of the radiation since, as we have seen, B stays at rest in S during this process.

Now let us apply the law of conservation of momentum to the process in S'.

The momentum of B in S' is Mv (from classical mechanics) along the positive y'-direction. Each pulse of radiation has energy $E/2$ and momentum $E/2c$ (from classical electromagnetism), the y'-components being $E/2c \sin \alpha$. Hence, before absorption takes place, the y'-component of momentum of the system is

$$Mv + 2\left(\frac{E}{2c}\right)\sin \alpha.$$

After absorption, body B has mass M' and its momentum is $M'v$ along the positive y'-direction. Equating y'-components of momentum before absorption to those after absorption we have

$$Mv + \frac{E}{c}\sin \alpha = M'v.$$

Now, since $v \ll c$, $\sin \alpha \cong \alpha = v/c$ (the classical aberration result) so that

$$Mv + \frac{E}{c}\frac{v}{c} = M'v.$$

Hence
$$M + \frac{E}{c^2} = M'$$

or
$$M' - M = \frac{E}{c^2}.$$

The energy increase E of body B, therefore, is connected to its mass increase, $\Delta M = M' - M$, as

$$E = \Delta M c^2.$$

In what way (if at all) did Einstein use special relativity theory in this derivation? What approximations were made? ◀

3.7 *The Transformation Properties of Momentum, Energy, Mass, and Force*

In Section 3-5 we investigated the dynamics of a single particle using the relativistic equation of motion that was found to be in agreement with experiment for the motion of high-speed charged particles. There we introduced the relativistic mass and the total energy, including the rest-mass energy. However, all the formulas that we used were applicable in one reference frame, which we called the laboratory frame. Often, as when analyzing nuclear reactions, it is useful to be able to transform these relations to other inertial reference frames, like the center-of-mass frame. Therefore, we present here the relations that connect the values of the momentum, energy, mass, and force in one frame S

to the corresponding values of these quantities in another frame S', which moves with uniform velocity $\mathbf{v}$ with respect to S along the common x-x' axes. We shall thereby gain some new insights into relativity. In later sections of the text, we shall use some of these results.*

We begin with a relation (easily verified; see Problem 37, Chapter Two) between the velocity of u of a particle in S and its velocity u' in S', namely

$$c^2 - u^2 = \frac{c^2(c^2 - u'^2)(c^2 - v^2)}{(c^2 + u_x'v)^2}.$$

If we divide throughout by c^2, invert, and take the square root, we find

$$\frac{1}{\sqrt{1 - u^2/c^2}} = \frac{1 + u_x'v/c^2}{\sqrt{1 - u'^2/c^2}\,\sqrt{1 - v^2/c^2}}, \qquad (3\text{-}29)$$

an equality that proves to be useful.

We now can easily obtain the transformations for the components of momentum and for the energy. In frame S we have (by definition)

$$p_x = \frac{m_0 u_x}{\sqrt{1 - u^2/c^2}}, \qquad p_y = \frac{m_0 u_y}{\sqrt{1 - u^2/c^2}},$$

$$p_z = \frac{m_0 u_z}{\sqrt{1 - u^2/c^2}}, \qquad E = \frac{m_0 c^2}{\sqrt{1 - u^2/c^2}}.$$

In frame S' the corresponding quantities are (by definition)

$$p_x' = \frac{m_0 u_x'}{\sqrt{1 - u'^2/c^2}}, \qquad p_y' = \frac{m_0 u_y'}{\sqrt{1 - u'^2/c^2}},$$

$$p_z' = \frac{m_0 u_z'}{\sqrt{1 - u'^2/c^2}}, \qquad E = \frac{m_0 c^2}{\sqrt{1 - u'^2/c^2}}.$$

Using Eq. 3-29 and the transformation equations for the velocity components (Eqs. 2-18 to 2-20), the student can easily verify that the relations between these quantities are

$$p_x = \frac{1}{\sqrt{1 - v^2/c^2}}\left(p_x' + \frac{E'v}{c^2}\right)$$

$$p_y = p_y',$$

$$p_z = p_z',$$

$$E = \frac{1}{\sqrt{1 - v^2/c^2}}(E' + vp_x') \qquad (3\text{-}30a)$$

*The instructor may prefer to postpone this section until he considers the material of Chapter Four.

The inverse relations, obtained by sending v to $-v$ and interchanging primed and unprimed quantities, are

$$p_x' = \frac{1}{\sqrt{1 - v^2/c^2}}\left(p_x - \frac{Ev}{c^2}\right)$$

$$p_y' = p_y,$$

$$p_z' = p_z,$$

$$E' = \frac{1}{\sqrt{1 - v^2/c^2}}(E - vp_x). \qquad (3\text{-}30b)$$

Equations 3-30a and 3-30b are the transformations for the components of momentum and the energy. We summarize them in Table 3-2.

If these results are compared to the original Lorentz transformations involving x, y, z, t and x', y', z', t' (see Table 2-1), we find a striking analogy (see Problem 39 and Question 18). The quantities p_x, p_y, p_z, and E/c^2 transform exactly as the space-time coordinates x, y, z, and t of a particle transform. This is an excellent way to remember the transformations. For example,

$$x' = \frac{x - vt}{\sqrt{1 - v^2/c^2}}$$

and

$$p_x' = \frac{p_x - v(E/c^2)}{\sqrt{1 - v^2/c^2}}.$$

$$t' = \frac{t - (v/c^2)x}{\sqrt{1 - v^2/c^2}}$$

and

$$\frac{E'}{c^2} = \frac{(E/c^2) - (v/c^2)p_x}{\sqrt{1 - v^2/c^2}}.$$

TABLE 3-2   THE RELATIVISTIC TRANSFORMATION FOR MOMENTUM AND ENERGY

$p_x' = \dfrac{p_x - Ev/c^2}{\sqrt{1 - v^2/c^2}}$	$p_x = \dfrac{p_x' + E'v/c^2}{\sqrt{1 - v^2/c^2}}$
$p_y' = p_y$	$p_y = p_y'$
$p_z' = p_z$	$p_z = p_z'$
$E' = \dfrac{E - vp_x}{\sqrt{1 - v^2/c^2}}$	$E = \dfrac{E' + vp_x'}{\sqrt{1 - v^2/c^2}}$

When relativity is put into its four-dimensional (space-time) form, a four-vector momentum naturally emerges whose "time" component is the energy. We have already seen in many equations of special relativity (e.g., Eqs., 3-18 to 3-20) the interdependence of energy E and momentum p of a particle. Perhaps the deepest connection between energy and momentum in relativity is this: If energy and momentum are conserved in an interaction according to one inertial observer, then necessarily energy and momentum are conserved in this interaction according to any other inertial observer; furthermore, if momentum is conserved, then energy must also be conserved. These results emerged in our study of collisions in Section 3-6. They can be shown to follow explicitly from the transformation equations (Eqs. 3-30) (see Problem 45). This emphasizes the internal consistency of the relativistic definitions of momentum and energy.

Notice that the transformation equations for the mass follow directly from the energy transformations. That is, $E = mc^2$ where $m = m_0/\sqrt{1 - u^2/c^2}$ and $E' = m'c^2$ where $m' = m_0\sqrt{1 - u'^2/c^2}$, so that, from the equations relating E and E', we have

$$m = \frac{m'\,(1 + u_x'v/c^2)}{\sqrt{1 - v^2/c^2}} \qquad (3\text{-}31a)$$

and its inverse

$$m' = \frac{m(1 - u_x'v/c^2)}{\sqrt{1 - v^2/c^2}}. \qquad (3\text{-}31b)$$

Equations 3-31a and 3-31b are the transformation equations for the mass.

Finally, we present the transformation equations for force.* In frame S, we have

$$F_x = \frac{d}{dt}(mu_x), \qquad F_y = \frac{d}{dt}(mu_y), \qquad F_z = \frac{d}{dt}(mu_z),$$

whereas the corresponding quantities in frame S' are

$$F_x' = \frac{d}{dt'}(m'u_x'), \qquad F_y' = \frac{d}{dt'}(m'u_y'), \qquad F_z' = \frac{d}{dt'}(m'u_z').$$

These are related by

*See Ref. 8 for a derivation.

$$F_x = F_x' + \frac{u_y'v}{(c^2 + u_x'v)} F_y' + \frac{u_z'v}{(c^2 + u_x'v)} F_z'$$

$$F_y = \frac{\sqrt{1 - v^2/c^2}}{(1 + u_x'v/c^2)} F_y'$$

$$F_z = \frac{\sqrt{1 - v^2/c^2}}{(1 + u_x'v/c^2)} F_z'$$

and the inverse relations are

$$F_x' = F_x - \frac{u_yv}{(c^2 - u_x'v)} F_y - \frac{u_zv}{(c^2 - u_xv)} F_z$$

$$F_y' = \frac{\sqrt{1 - v^2/c^2}}{(1 - u_xv/c^2)} F_y$$

$$F_z' = \frac{\sqrt{1 - v^2/c^2}}{(1 - u_xv/c^2)} F_z.$$

These can be written more compactly by letting $1/\sqrt{1 - v^2/c^2} = \gamma$ and by using the dot product of **u** and **F**. Thus,

$$F_x = \frac{F_x' + (v/c^2)\,\mathbf{u}' \cdot \mathbf{F}'}{(1 + u_x'v/c^2)}, \qquad F_y = \frac{F_y'}{\gamma(1 + u_x'v/c^2)},$$

$$F_z = \frac{F_z'}{\gamma(1 + u_x'v/c^2)} \qquad\qquad (3\text{-}32a)$$

and

$$F_x' = \frac{F_x - (v/c^2)\,\mathbf{u} \cdot \mathbf{F}}{(1 - u_xv/c^2)}, \qquad F_y' = \frac{F_y}{\gamma(1 - u_xv/c^2)},$$

$$F_z' = \frac{F_z}{\gamma(1 - u_xv/c^2)}. \qquad\qquad (3\text{-}32b)$$

Equations 3-32a and 3-32b are the transformation equations for the components of force. As a check, note in the Newtonian limit where $v/c \ll 1$, these equations reduce to $\mathbf{F} = \mathbf{F}'$, as required.

An interesting aspect of these equations is that the force in one frame, F_x, for instance, is related to the power developed by the force in another frame, $\mathbf{u}' \cdot \mathbf{F}'$. This is analogous to the dependence of p_x, in Eq. 3-30, on E'. It suggests that just as energy and momentum are related when relativity is put in four-dimensional (space-time) form, so may power and force be related. Indeed, we can easily show that a fourth relation belonging in Eqs. 3-32 involves the power, namely

$$\mathbf{u} \cdot \mathbf{F} = \frac{\mathbf{u}' \cdot \mathbf{F}' + vF_x'}{(1 + u_x'v/c^2)}$$

and the inverse relation

$$\mathbf{u}' \cdot \mathbf{F}' = \frac{\mathbf{u} \cdot \mathbf{F} - vF_x}{(1 - u_xv/c^2)}.$$

All this suggests the great generalizing nature of relativity theory. It is relevant to an issue in the history of classical mechanics wherein the effect of a force over time, $F\,dt = dp$, was regarded as the significant measure of a force by some, whereas the effect of a force over distance, $F\,dx = dE$, was regarded as the significant quantity by others. That is, F can be regarded as the time rate of change of momentum, dp/dt, or the space rate of change of energy, dE/dx. In the relativistic equations *both* concepts are used, for F_x' depends not only on $F_x = dp/dt$ but also on $\mathbf{F} \cdot \mathbf{u}$, which has the form $(dE/dx) \cdot (dx/dt)$.

Finally, let us look at a special case of Eqs. 3-32, which is both useful and simple. Consider a particle at rest instantaneously in the S'-frame, where it is subject to a force with components F_x', F_y', and F_z'. Since $u' = 0$, in this proper frame, the force transformations become

$$F_x = F_x'$$

$$F_y = \frac{F_y'}{\gamma} = F_y'\sqrt{1 - v^2/c^2}$$

$$F_z = \frac{F_z'}{\gamma} = F_z'\sqrt{1 - v^2/c^2} \tag{3-33}$$

where F_x, F_y, and F_z are the components of force in some other (non-proper) frame. Notice that the force in the particle's instantaneous rest frame is greater than the corresponding force in any other frame.

The method of obtaining the force transformations, although algebraically involved, is straightforward in principle, for we simply use transformation equations that are already known and understood. The purpose in writing down the force transformations will become clearer in the next chapter, where we investigate how the numerical value of electric and magnetic fields depends upon the frame of the observer.

Questions

1. Does **F** equal $m\mathbf{a}$ in relativity? Does $m\mathbf{a}$ equal $\dfrac{d}{dt}\,(m\mathbf{u})$ in relativity?

2. Distinguish between a variable-mass problem in classical physics and the relativistic variation of mass.

3. Can we simply substitute m for m_0 in classical equations to obtain the correct corresponding relativistic equation? Give examples.

4. Suppose **F** is neither parallel nor perpendicular to **u**. Can **F** and **a** then be parallel? (*Hint.* Consider $\mathbf{u} = 0$.)

5. We found that **F** and **a** are parallel either when **F** is parallel to **u** or when **F** is perpendicular to **u**. In view of the fact that we can always resolve **F** into two such components, why is **F** not always parallel to **a?**

6. Any force can be resolved into two components, one along the line of motion and the other perpendicular to the line of motion. Can the resulting acceleration, then, be predicted from the longitudinal and transverse mass relations?

7. Can a body be accelerated to the speed of light? Explain.

8. Explain how it happens, in Example 4, that although total energy is conserved in each frame, the value assigned to the total energy in S does not equal numerically the value in S'.

9. We have seen that, in an elastic collision between two spheres, both the rest mass of the sphere and its relativistic mass before collision are equal to the corresponding quantities after collision. What happens to these quantities *during* the collision? (*Hint.* The impulsive forces exerted by the spheres on one another are equivalent to a changing internal elastic potential energy.)

10. How would you expect the relativistic variation of mass to affect the performance of a cyclotron?

11. Is it true that a particle that has energy must also have momentum? What if the particle has no rest mass?

12. If photons have a speed c in one reference frame, can they be found at rest in any other frame? Can photons have a speed other than c?

13. Radiation, being a transfer of energy, involves a transfer of mass and carries momentum. Hence, radiation should exert pressure on bodies it falls upon. Give some examples.

14. Under what circumstances is the rest (or proper) mass of a body a constant quantity? Under what circumstances can we speak of a varying proper mass?

15. A hot metallic sphere cools off on a scale. Does the scale indicate a change in rest mass?

16. What role does potential energy play in the equivalence of mass and energy?

17. A spring is kept compressed by tying its ends together tightly. It is then placed in acid and dissolves. What happens to its stored potential energy?

18. Show that momentum is analogous to displacement in the sense that momentum is obtained from displacement merely by multiplication by an invariant factor $m_0/d\tau$. Show, similarly, that energy is analogous to time in the sense that energy is obtained from time merely by multiplication by an invariant factor $m_0c^2/d\tau$ (see Sections 3-4 and 3-7).

Problems

1. Consider a box at rest with sides a, b, and c, as shown in Fig. 3-10. Its rest mass is m_0, and its rest mass per unit volume is $\rho_0 = m_0/abc$. (*a*) What is the volume of the box as viewed by an observer moving relative to the box with speed u in the x-direction? (*b*) What is the mass measured by this observer? (*c*) What is the density of the box, in terms of ρ_0, as measured by this observer?

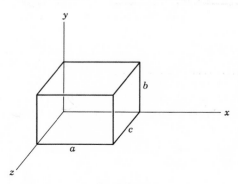

Fig. 3-10.

2. Consider the following elastic collision: particle A has rest mass m_0 and particle B has rest mass $2m_0$; before the collision, particle A moves in the $+x$-direction with a speed of $0.6c$ and particle B is at rest; after the collision, particle A is found to be moving in the $+y$-direction, and particle B is found to be moving at an angle δ to the $+x$-direction. Write down the three equations (do not solve them) from which we could determine the angle δ and the speeds of A and B after the collision.

3. What is the speed of an electron whose kinetic energy equals its rest energy? Does the result depend on the mass of the electron?

4. The average lifetime of μ-mesons at rest is 2.3×10^{-6} sec. A laboratory measurement on μ-mesons yields an average lifetime of 6.9×10^{-6} sec. (*a*) What is the speed of the mesons in the laboratory? (*b*) The rest mass of a μ-meson is $207 \, m_e$. What is the effective mass of such a meson when moving at this speed? (*c*) What is its kinetic energy? What is its momentum?

5. An electron is accelerated in a synchrotron to an energy of 1.0 Bev. (*a*) What is the effective mass of this electron in terms of its rest mass? (*b*) What is the speed of this electron in terms of the speed of light? (*c*) What are the answers to (*a*) and (*b*) if the energy of the electron is 1.0 Mev instead?

6. Compute the speed of (*a*) electrons and (*b*) protons which fall through an electrostatic potential difference of 10 million volts. (*c*) What is the ratio of relativistic mass to rest mass in each case?

7. Prove that if $u/c \ll 1$, the kinetic energy K of a moving particle will always be much less than its rest energy $m_0 c^2$.

8. Derive the relation $K = (m - m_0)c^2$ for motion in three dimensions.

9. Prove that, in Fig. 3-3, $\sin \theta = u/c = \beta$ and that $\sin \phi = \sqrt{1 - u^2/c^2} = \sqrt{1 - \beta^2}$.

10. (*a*) Verify Eq. 3-18*a* connecting K and p by eliminating u between Eqs. 3-11 and 3-16*b*. (*b*) Derive the following useful relations between p, E, K, and m_0 for relativistic particles, starting from Eqs. 3-18*a* and 3.18*b*.

$$(1) \quad K = c\sqrt{m_0^2 c^2 + p^2} - m_0 c^2.$$

$$(2) \quad p = \frac{\sqrt{K^2 + 2m_0 c^2 K}}{c}.$$

$$(3) \quad m_0 = \frac{\sqrt{E^2 - p^2 c^2}}{c^2}.$$

11. Show (when **F** is parallel to **u**) that substitution of $m = m_0/\sqrt{1 - u^2/c^2}$ into $F = m(du/dt) + u(dm/dt)$ leads to $F = m_0 a/(1 - u^2/c^2)^{3/2}$.

12. Show that, although **a** and **F** are not parallel in general (Eq. 3-22), the angle between them is always *less* than $90°$.

13. (*a*) What potential difference will accelerate electrons to the speed of light, according to classical physics? (*b*) With this potential difference, what speed would an electron acquire relativistically? (*c*) What would its mass be at this speed? Its kinetic energy?

14. A charge q at $x = 0$ accelerates from rest in a uniform electric field **E**, which is directed along the positive x-axis.

(a) Show that the acceleration of the charge is given by

$$a_x = \frac{qE}{m_0}\left(1 - \frac{u^2}{c^2}\right)^{3/2}.$$

(b) Show that the velocity of the charge at any time t is given by

$$u_x = \frac{qEt/m_0}{\sqrt{1 + (qEt/m_0c)^2}}$$

(c) Show that the distance the charge moves in a time t is given by

$$x = \frac{m_0c^2}{qE}\left(\sqrt{1 + (qEt/m_0c)^2} - 1\right).$$

(d) Show that when t is large, u_x approaches c, and x approaches ct.

(e) Show that if $qEt/m_0 \ll c$ we obtain the classical results for a_x, u_x, and x.

15. (a) Show that when $u/c < 1/10$ or when $K/m_0c^2 < 1/200$ the classical expressions for kinetic energy and momentum, that is, $K = \frac{1}{2}m_0u^2$ and $p = m_0u$, may be used with an error of less than 1 percent. (b) Show that when $u/c > 99/100$ or when $K/m_0c^2 > 7$, the relativistic relation $p = E/c$ for a zero rest-mass particle may be used for a particle of rest mass m_0 with an error of less than 1 percent.

16. (a) Show that a particle which travels at the speed of light must have a zero rest mass. (b) Show that for a particle of zero rest mass, $u = c$, $K = E$, and $p = E/c$.

17. Make a plot of the total energy E versus the momentum p for a particle of rest mass m_0 for the cases (a) classical particle (b) relativistic particle and (c) zero rest-mass particle. (d) In what region does curve (b) approach curve (a) and in what region does curve (b) approach curve (c)? (e) Explain briefly the physical significance of the intercepts of the curves with the axes and of their slopes (derivatives).

18. A 0.50 Mev electron moves at right angles to a magnetic field in a path whose radius of curvature is 2.0 cm. (a) What is the magnetic induction B? (b) By what factor does the effective mass of the electron exceed its rest mass?

19. A cosmic-ray proton of energy 10 Bev approaches the earth in its equatorial plane in a region where the earth's magnetic induction has a value 5.5×10^{-5} webers/m^2. What is the radius of its curved path in that region?

20. Show that the angular frequency of a charge moving in a uniform magnetic field is given by $\omega = (qB/m)\sqrt{1 - u^2/c^2}$. (b) Compare this with the classical result upon which some cyclotron designs are based and explain qualitatively how the design must be modified relativistically.

21. The general magnetic field in the solar system is 2×10^{-19} tesla (a tesla is one weber/meter^2). Find the radius of curvature of a 10 Bev cosmic-ray proton in such a field. Compare this radius to the radius of the earth's orbit around the sun.

22. Ionization measurements show that a particular charged particle is moving with a speed given by $\beta = u/c = 0.71$, and that its radius of curvature is 0.46 m in a field of magnetic induction of 1.0 tesla. Find the mass of the particle and identify it.

23. In a high-energy collision of a primary cosmic-ray particle near the top of the Earth's atmosphere, 120 km above sea level, a π^+ meson is created with a total energy of 1.35×10^5 Mev, travelling vertically downward. In its proper frame it disintegrates 2.0×10^{-8} sec after its creation. At what altitude above sea level does the disintegration occur? The π-meson rest-mass energy is 139.6 Mev.

24. The "effective mass" of a photon (bundle of electromagnetic radiation of zero rest mass and energy $h\nu$) can be determined from the relation $m = E/c^2$. Compute the "effective mass" for a photon of wavelength 5000 Å (visible region), and for a photon of wavelength 1.0 Å (X-ray region).

25. Using data in Example 8, find the pressure of solar radiation at the earth.

26. What is the equivalent in energy units of one gram of a substance?

28. A ton of water is heated from the freezing point to the boiling point. By how much, in kilograms and as a percentage of the original mass, does its mass increase?

28. (a) Prove that 1 a.m.u. = 931.5 Mev/c^2. (b) Find the energy equivalent to the rest mass of the electron, and to the rest mass of the proton.

29. (a) How much energy is released in the explosion of a fission bomb containing 3.0 kg of fissionable material? Assume that 0.1 percent of the rest mass is converted to released energy. (b) What mass of TNT would have to explode to provide the same energy release? Assume that each mole of TNT liberates 820,000 calories on exploding. The molecular weight of TNT is 0.227 kg/mole. (c) For the same mass of explosive, how much more effective are fission explosions than TNT explosions? That is, compare the fractions of rest mass converted to released energy for the two cases.

30. The nucleus C^{12} consists of six protons (H^1) and six neutrons (n) held in close association by strong nuclear forces. The rest masses are

$$
\begin{array}{ll}
C^{12} & 12.000000 \text{ a.m.u.,} \\
H^1 & 1.007825 \text{ a.m.u.,} \\
n & 1.008665 \text{ a.m.u.}
\end{array}
$$

How much energy would be required to separate a C^{12} nucleus into its constituent protons and neutrons? This energy is called the binding energy of the C^{12} nucleus. (The masses are really those of the neutral atoms, but the extranuclear electrons have relatively negligible binding energy and are of equal number before and after the breakup of C^{12}.)

31. A positron and an electron at rest in frame S combine and annihilate one another, producing two photons. (*a*) What is the energy and momentum of each photon in this frame? What quantities are conserved in this process? (*b*) Prove that the positron and electron cannot combine to produce only *one* photon.

32. A body of rest mass m_0, travelling initially at a speed $0.6c$, makes a completely inelastic collision with an identical body initially at rest. (*a*) What is the speed of the resulting single body? (*b*) What is its rest mass?

33. An excited atom of mass m, initially at rest in frame S, emits a photon and recoils. The internal energy of the atom decreases by ΔE and the energy of the photon is $h\nu$. Show that $h\nu = \Delta E (1 - \Delta E/2mc^2)$.

34. The nucleus of a carbon atom initially at rest in the laboratory goes from one state to another by emitting a photon of energy 4.43 Mev. The atom in its final state has a rest mass of 12.0000 atomic mass units. (1 a.m.u. corresponds to 931.478 Mev). (*a*) What is the momentum of the carbon atom after the decay, as measured in the laboratory? (*b*) What is the kinetic energy, *in Mev*, of the carbon atom after the decay, as measured in the laboratory system?

35. A body of mass m at rest breaks up spontaneously into two parts, having rest masses m_1 and m_2 and respective speeds v_1 and v_2. Show that $m > m_1 + m_2$, using conservation of mass-energy.

36. A charged π-meson (rest mass $= 273\ m_e$) at rest decays into a neutrino (zero rest mass) and a μ-meson (rest mass $= 207\ m_e$). Find the kinetic energies of the neutrino and the μ-meson.

37. A gamma ray creates an electron-positron pair. (*a*) Show directly that, without the presence of a third body to take up some of the momentum, energy and momentum cannot both be conserved. (*Hint.* Set the energies equal and show that this leads to unequal momenta before and after the interaction.) (*b*) Show the result of part (*a*) by employing the relativity postulates. (*Hint.* The gamma ray must have at least an energy of $2\ m_0c^2$ to create the pair. Suppose that, in frame S, this condition is satisfied. What would an observer in frame S', moving away from the photon, see?) (*c*) Show the result of part (*a*) directly from the diagram of Problem 17.

We can see from this problem that pair creation cannot occur in free space. In order to satisfy the conservation laws, as well as to explain an interesting paradox suggested by (*b*), there must be another body around to take up some of the recoil momentum of the interaction.

38. A gamma ray (passing near a nucleus) creates an electron-positron pair, which enter a magnetic field whose intensity is 0.10 weber/m². The magnetic field is perpendicular to the flight paths of both particles, which are observed to be circular arcs of radii 4.0 cm and 10.0 cm respectively. (*a*) Find the energy of the incident gamma ray. (*b*) Would the energy calculated above be different if the observed radii were the same when the particles moved in a plane inclined at 30° to a magnetic field of the same value? Explain briefly.

39. Using Eq. 3-29 and the transformation equations for the velocity components (Eqs. 2-18 through 2-20), derive the transformation equations for the components of momentum and the energy, Eqs. 3-20*a* and 3-20*b*.

40. The quantity $c^2t^2 - (x^2 + y^2 + z^2)$ of an event is an invariant (the same for all observers) equal to $c^2\tau^2$, where τ is the proper time. That is, $c^2t^2 - (x^2 + y^2 + z^2) = c^2t'^2 - (x'^2 + y'^2 + z'^2) = c^2\tau^2$. Show that, analogously, the quantity $(E^2/c^2) - (p_x^2 + p_y^2 + p_z^2)$ for a particle is an invariant equal to $m_0^2c^2$.

41. An electron moves in the positive *x*-direction in frame S at a speed $v = 0.8c$. (*a*) What are its momentum and its energy in frame S? (*b*) Frame S' moves to the right at a speed $0.6c$ with respect to S. Find the momentum and energy of the electron in this frame.

42. Consider electromagnetic radiation to consist of photons, that is, particles of zero rest mass and of energy $E = h\nu$. Show that the Doppler and aberration formula of Chapter Two can be obtained from the transformation laws for the components of momentum and the energy (Table 3-2).

43. For a system of interacting particles, in the absence of external forces, the laws of momentum and energy in S can be written as $\Sigma_i m_i \mathbf{u}_i =$ constant and $\Sigma_i m_i c^2 =$ constant, where the relativistic mass is $m_i = m_{0i}/\sqrt{1 - u_i^2/c^2}$ for the *i*th particle. Show that if these laws are true in S, then (using the Lorentz transformation) they are true (in form) in S'.

44. Show that when $\mathbf{F}$ (as defined by Eq. 3-13) is not zero, then if, for a system of interacting particles, the total relativistic momentum changes by an amount $\Delta\mathbf{P}$, this change is equal to $\int \mathbf{F}\,dt$, the total impulse given to the system.

45. (*a*) Write the transformation equations for momentum and energy (see Table 3-2) in terms of the differences (Δp_x, Δp_y, and Δp_z) in initial and final components of momenta, and the difference (ΔE) in initial and final energy of a system of interacting particles. Justify your procedure. (*b*) Now show that if momentum and energy are conserved in frame S (i.e., $\Delta p_x = \Delta p_y = \Delta p_z = \Delta E = 0$) they are also conserved in frame S'. (*c*) Show finally that, if momentum is conserved, then energy must be conserved. Compare this result to that of Problem 3 of Chapter One.

References

1. A. H. Bucherer, *Ann. Physik,* **28,** 513 (1909)
2. R. Fleischmann and R. Kollath, "Method for Measurement of the Charge of Fast Moving Electrons," *Zeitschrift fur Physik,* **134,** 526 (1953).
3. R. Kollath and D. Menzel, "Measurement of the Charge on Moving Electrons," *Zeitschrift fur Physik,* **134,** 530 (1953).
4. W. Bertozzi, "Speed and Kinetic Energy of Relativistic Electrons," *Am. J. Phys.* **32,** 551 (1964).
5. R. T. Weidner, "On Weighing Photons," *Am. J. Phys.* **35,** 443 (1967).
6. *The Principle of Relativity,* Dover Publications, 1923, p. 29. (A collection of original papers by Einstein, Lorentz, Weyl, and Minkowski.)
7. Albert Einstein, *Out of My Later Years,* Philosophical Library, New York, 1950, pp. 116–119.
8. W. G. V. Rosser, *Contemp. Physics,* **1,** 453 (1960).

Chapter Four
Relativity and Electromagnetism

4.1 *Introduction*

We have seen how kinematics and dynamics must be generalized from their classical form to meet the requirements of special relativity. And we have seen the role that optical experiments played in the development of relativity theory and the new interpretation that is given to such experiments. It remains to investigate classical electricity and magnetism in order to discover what modifications need to be made there because of relativistic considerations. We shall confine our investigation to electromagnetic fields in vacuum.

Classical electromagnetism is consistent with special relativity. Maxwell's equations are invariant under a Lorentz transformation and do not need to be modified. Indeed, Lorentz originally arrived at his transformation equations by requiring the invariance of Maxwell's equations. In a statement [1] sent to a meeting in 1952 honoring the centenary of Michelson's birth, Albert Einstein wrote:

"The influence of the crucial Michelson-Morley experiment upon my own efforts has been rather indirect. I learned of it through H. A. Lorentz's decisive investigation of the electrodynamics of moving bodies (1895) with which I was acquainted before developing the special theory of relativity .... What led me more or less directly to the special theory of relativity was the conviction that the electromotive force acting on a body in motion in a magnetic field was nothing else but an electric field."

Hence, we could confine our considerations to the proof of the invariance of Maxwell's equations (as is done in Section 4-7) and end the discussion there. However, this would rob us of the real merits of the relativistic approach to electromagnetism. Relativity gives us a new point of view that enhances our understanding of electromagnetism. And the techniques of relativity are often much simpler than the classical techniques for solving electromagnetic problems, so that relativity theory is also a practical aid in problem solving. In the succeeding sections, we

157

shall give examples of the relativistic point of view and its practicality.

The following is a problem that suggests at once the possible value of such considerations. Consider a charge that is in motion in an inertial reference frame S. This charge, which we may call the source charge q_s, sets up a field of magnetic induction $\mathbf{B}$. Let another charge, called a test charge q_t, move through this field with a velocity $\mathbf{u}$. Then the test charge will experience a magnetic force $\mathbf{F}_m = q_t(\mathbf{u} \times \mathbf{B})$ in the S-frame. Now, consider an observer in an inertial frame S' which moves relative to S, either with the velocity $\mathbf{u}$ of the test charge or with the velocity of the source charge in S. In either one of these frames there will be no magnetic force, for either the velocity of the test charge is zero, or the source charge is at rest and there is no magnetic field; hence, $F_m' = 0$. But inertial frames are equivalent; none is preferred over another. Then is there or isn't there a magnetic force? The resolution of this paradox is simple in relativistic terms. We shall return to it later.

4.2   *The Interdependence of Electric and Magnetic Fields*

Paradoxes such as the one just raised are resolved by the fact, shown so clearly in relativity, that magnetic fields and electric fields have no separate meaning; instead, we have the single concept of an electromagnetic field. A field that is purely electric, or purely magnetic, in one frame, for example, will have both electric and magnetic components in another frame, in general. All this can be shown directly when we find how the field vectors $\mathbf{E}$ and $\mathbf{B}$ transform from one frame to another (Section 4-3). Before we do that, however, it is instructive to examine, in a semiquantitative way, a current-carrying wire viewed from two inertial frames. This will give us some insight into the interdependence of electric and magnetic fields.

We begin by considering a volume element containing charge. For simplicity, let the volume element be a cube whose edges have rest length l_0 and let there be N electrons in the cube. The charge in the cube is Ne, then, and the charge density (the charge per unit volume) is $\rho_0 = Ne/l_0^3$. If the charges are at rest in frame S' then there will be no current in S' and the current density* (current per unit cross-sectional area) will

---

*The current density is related to the current by $i = \int \mathbf{j} \cdot d\mathbf{S}$, where $\mathbf{j}$ is the (vector) current density, $d\mathbf{S}$ is a (vector) element of surface area of a conductor, and i is the current. The current is the flux

be $j_0 = 0$. Now, consider the volume element from a frame S in which it moves with velocity $\mathbf{u}$. Again, for simplicity, take $\mathbf{u}$ to be in the direction of one edge of the cube. This edge will have the measured length $l_0 \sqrt{1 - u^2/c^2}$ in S whereas the transverse edges will measure l_0 each. Hence, the volume of the cube in S is $l_0{}^3 \sqrt{1 - u^2/c^2}$. However, the number of electrons and the charge on each do not change, so that the S observer will find a charge density $\rho = Ne/l_0{}^3 \sqrt{1 - u^2/c^2}$. Combining this with ρ_0, we obtain

$$\rho = \frac{\rho_0}{\sqrt{1 - u^2/c^2}}. \tag{4-1}$$

The charges move with the velocity u in S so that j, the measured current density there (the current per unit cross-sectional area), will be the charge density of the cube times the velocity of the cube; that is, $j = \rho u = Neu/l_0{}^3 \sqrt{1 - u^2/c^2}$. Combining this with ρ_0, we obtain

$$j = \frac{\rho_0 u}{\sqrt{1 - u^2/c^2}}. \tag{4-2}$$

If we had considered a current density $\mathbf{j}$ with components j_x, j_y, and j_z, we obviously would have obtained the general result

$$j_x = \frac{\rho_0 u_x}{\sqrt{1 - u^2/c^2}}, \qquad j_y = \frac{\rho_0 u_y}{\sqrt{1 - u^2/c^2}},$$

$$j_z = \frac{\rho_0 u_z}{\sqrt{1 - u^2/c^2}}, \qquad \rho = \frac{\rho_0}{\sqrt{1 - u^2/c^2}}. \tag{4-3}$$

Now we notice a very interesting analogy. The relation between current density and charge density is similar to that between momentum and energy and to that between space and time coordinates. In fact, just as $c^2 t^2 - (x^2 + y^2 + z^2)$ is an invariant quantity equal to $c^2 \tau^2$, and just as $c^2 m^2 - (p_x{}^2 + p_y{}^2 + p_z{}^2)$ is an invariant quantity equal to $c^2 m_0{}^2$ (see Problem 3-40, for example), so we can analogously derive an invariant quantity formed from $\mathbf{j}$ and ρ. It is easily shown (Problem 4-1) that

---

of the vector $\mathbf{j}$ over the surface. In the case we are considering, the current is distributed uniformly across a conductor of cross-sectional area $A(= l_0{}^2)$ so that $i = jA$ or $j = i/A$. That is, $\mathbf{j}$ is constant over the (vector) surface of the integration and at right angles to it. The current density is current per unit cross-sectional area.

$c^2\rho^2 - (j_x{}^2 + j_y{}^2 + j_z{}^2) = c^2\rho_0{}^2$. The three analogous relations above may be written simply as

$$c^2t^2 - r^2 = c^2\tau^2,$$
$$c^2m^2 - p^2 = c^2m_0{}^2,$$
and
$$c^2\rho^2 - j^2 = c^2\rho_0{}^2.$$

In fact, Eqs. 4-1 and 4-2 can also be written as

$$\rho = \frac{\rho_0}{m_0} m \qquad \text{and} \qquad \mathbf{j} = \frac{\rho_0}{m_0} \mathbf{p}. \tag{4-3}$$

We see at once then that the quantities $\mathbf{j}$ and ρ transform exactly as $\mathbf{p}$ and m, respectively. Hence, from Eqs. 3-30, we immediately obtain the transformation equations

$$j_x{}' = \frac{j_x - \rho v}{\sqrt{1 - v^2/c^2}}, \qquad j_y{}' = j_y, \qquad j_z{}' = j_z,$$
$$\rho' = \frac{\rho - vj_x/c^2}{\sqrt{1 - v^2/c^2}}, \tag{4-4a}$$

and their inverses

$$j_x = \frac{j_x{}' + \rho'v}{\sqrt{1 - v^2/c^2}}, \qquad j_y = j_y{}', \qquad j_z = j_z{}',$$
$$\rho = \frac{\rho' + vj_x{}'/c^2}{\sqrt{1 - v^2/c^2}}. \tag{4-4b}$$

As usual, we assume that frame S' moves with a velocity v with respect to frame S along their common x-x' axes.

We shall now use these relations to analyze the fields around a current-carrying wire. Consider a long straight wire (frame S) in which free electrons move with a (drift) velocity u to the right. We take the number of free electrons per unit volume, n, to be equal to the number of positive ions per unit volume, so that the net charge in any volume element of the wire is zero. Because of these circumstances, the separation between electrons must be the same as the separation between positive ions (see Fig. 4-1). The positive charge, however, is at rest in frame S whereas the electrons are in motion.

Let us write down the charge density and the current density in S. The negative-charge density (caused by electrons) is $\rho^- = -ne$, where e is the magnitude of an electronic charge, whereas the positive-charge density

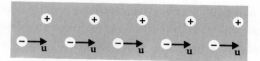

Fig. 4-1. One-dimensional schematic drawing of current-carrying wire at rest in frame S. The positive ions are at rest and the free electrons move at constant speed u to the right. The system is electrically neutral, the (measured) separation between electrons being equal to that between positive ions.

(caused by the ions) is $\rho^+ = +ne$. The net charge density, $\rho = \rho^- + \rho^+$, is zero. As for the current density, we have $j_x^- = -neu = \rho^- u$ and $j_x^+ = 0$, so that $j_x = j_x^+ + j_x^- = \rho^- u$.

Now we consider the situation in S', an inertial frame moving with speed v to the right relative to S. This observer will declare that the positive charge is in motion (to the left) but, what is more interesting, he will find that the wire is not electrically neutral. For, consider the charge density, obtained from Eq. 4-4a, in S'. We have, in general,

$$\rho^{-\prime} = \frac{\rho^- - vj_x^-/c^2}{\sqrt{1 - v^2/c^2}} \qquad \text{and} \qquad \rho^{+\prime} = \frac{\rho^+ - j_x^+/c^2}{\sqrt{1 - v^2/c^2}}$$

and with $j_x^- = \rho^- u$ and $j_x^+ = 0$, we obtain

$$\rho^{-\prime} = \rho^- \frac{(1 - vu/c^2)}{\sqrt{1 - v^2/c^2}} \qquad \text{and} \qquad \rho^{+\prime} = \frac{\rho^+}{\sqrt{1 - v^2/c^2}}.$$

Substituting $\rho^- = -ne$ and $\rho^+ = +ne$, we get for the net charge density, $[\rho' = \rho^{+\prime} + \rho^{-\prime}]$,

$$\rho' = \frac{ne}{\sqrt{1 - v^2/c^2}} - \frac{ne(1 - vu/c^2)}{\sqrt{1 - v^2/c^2}} = \frac{ne\,vu/c^2}{\sqrt{1 - v^2/c^2}},$$

which is positive and *not* zero. The primed observer finds the wire to be positively charged.

Let us summarize the results. In the S-frame, the net charge density is zero and there is no observed electric field; there is a net current density, however, so that a magnetic field **B** exists around the wire. Hence, in the S frame there is *only* a magnetic field. In the S'-frame, on the other hand, there is a positive net charge density as well as a current density so that *both* an electric field **E**$'$ and a magnetic field **B**$'$ exist. This specific example illustrates the general result that whether an electromagnetic field is purely magnetic or purely electric, or electric and magnetic, depends on the inertial frame in which the sources are observed.

With the qualitative insight of this example in mind, we now seek the result of the general case: given an electromagnetic field having values **E'** and **B'** for its electric and magnetic components in one inertial frame (S'), how do we obtain the values **E** and **B** of the corresponding field in another inertial frame (S)? Once we obtain this result, we shall be able to apply it to familiar problems, including "paradox" problem of Section 4-1.

The student may wonder what the origin is of the net positive-charge density in S' in the above example. The origin is the relativity of simultaneity. In some respects, the situation is like the length contraction of relativistic kinematics. Let us see how this is so. First, consider the wire before we apply an emf, that is, before there is a current. Both the positive ions and the electrons are stationary in S; the positive-charge density and negative-charge density are equal, and the wire is electrically neutral. Now apply an emf such that, in S, all the electrons begin moving in the same way at the same instant.* In a circular turn of wire, for example, this can be achieved by plunging a magnet through its center. Then, in S, the wire remains neutral, for the separation between electrons remains the same as before (see Problem 21 and Question 4). But what is the situation in S'? Here the positive ions are moving and the measured separation of the ions is contracted compared to the rest separation, thereby increasing the positive-charge density. Likewise, the measured separation of the electrons in S' may be increased (here the electrons can be at rest if $\mathbf{v} = \mathbf{u}$, for example) thereby decreasing the negative-charge density. In this respect, the separation between adjacent positive ions may be considered as a moving rod and the separation between adjacent electrons as another moving rod; the two observers, S and S', disagree on the simultaneity of the measurements on the end-point positions, thereby measuring different separations. This leads to different measured charge densities so that a net positive-charge density results in S' if the net charge density is zero in S. What about charge invariance then? Is the total charge in S' different than that in S? No, it is not. In a complete circuit, the direction of motion of the electrons is different in different parts of the circuit. Hence, one segment of the wire may be positively charged in S' and another segment negatively charged (see Question 3). The circuit as a whole, however, remains electrically neutral.

---

*Notice that this is *not* the way particles in a rod behave when the rod is pushed from a rest position at one end. It takes time for the signal to get to each particle and successive particles start moving later in time.

4.3   *The Transformation for* **E** *and* **B**

The electromagnetic (or *Lorentz*) force on a particle of charge q moving with velocity **u**, at a point and a time at which the electric field is **E** and the magnetic field is **B**, is

$$\mathbf{F} = q(\mathbf{E} + \mathbf{u} \times \mathbf{B}).$$

Although the electric force does not depend on the motion of the test charge, the magnetic force does. However, the motion of a particle depends on the frame in which it is described, so that we should not be surprised that the fields also depend on the frame in which they are described. We shall derive the field transformations here from special cases, the results, however, being quite generally true.

We saw (Section 3-6) that the force transformation equations between a frame S and another frame S', in which the particle experiencing the force is instantaneously at rest, is

$$F_x = F_x',$$
$$F_y = F_y'\sqrt{1 - v^2/c^2} = \frac{F_y'}{\gamma}, \tag{3-33}$$
$$F_z = F_z'\sqrt{1 - v^2/c^2} = \frac{F_z'}{\gamma}.$$

Consider a particle of charge q to be instantaneously at rest in S', wherein there is an electric field **E'** and a magnetic field **B'**. The electromagnetic force on the particle will be $\mathbf{F'} = q\mathbf{E'}$, there being no magnetic force on a particle at rest. In frame S the corresponding force is given by $\mathbf{F} = q(\mathbf{E} + \mathbf{v} \times \mathbf{B})$, for in this frame the charge has a velocity **v**, the velocity of S' relative to S. We take **v** to be along the common x-x' axes so that $v_x = v$ and $v_y = v_z = 0$.

Let us now use Eqs. 3-33, one at a time. We find, with $(\mathbf{v} \times \mathbf{B})_x = v_y B_z - v_z B_y = 0$, that $F_x = q[E_x + (\mathbf{v} \times \mathbf{B})_x] = qE_x$ and $F_x' = qE_x'$. Then, the equation $F_x' = F_x$ gives us $qE_x' = qE_x$, and we have

$$E_x' = E_x$$

as the transformation equation for E_x'.

Using the y-component equation, we obtain $qE_y'/\gamma = q[E_y + (\mathbf{v} \times \mathbf{B})_y]$ or, since $(\mathbf{v} \times \mathbf{B})_y = v_z B_x - v_x B_z = vB_z$, the transformation equation for E_y' is

$$E_y' = \gamma(E_y - vB_z).$$

Similarly, from the z-component equation we obtain the transformation equation for E_z', namely

$$E_z' = \gamma(E_z + vB_y).$$

Hence, we can summarize *the transformation for the electric field components* as

$$
\begin{aligned}
E_x' &= E_x & E_x &= E_x' \\
E_y' &= \gamma(E_y - vB_z) & E_y &= \gamma(E_y' + vB_z') \\
E_z' &= \gamma(E_z + vB_y) & E_z &= \gamma(E_z' - vB_y').
\end{aligned}
\tag{4-5}
$$

The left-hand set of equations was just derived. The right-hand set gives the inverse equations, obtained by sending v to $-v$ and interchanging primes and unprimes.

Actually, the restriction that the relative velocity $\mathbf{v}$ of S' with respect to S be along the x-axis is unnecessary, because the orientation of this axis is arbitrary. If, instead, we introduce components of the fields parallel ($\parallel$) and perpendicular ($\perp$) to the direction of the relative velocity, then we can write these transformations quite generally as

$$E_\parallel' = E_\parallel \tag{4-6}$$

and
$$E_\perp' = \gamma[E_\perp + (\mathbf{v} \times \mathbf{B})_\perp]$$

which assert that the component of $\mathbf{E}$ parallel to the relative velocity of the two frames is unchanged, whereas the components of $\mathbf{E}$ perpendicular to the relative velocity transform to mixed electric and magnetic fields.

Now let us investigate the transformation of the *magnetic* field components. Again we pick a relatively simple case whose results are nevertheless general. As before, the relative motion of the two frames, S and S', is along the common x-x' axes. Consider a particle of charge q moving in the S' frame in the y'-direction only, with speed u'. Then, with $u' = u_y'$, the force in S', $\mathbf{F}' = q(\mathbf{E}' + \mathbf{u}' \times \mathbf{B}')$, has components $F_x' = q(E_x' + u_y'B_z')$, $F_y' = qE_y'$, and $F_z' = q(E_z' - u_y'B_x')$ in the primed frame (S'). To get the force in S, we first must know what the particle's velocity is in this unprimed (S) frame. Here we need the velocity transformation equations, Eqs. 2-18 to 2-20, from which we find $u_x = v$, $u_y = u_y'/\gamma$, and $u_z = 0$. That is, although in S' the particle moves only along the y'-direction, in S the particle velocity has a component along x as well as along y. Hence, the force $\mathbf{F} = q(\mathbf{E} + \mathbf{u} \times \mathbf{B})$ in S has components $F_x = q(E_x + u_yB_z)$, $F_y = q(E_y - vB_z)$, and $F_z = q(E_z + vB_y - u_yB_x)$.

Now that we have the components of force in each inertial frame, we must substitute them into the general force transformation equations (Eqs. 3-32*a* or 3-32*b*) to obtain relations between the fields. If we do this, and use also Eqs. 4-5, relations already derived, we shall find (see Problem 3) that $B_x' = B_x$ and $B_z' = \gamma[B_z - (v/c^2)E_y]$. In order to find how the *y*-component of the magnetic field transforms, we would need to let the charge move in the *z'*-direction instead of in the *y'*-direction. We would find (see Problem 3), by a similar procedure, that $B_y' = \gamma[B_y + (v/c^2)E_z]$. Hence, we can summarize the *transformations for the magnetic field components* as

$$B_x' = B_x \qquad\qquad\qquad B_x = B_x'$$

$$B_y' = \gamma\left(B_y + \frac{v}{c^2}E_z\right) \qquad B_y = \gamma\left(B_y' - \frac{v}{c^2}E_z'\right) \qquad (4\text{-}7)$$

$$B_z' = \gamma\left(B_z - \frac{v}{c^2}E_y\right) \qquad B_z = \gamma\left(B_z' + \frac{v}{c^2}E_y'\right).$$

Once again, we need not restrict the relative velocity **v** of *S'* with respect to *S* to be along the *x*-axis. Taking the field components parallel and perpendicular to the direction of the relative velocity, we can write these transformations quite generally as

$$B_\parallel' = B_\parallel$$

and

$$B_\perp' = \gamma\left[B_\perp - \frac{1}{c^2}(\mathbf{v} \times \mathbf{E})_\perp\right] \qquad (4\text{-}8)$$

which assert that the components of **B** parallel to the relative velocity of the two frames is unchanged, whereas the components of **B** perpendicular to the relative velocity transform to mixed magnetic and electric fields.

There is a similarity between the transformation for **E** (Eq. 4-5 or Eq. 4-6) and those for **B** (Eq. 4-7 or Eq. 4-8), with only a sign difference and a factor c^2 in the **B** equations compared to those for **E**.

As a good consistency check, the student can show (see Problem 10) that Eqs. 4-5 and 4-7 have the property that the first three equations in each set may be inverted (solved for the unprimed fields in terms of the primed ones) to yield the last three equations in each set. To do this, however, we must consider the *six* as a set, not two sets of three each. In this way, we can justify explicitly the procedure for obtaining the inverse transformations by merely replacing **v** and $-\mathbf{v}$ and interchang-

TABLE **4-1**   RELATIVISTIC TRANSFORMATIONS FOR THE ELECTROMAGNETIC FIELD

$E_x' = E_x$	$E_x = E_x'$
$E_y' = \gamma(E_y - vB_z)$	$E_y = \gamma(E_y' + vB_z')$
$E_z' = \gamma(E_z + vB_y)$	$E_z = \gamma(E_z' - vB_y')$
$B_x' = B_x$	$B_x = B_x'$
$B_y' = \gamma(B_y + vE_z/c^2)$	$B_y = \gamma(B_y' - vE_z'/c^2)$
$B_z' = \gamma(B_z - vE_y/c^2)$	$B_z = \gamma(B_z' + vE_y'/c^2)$

ing primes and unprimes. And, at the same time, we see in another way the interdependence of **E** and **B**, since our transformation law relates all six components of **E** and **B** rather than giving us two separate laws of transformation, one for **E** and one for **B**. Electric and magnetic fields cannot exist independently as separate quantities but are interdependent.*

We summarize the transformation for the electromagnetic field in Table 4-1.

◗ *Example* 1. (*a*) Suppose that an electromagnetic field is *purely electric* in inertial frame *S*; that is, **E** $\neq$ 0 but **B** = 0. Describe this field in inertial frame *S'*.

From Eqs. 4-6 and 4-8 we find that, in *S'*,

$$E_\parallel' = E_\parallel \qquad B_\parallel' = 0$$

$$E_\perp' = \gamma E_\perp \qquad B_\perp' = -\frac{\gamma}{c^2}(\mathbf{v} \times \mathbf{E})_\perp$$

But $$(\mathbf{v} \times \mathbf{E}) = \mathbf{v} \times \mathbf{E}_\perp = \frac{\mathbf{v} \times \mathbf{E}_\perp'}{\gamma} = \frac{\mathbf{v} \times \mathbf{E}'}{\gamma}.$$

Hence $$\mathbf{B}' = \mathbf{B}_\perp' = \frac{-\gamma}{c^2}(\mathbf{v} \times \mathbf{E}) = -\frac{\mathbf{v} \times \mathbf{E}'}{c^2}.$$

There *is* a magnetic field **B'** in the primed frame, as well as an electric field **E'**, so that what appears to observer *S* as a pure electric field **E** appears to observer *S'* as both an electric and a magnetic field.

(*b*) Suppose that an electromagnetic field is *purely magnetic* in inertial frame *S*; that is, **E** = 0 but **B** $\neq$ 0. Describe this field in inertial frame *S'*.

From Eqs. 4-6 and 4-8 we find that, in *S'*,

$$E_\parallel' = 0 \qquad\qquad B_\parallel' = B_\parallel$$

$$E_\perp' = \gamma(\mathbf{v} \times \mathbf{B})_\perp \qquad B_\perp' = \gamma B_\perp$$

---

*Although **E**, **B**, or any combination of them do not form a four-vector, we can combine **E** and **B** to form a single quantity, a four-tensor, called the electromagnetic field tensor.

But $$\mathbf{v} \times \mathbf{B} = \mathbf{v} \times \mathbf{B}_{\perp} = \frac{\mathbf{v} \times \mathbf{B}_{\perp}{}'}{\gamma} = \frac{\mathbf{v} \times \mathbf{B}'}{\gamma}.$$

Hence $$\mathbf{E}' = \mathbf{E}_{\perp}{}' = \gamma(\mathbf{v} \times \mathbf{B}) = \mathbf{v} \times \mathbf{B}'.$$

There *is* an electric field $\mathbf{E}'$ in the primed frame, as well as magnetic field $\mathbf{B}'$, so that what appears to observer S as a pure magnetic field $\mathbf{B}$ appears to observer S' as both an electric and a magnetic field.

This example relates directly to Einstein's comment "that the electromotive force acting on a body in motion in a magnetic field (is) nothing else but an electric field." ◀

We have seen directly in the transformation equations that electric and magnetic fields do not have separate existences. These equations also suggest a very practical benefit. We may be able to solve difficult problems by choosing a reference system in which the answer is easier to find and then transforming the results back to the system we deal with in the laboratory. We illustrate this in succeeding sections.

4.4   *The Field of a Uniformly Moving Point Charge*

Consider a particle of charge q moving with uniform velocity $\mathbf{u}$ in frame S. We wish to calculate the electric and magnetic fields in S caused by this moving charge. We can get an exact solution to this problem in a simple way by choosing an inertial frame S' in which this charge is at rest at the origin and in which, therefore, the field is merely the static electric field of a point charge. Then we use the transformation equations for the electromagnetic field and immediately obtain the fields corresponding to the charge moving in S.

In Fig. 4-2 we show the charge q at rest at the origin of S', moving relative to S with a velocity $\mathbf{u}$ along the common x-x' axis. Let the position of the charge along the x-axis at time t be given by $X = ut$, so that in S the space coordinates of q are $(X,0,0)$. Now the field of the charge in S' (it's rest frame) is purely electric, that is,

$$\mathbf{E}' = \frac{q}{4\pi\epsilon_0}\frac{\mathbf{r}'}{r'^3} \qquad \mathbf{B}' = 0, \qquad (4\text{-}9)$$

the electric field lines diverging from q with spherical symmetry, as in Fig. 4-3a. Here,

$$r' = (x'^2 + y'^2 + z'^2)^{1/2} \qquad (4\text{-}10)$$

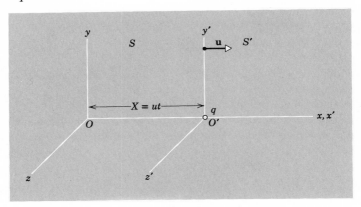

Fig. 4-2. Charge q, at rest in S' at the origin O', is at the position $(X, 0, 0)$ in S where $X = ut$.

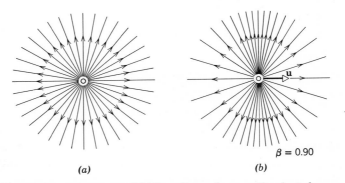

$\beta = 0.90$

(a)   (b)

Fig. 4-3. (a) The electric field lines diverge from q with spherical symmetry in its rest frame. (b) In a frame in which q moves with high speed, the electric field lines concentrate in the transverse direction.

is the distance from O' to the point at which the field strength is measured.* The field depends inversely on the square of r', as required by Coulomb's law.

In order to obtain the fields **E** and **B** in inertial frame S, corresponding to the moving charge, we simply use the transformation equations, Eqs. 4-5 and 4-7. We should note first, however, that $\mathbf{r}'$ has components (x',y',z') and that the field in S must be expressed in terms of x, y, and z.

---

*We emphasize that the coordinates (X,Y,Z), which here equal $(ut,0,0)$, are the coordinates of the source of the field (i.e., the source charge) whereas the coordinates (x,y,z) are those of the point at which the field is being evaluated. We can relate the space-time field point (x,y,z,t) in S to the *same* space-time field point (x',y',z',t') in the S' via the Lorentz transformations.

Hence, we must use the Lorentz transformation equations also, so that, for example,

$$r' = (x'^2 + y'^2 + z'^2)^{1/2} = [\gamma^2(x - ut)^2 + y^2 + z^2]^{1/2}$$

where $\gamma = 1/\sqrt{1 - u^2/c^2}$. Then, with

$$E_x' = \frac{qx'}{4\pi\epsilon_0 r'^3}, \qquad E_y' = \frac{qy'}{4\pi\epsilon_0 r'^3},$$

and

$$E_z' = \frac{qz'}{4\pi\epsilon_0 r'^3},$$

Eq. 4-5 gives

$$E_x = E_x' = \frac{qx'}{4\pi\epsilon_0 r'^3} = \frac{q\gamma(x - ut)}{4\pi\epsilon_0[\gamma^2(x - ut)^2 + y^2 + z^2]^{3/2}};$$

or, with $X = ut$ giving the location of the charge in S,

$$E_x = \frac{q\gamma(x - X)}{4\pi\epsilon_0[\gamma^2(x - X)^2 + y^2 + z^2]^{3/2}}$$

$$E_y = \frac{q\gamma y}{4\pi\epsilon_0[\gamma^2(x - X)^2 + y^2 + z^2]^{3/2}} \qquad (4\text{-}11)$$

$$E_z = \frac{q\gamma z}{4\pi\epsilon_0[\gamma^2(x - X)^2 + y^2 + z^2]^{3/2}}$$

give the electric field components at the point x, y, z in the S frame.

Similarly, the components of the magnetic field **B** in S follow explicitly from substituting **E'** and **B'** into the transformation equations for the magnetic field components (Eq. 4-7). Actually, from (the inverse of) Eq. 4-8 we obtain at once $\mathbf{B}_\| = 0$ and $\mathbf{B}_\perp = (\mathbf{u} \times \mathbf{E})/c^2$, or (since **u** is along the x-axis)

$$\mathbf{B} = \frac{\mathbf{u} \times \mathbf{E}}{c^2}. \qquad (4\text{-}12)$$

If we want the components of **B** at the field point x, y, z, we substitute the equations for E_z and E_y given above into

$$B_x = 0,$$

$$B_y = -\frac{u}{c^2}E_z, \qquad (4\text{-}13)$$

and

$$B_z = \frac{u}{c^2}E_y.$$

Equations 4-11 and 4-13 are the exact expressions for the electric and magnetic fields of a uniformly moving charge and our problem is solved. Notice that, because $X = ut$, these fields depend upon the time t as well as on x, y, and z. Notice, too, the symmetric appearance of γ in these expressions.

It is interesting to investigate how the electric field, which is a radial, inverse square, spherically symmetric field in the rest (S') frame, appears in the S-frame. Consider the field at the instant, $t = 0$, that the moving charge is at the origin 0 of frame S; at other instants the field will look the same, although translated to the right by an amount ut. With $X(= ut) = 0$, Eqs. 4-11 reduce to

$$E = \frac{q\gamma\mathbf{r}}{4\pi\epsilon_0[\gamma^2 x^2 + y^2 + z^2)^{3/2}} \tag{4-14}$$

Hence, $\mathbf{E}$ is still a radial field, directed out along $\mathbf{r}$. [$\mathbf{B}$, incidently, is perpendicular to the plane formed by $\mathbf{E}$ and $\mathbf{u}$, as given in Eq. 4-12.] Is the electric field still an inverse square one and still spherically symmetric? Let θ be the angle made by $\mathbf{r}$ with the x-axis, so that $x = r\cos\theta$ and $y^2 + z^2 = r^2\sin^2\theta$. Then, with $\beta = u/c$ and $\gamma = 1/\sqrt{1 - \beta^2}$, the student can easily show that $\gamma^2 x^2 + y^2 + z^2 = r^2\gamma^2(1 - \beta^2\sin^2\theta)$. Substituting this into Eq. 4-14, we obtain

$$E = \frac{q(1 - \beta^2)}{4\pi\epsilon_0 r^2(1 - \beta^2\sin^2\theta)^{3/2}}\frac{\mathbf{r}}{r}. \tag{4-15}$$

Hence, the field is an inverse square one, insofar as its dependence on the radial distance r goes as $1/r^2$, but the strength of the field at a given radial distance depends on the direction and the field is *not* spherically symmetric.

▶ *Example 2.* Calculate the strength of the electric field from Eq. 4-15 for the limiting cases (*a*) $\theta = 0°$, (*b*) $\theta = 90°$, and (*c*) $\beta = 0$.

(*a*) $\theta = 0$ means directly in front of the charge along its line of motion. This is equivalent to calculating $E_\parallel$. Then, with $\sin^2\theta = 0$, we obtain

$$E_\parallel = \frac{q}{4\pi\epsilon_0 r^2}(1 - \beta^2)$$

(*b*) $\theta = 90°$ means perpendicular to the x-axis, or perpendicular to the line of motion, and is equivalent to calculating $E_\perp$. Then, with $\sin^2\theta = 1$,

$$E_\perp = \frac{q}{4\pi\epsilon_0 r^2} \frac{1}{\sqrt{1-\beta^2}}.$$

Hence, for a high-speed charged particle (i.e., for β^2 not negligible) $E_\parallel$ is small and $E_\perp$ is large compared to the static field. In Fig. 4-3*b* we show this relativistic effect, the electric field lines concentrating in the transverse directions.

(*c*) When $\beta = 0$, we obtain, from Eq. 4-15,

$$E = \frac{q}{4\pi\epsilon_0 r^2} \qquad \text{and} \qquad E_\parallel = E_\perp.$$

Hence, if the charged particle is a low-speed one (i.e., $\beta \ll 1$) the electric field components are approximately equal to those of the static field in Fig. 4-3*a*. ◀

The results of the previous example can be related to the invariance of the charge. The quantity of charge is defined by Gauss' law, $q = \epsilon_0 \oint \mathbf{E} \cdot d\mathbf{S}$. If the charge q is invariant, then by definition the electric flux over a surface enclosing the charge (the integral above) must be invariant. Imagine now a cylindrical pillbox (Fig. 4-4*a*) enclosing the charge in frame S', the axis of the cylinder being along the *x-x'* axes. Surfaces perpendicular to x' (i.e., the flat end surfaces whose surface area vectors are directed along *x-x'*) do not contract as seen by S, for whom the pillbox is in motion (Fig. 4-4*b*). But surfaces parallel to x' (i.e., the cylindrical surface whose surface area vectors are perpendicular to x') *do* con-

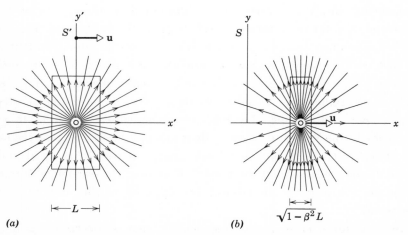

(*a*)   (*b*)

Fig. 4-4. Gauss' law as applied to a moving charge. The charge q is surrounded by a Gaussian surface in the shape of a pillbox. The flux through the sides of the box is the same measured in either frame, as is the flux through the ends of the box.

tract, their area changing by a factor $\sqrt{1 - \beta^2} = 1/\gamma$. Compared to its rest shape, the pillbox appears compressed to S. The electric flux through the surfaces of the pillbox must be the same for each observer, however, if charge is to be invariant. That is, if $q = q'$ then $\oint \mathbf{E} \cdot d\mathbf{S} = \oint \mathbf{E'} \cdot d\mathbf{S'}$. A simple way in which this result can be achieved is to require that the flux through the end surfaces remain the same and that the flux through the cylindrical surfaces remain the same. Then, $E_x = E_x{}'$, the electric field components along the common x-x' axes being unchanged because the flat end surfaces are unchanged; and $E_y = \gamma E_y{}'$ and $E_z = \gamma E_z{}'$, the electric field components perpendicular to x-x' changing to S by a factor γ because the cylindrical surface area changed to S by a factor $1/\gamma$. That charge is invariant in our example, and that the flux invariance is achieved in the simple way we considered, follow from the fact that our results are identical to the transformation equations (Eqs. 4-5), which were the starting point of our example. For a charge stationary in S', wherein $B' = 0$, we obtain, from Eqs. 4-5, $E_x = E_x{}'$, $E_y = \gamma E_y{}'$, and $E_z = \gamma E_z{}'$, exactly as above.

4.5   *Forces and Fields Near a Current-Carrying Wire*

We return now to the current-carrying wire discussed in Section 4-2. There we used such a wire to show the interdependence of electric and magnetic fields; the description of the field depends on the inertial frame in which the sources are observed. Here we shall use the field transformations, which relate these different descriptions of the same field, and examine the forces on a test charge in the field outside the wire.

Consider a test charge q at rest in frame S outside a long straight stationary wire carrying a current. It simplifies the algebra to characterize the charges in the wire in terms of a linear charge density λ (charge per unit length) rather than, as before, in terms of a volume charge density ρ (charge per unit volume). Let the current be caused by the motion of electrons in the wire and let their drift velocity be u. The positive ions are at rest in frame S, but their linear charge density λ^+ is equal to the linear charge density λ^- of the moving electrons. The current in frame S is simply $i = \lambda^- u$, its direction being opposite to the motion of the electrons.

Because there is no net charge density, that is, because $\lambda = \lambda^+ + \lambda^- = 0$, there is no electric field outside the wire in frame S. (If λ were *not* equal to zero, the electric field would be given by $E = (\lambda/2\pi\epsilon_0)/r$, where r is the perpendicular distance from the wire, and would be radially directed.) However, there *is* a magnetic field outside the wire, given by $B = (\mu_0/2\pi)i/r$, forming concentric circles around it (see Fig. 4-5). Hence, with $i = \lambda^- u$, we have

$$E = 0 \qquad \text{and} \qquad B = \frac{\mu_0 \lambda^- u}{2\pi r}$$

as the fields in frame S. What is the force on the test charge in these fields? It is zero; for the electric field is zero (no electric force) and the test charge is not moving (no magnetic force).

Consider the situation in frame S' which moves relative to S at a velocity $\mathbf{v} = \mathbf{u}$, such that, in this frame, the electrons in the wire are at rest. The force transformation laws tell us at once that the force on the charge in S' must also be zero; but we know that if a charge does not accelerate in one inertial frame, it does not accelerate in any inertial frame, so this result is expected. What is interesting here is that in S' there *is* an electric field (see Section 4-2), so there must be an electric

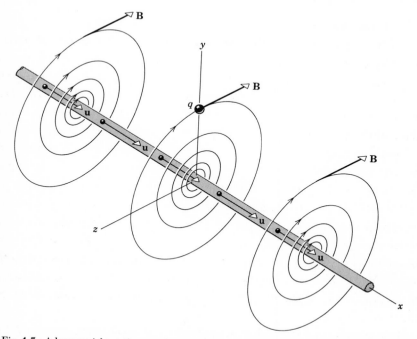

Fig. 4-5. A long straight stationary wire carrying a current sets up a magnetic field **B** in frame S. Electrons of linear charge density λ^- drift with speed u along the positive x-direction. The current, $i = \lambda u$, is directed along the negative x-direction. A test charge q is at rest on the y-axis.

force on q; if the net force is zero then there must also be a magnetic force which cancels the electric force. This is now possible, of course, because in S' the test charge is not at rest but is moving. We can prove that $F' = 0$ by direct application of the transformation for $\mathbf{E}$ and $\mathbf{B}$.

Let the charge be at some point on the y-axis in frame S (see Fig. 4-5). At this point, since there is no electric field in S,

$$E_x = 0, \qquad E_y = 0, \qquad E_z = 0,$$

$$B_x = 0, \qquad B_y = 0, \qquad B_z = -\frac{\mu_0 \lambda^- u}{2\pi r},$$

where the minus sign on B_z indicates that $\mathbf{B}$ points along the negative z-direction. Now, with $v = u$, let us find the components of $\mathbf{E}'$ and $\mathbf{B}'$ in the primed frame from Eqs. 4-5 and 4-7. We have, from Eqs. 4-5,

$$E_x' = E_x = 0$$

$$E_y' = \gamma(E_y - uB_z) = \gamma\left(0 + u\frac{\mu_0 \lambda^- u}{2\pi r}\right) = \gamma u^2 \frac{\mu_0 \lambda^-}{2\pi r}$$

$$E_z' = \gamma(E_z + uB_y) = \gamma(0 + 0) = 0.$$

The electric field points along y' away from the wire and the electric force on charge q in S' is directed along the positive y'-direction with a magnitude of

$$F_E' = qE' = q\gamma u^2 \frac{\mu_0 \lambda^-}{2\pi r}.$$

The magnetic field components, from Eqs. 4-7, are

$$B_x' = B_x = 0$$

$$B_y' = \gamma\left(B_y + \frac{u}{c^2}E_z\right) = \gamma(0 + 0) = 0$$

$$B_z' = \gamma\left(B_z - \frac{u}{c^2}E_y\right) = \gamma\left(-\frac{\mu_0 \lambda^- u}{2\pi r} - 0\right) = -\gamma\frac{\mu_0 \lambda^- u}{2\pi r}.$$

In S', charge q moves to the left (along x') with speed u so that, with B_z' along the negative z-direction, the magnetic force is directed toward the wire along with negative y'-direction with a magnitude

$$F_B' = |q(\mathbf{v} \times \mathbf{B}')| = qu\gamma\frac{\mu_0 \lambda^- u}{2\pi r} = q\gamma u^2 \frac{\mu_0 \lambda^-}{2\pi r}.$$

Hence, the net force $\mathbf{F}' = \mathbf{F}_E' + \mathbf{F}_B' = 0$, as we set out to prove.

The student should now be able to resolve the paradox presented in Section 4-1, for in frame S' there *is* a magnetic force on the test charge whereas in frame S there is *not* a magnetic force on the test charge, exactly the situation presented earlier.

Notice that, throughout, we have assumed the invariance of electric charge; that is, the charge was taken to be the same as measured by each inertial observer ($q \equiv q'$). This is not only confirmed by the consistency of all the results based on this assumption and the agreement of such results with experiment, but also by direct experimental confirmation of charge invariance (see, for example, Refs. 2).

4.6 *Forces Between Moving Charges*

As a final example of the insights into electromagnetism that are provided by relativity theory, we consider two particles of equal charge q moving with equal uniform velocity **u**. Let **u** be along the x-axis of frame S and let the particles have the same x-coordinate, for simplicity, their separation being r (see Fig. 4-6a). We expect the charges to exert forces upon one another, a repulsive electrical force and an attractive magnetic force. Are these forces equal?

Guided by our earlier example, we pick another inertial frame S' in which the problem is simpler. Let S' move with uniform velocity $v = u$ relative to S along the common x-x' axis, so that the charges are at rest in S' (see Fig. 4-6b). Here, there is no magnetic force at all and the elec-

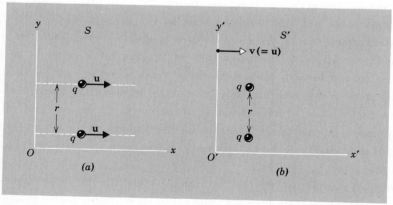

Fig. 4-6. (a) Two particles of equal charge q move with equal uniform velocity **u** in frame S, their separation being r. (b) The same situation in S', which moves relative to S with a velocity $v = u$.

trical force is a repulsion; the charges would tend to move apart along the y'-direction, each exerting a force on the other of magnitude

$$F_y' = \frac{1}{4\pi\epsilon_0} \frac{q^2}{r^2}.$$

The force on the upper charge is $+F_y'$ and that on the lower charge is $-F_y'$. Notice once again that charge invariance is assumed. Notice also that the separation r is unchanged by the transformation from S to S' (it is measured in the y or y' direction, and $y' = y$).

Now let us use the force transformation equations (Eqs. 3-33) in which a particle is at rest instantaneously in the S'-frame, subject to a force with components F_x', F_y', and F_z', to obtain the force components F_x, F_y, and F_z acting on the particle in the S-frame. We know that in inertial frame S, in which the charges are in motion, there will be both magnetic and electrical forces on each particle, but what will the net force be? From Eq. 3-33 we find, for the force on the upper charge, that

$$F_x = F_x' = 0$$
$$F_z = F_z'/\gamma = 0$$

and $$F_y = F_y'/\gamma = F_y'\sqrt{1 - v^2/c^2} = \frac{q^2}{4\pi\epsilon_0 r^2}\sqrt{1 - v^2/c^2}$$

Hence, the net force is in the positive y-direction. The charged particles *repel* one another and the electrical force of repulsion must exceed the magnetic force of attraction.

This example is rich in insights. Notice, for example, that only when $v = c$ does the net force become zero, so that the charges repel in *all* inertial frames, that is, the electric force is always greater than the magnetic force. Although the magnitude of the net force depends on the frame, the net force is always repulsive. Also, when $v \to 0$, we return to the static result wherein only an electric force exists. Clearly, then, the magnetic force, which exists only when $v \neq 0$, is a second-order effect compared to the electrical force, for its effect enters as the square of the ratio of the velocity of the charges to the velocity of light, that is, it enters as $(v/c)^2$.

In this example, we start with Coulomb's law for the forces between electrostatic charges (in frame S') and calculate magnetic forces produced by moving charges as well (in frame S). All we assumed were the force transformations of special relativity and the invariance of charge. We did *not* use the electromagnetic field component transformations. Hence, the deepest insight given by this example is that magnetic forces can be interpreted as relativistic forces; they are that part of the force, transformed from the rest frame, which depends on the velocity of the test charge relative to the observer. To put it all in another way, if all we knew in electromagnetism was Coulomb's law, then, by using special relativity and the invariance of charge, we could prove that magnetic fields must exist. The magnetic field enters relativity in a most natural way as a field that is produced by a source charge in motion and that exerts a force on a test charge that depends on its velocity relative to the observer. The Lorentz force law is found to apply, and Maxwell's equations and the transformation equations of the electromagnetic field can then all be deduced. In this way, electromagnetism can be derived from relativity theory, the exact opposite of the historical development of these subjects.*

If we had considered the more general case in which the two charges had different uniform velocities, we would have found that the magnetic force, compared to the electric force, is smaller by a factor uv/c^2, where v is the speed of the source charge and u that of the test charge. We might wonder how we can observe magnetic forces at all, then, when u and v are ordinary speeds; the electric forces would entirely mask the magnetic forces, in practice, it seems. The answer, of course, is that we can eliminate the electrical forces entirely in many situations, leaving the magnetic force as the only one observed. The current-carrying wire is an example in point, for although there are many charges present, they are equally positive and negative, so that no electric field exists. The moving electrons set up a magnetic field which exerts forces on charges moving through it. Actually, the magnetic forces can be reasonably large (as you know from simple freshman laboratory apparatus) because of the largeness of Avogadro's number (there are so many moving electrons). Indeed, considering that electron drift velocities are so small, about 1 mm/sec (see, for example, Ref. 4), and that the magnetic force can be regarded as a relativistic effect, the statement that relativity is important only for speeds near that of light must be taken with a grain of salt.

*See Ref. 3 for a complete development of this approach.

4.7   *The Invariance of Maxwell's Equations*

Let us review what we have done in relativistic dynamics. By consideration of mechanical collisions and the Lorentz transformation equations, we derived the relativistic force and its transformation from one inertial frame to another. Then, by taking the Lorentz force law, $\mathbf{F} = q[\mathbf{E} + (\mathbf{u} \times \mathbf{B})]$, as the correct force between moving charges, and assuming that electric charge is invariant, we derived the transformation formulas for the $\mathbf{E}$ and $\mathbf{B}$ fields.

Now, we can do the following, as well. We can start with the Lorentz transformation equations and require that Maxwell's equations should be relativistically invariant. We can then derive what the transformation formula for the $\mathbf{E}$ and $\mathbf{B}$ fields must be in order to satisfy this requirement. We shall find that we get the same result as before.

Thus, once again special relativity is shown to be internally consistent. But more than that, this constitutes a proof that the force transformations that we derived by considering collisions applies as well to electromagnetic forces. Indeed, once we have shown explicitly that Maxwell's equations transform correctly, we have fully solved the original problem of special relativity. Let us now show how this can be done.

We begin by writing down Maxwell's equations in differential form [see Ref. 5]. They are

$$\epsilon_0 \operatorname{div} \mathbf{E} = \rho \tag{4-16}$$
$$\operatorname{div} \mathbf{B} = 0, \tag{4-17}$$
$$\operatorname{curl} \mathbf{B} = \mu_0(\mathbf{j} + \epsilon_0\, \partial \mathbf{E}/\partial t), \tag{4-18}$$
and
$$\operatorname{curl} \mathbf{E} = -\, \partial \mathbf{B}/\partial t. \tag{4-19}$$

Equations 4-17 and 4-19 do not contain the quantities ϵ_0, μ_0, ρ, or $\mathbf{j}$ and have the same form in vacuum as in a material medium. They contain only the field quantities $\mathbf{E}$ and $\mathbf{B}$. It will be simpler to work with them to show how the invariance of Maxwell's equations can be proved. We confine our discussion to those equations, therefore, but assert that a similar procedure* gives the same results starting from Eqs. 4-16 and 4-18.

The spatial components of the vector equations (Eqs. 4-19 and 4-17) can be written as

---

*We would have to use the transformations for the current density $\mathbf{j}$ and the charge density ρ (see Eqs. 4-4a and 4-4b) in this case, as well as the Lorentz equations.

$$\frac{\partial}{\partial y} E_z - \frac{\partial}{\partial z} E_y = -\frac{\partial B_x}{\partial t}, \tag{4-20}$$

$$\frac{\partial}{\partial z} E_x - \frac{\partial}{\partial x} E_z = -\frac{\partial B_y}{\partial t} \tag{4-21}$$

$$\frac{\partial}{\partial x} E_y - \frac{\partial}{\partial y} E_x = -\frac{\partial B_z}{\partial t}, \tag{4-22}$$

and
$$\frac{\partial}{\partial x} B_x + \frac{\partial}{\partial y} B_y + \frac{\partial}{\partial z} B_z = 0. \tag{4-23}$$

These equations are a set of coupled partial differential equations involving the components of the **E** field (E_x, E_y, E_z) and the **B** field (B_x, B_y, B_z) and apply at a point x, y, z and a time t in the inertial frame S. We now require that they have the same form in inertial frame S', which moves at uniform velocity **v** relative to S along the common x-x' axes. That is, we require that at the space-time coordinates x', y', z', t' in S', which corresponds (by means of the Lorentz transformations) to x, y, z, t in S, these same fields, now designated **E′** and **B′**, be related by

$$\text{curl } \mathbf{E'} = -\partial \mathbf{B'}/\partial t' \tag{4-19'}$$

and
$$\text{div } \mathbf{B'} = 0 \tag{4-17'}$$

or, in component form, by

$$\frac{\partial E_z'}{\partial y'} - \frac{\partial E_y'}{\partial z'} = -\frac{\partial B_x'}{\partial t'}, \tag{4-20'}$$

$$\frac{\partial E_x'}{\partial z'} - \frac{\partial E_z'}{\partial x'} = -\frac{\partial B_y'}{\partial t'}, \tag{4-21'}$$

$$\frac{\partial E_y'}{\partial x'} - \frac{\partial E_x'}{\partial y'} = -\frac{\partial B_z'}{\partial t'}, \tag{4-22'}$$

and
$$\frac{\partial B_x'}{\partial x'} + \frac{\partial B_y'}{\partial y'} + \frac{\partial B_z'}{\partial z'} = 0. \tag{4-23'}$$

We need to know the relation between partial differentiation with respect to one set of variables (x, y, z, t) and the corresponding partial differentiation with respect to the other set of variables (x', y', z', t'). The variables themselves are related by the Lorentz transformation equations (see Table 2-1), which we can write compactly, with $\gamma = 1/\sqrt{1 - v^2/c^2}$, as $x' = \gamma(x - vt)$, $y' = y$, $z' = z$, and $t' = \gamma(t - xv/c^2)$. The relation for $\partial/\partial x$ is

$$\partial/\partial x = \frac{\partial x'}{\partial x}\frac{\partial}{\partial x'} + \frac{\partial y'}{\partial x}\frac{\partial}{\partial y'} + \frac{\partial z'}{\partial x}\frac{\partial}{\partial z'} + \frac{\partial t'}{\partial x}\frac{\partial}{\partial t'} \qquad (4\text{-}24)$$

with corresponding relations for $\partial/\partial y$, $\partial/\partial z$, and $\partial/\partial t$ (simply replace x by y, z, or t, respectively). However, we find from the Lorentz equations that

$$\frac{\partial x'}{\partial x} = \gamma, \qquad \frac{\partial y'}{\partial x} = 0, \qquad \frac{\partial z'}{\partial x} = 0, \qquad \text{and} \qquad \frac{\partial t'}{\partial x} = -\frac{\gamma v}{c^2}$$

so that

$$\frac{\partial}{\partial x} = \gamma\left(\frac{\partial}{\partial x'} - \frac{v}{c^2}\frac{\partial}{\partial t'}\right). \qquad (4\text{-}25)$$

In the same way, we find

$$\frac{\partial}{\partial y} = \frac{\partial}{\partial y'}, \qquad (4\text{-}26)$$

$$\frac{\partial}{\partial z} = \frac{\partial}{\partial z'} \qquad (4\text{-}27)$$

and

$$\frac{\partial}{\partial t} = \gamma\left(\frac{\partial}{\partial t'} - v\frac{\partial}{\partial x'}\right) \qquad (4\text{-}28)$$

The next step is make these substitutions into Eqs. 4-20 through 4-23. We find, on doing this for Eq. 4-21, for example, that this equation becomes

$$\frac{\partial}{\partial z'}E_x - \frac{\partial}{\partial x'}[\gamma(E_z + vB_y)] = -\frac{\partial}{\partial t'}\left[\gamma\left(B_y + \frac{vE_z}{c^2}\right)\right] \qquad (4\text{-}29)$$

If Eq. 4-21 is to be invariant in form, then in S' it must be Eq. 4-21',

$$\frac{\partial}{\partial z'}E_x' - \frac{\partial}{\partial x'}E_z' = -\frac{\partial}{\partial t'}B_y'.$$

If we put

$$E_x' = E_x$$
$$E_z' = \gamma(E_z + vB_y)$$

and

$$B_y' = \gamma\left(B_y + \frac{vE_z}{c^2}\right)$$

then Eqs. 4-29 and 4-21' are identical. But these relations are exactly the transformations for the electromagnetic field components that we found before (see Table 4-1).

In the same way, if we substitute the partial differentiation relations into Eq. 4-22 and require that the result be identical to Eq. 4-22', we find

$$E_x' = E_x$$
$$E_y' = \gamma(E_y - vB_z)$$

and
$$B_z' = \gamma\left(B_z - \frac{vE_y}{c^2}\right)$$

which also are transformations found before (Table 4-1). To complete the process, we must find how B_x transforms, for we have all the other relations of transformation of the electromagnetic field. We find this by substituting Eqs. 4-25 through 4-28 into the remaining Maxwell equations, Eqs. 4-20 and 4-23. After some manipulation, we find that Eq. 4-20 becomes Eq. 4-20' and that Eq. 4-23 becomes Eq. 4-23' if we set

$$B_x' = B_x$$

which completes the set of relations of transformation of the field components.

Hence, when we transform the space-time coordinates by means of the Lorentz transformation equations, we find that Maxwell's equations are invariant in form, providing that the electromagnetic field transforms, as deduced earlier from other considerations, according to Table 4-1.

4.8 *The Possible Limitations of Special Relativity*

We have now completed our original program of finding the transformation (the Lorentz transformation) which keeps the velocity of light constant and finding the invariant form of the laws of mechanics and electromagnetism. The (Einstein) principle of relativity appears to apply to all* the laws of physics.

Although, on the basis of present knowledge, special relativity theory is as consistent with experiment as is any part of physics, we cannot be certain, of course, that it too will not give way eventually to another theory. Particularly in the domain of the very small (elementary particle physics) or the very large (cosmology), new levels of understanding may

---

*Not only the electromagnetic force but all forces whose properties we know can be put into a relativistically invariant form.

emerge that require a revision of our basic assumptions. And, just as relativity involved a radical departure from Newtonian ideas but can be regarded as a logical extension of them, so a new theory may have the same attributes compared to relativity. The same critical probing and analysis that characterized the birth and development of relativity is now being brought to bear in the subatomic and astronomical domains.

Blokhintsev [6], for example, suggests that there might exist an elementary interval which serves as a scale for that region of space-time in which the structure of space-time may differ from that in the relativistic domain. Such an interval may be associated with the region of space-time near a system of interacting elementary particles or with the physical vacuum. In such a situation, we can check experimentally the consequences or assumptions of relativity, such as causality and the homogeneity and isotropy of space-time. Blokhintsev concludes as follows:

"Experimental data available to present day physics are restricted to dimensions $a_0 > (\hbar/Mc)(Mc^2/E) \sim 10^{-15}$ cm in the laboratory coordinate system. . . . The set of facts which are known in this domain does not contradict relativistic kinematics, and on the average this kinematics holds with an accuracy of approximately 1 per cent. The dependence of mass on velocity has been verified with considerable greater accuracy (up to 0.01 per cent). [However] possible large (but of low probability) deviations from relativistic kinematics remain uninvestigated . . . they could be due to a violation of homogeneity or isotropy of space-time on a small scale. Such deviations could occur within limits of $\cong 1$ per cent. More disturbing is the situation with local field theory which is closely related to the assumed form of geometry and to causality. If the indicated disagreement between theory and experiment is confirmed, it would serve as a serious foundation for a radical revaluation of the basic postulates of contemporary theory. In view of the importance of this problem it is necessary to make the measurements still more accurate and to perfect the calculations."

Questions

1. If total charge is an invariant quantity (the same in all inertial frames) how can it be that a neutral wire in one frame appears to be charged in another frame?

2. In the example discussed in Section 4-2, where the current in S is caused by electron motion, we found the charge density in S' to be positive. Suppose that **u** and **v**, instead of being parallel, were antiparallel. Would the charge density in S' still be positive? Would it be different from that in S?

3. Explain carefully how the S' observer can find one segment of a complete circuit positively charged and another segment negatively charged, all segments appearing neutral to the S observer. (See Problem 21 and Topical Appendix A.)

4. If a current is started in a circuit by closing the switch to a battery in it, will all the conduction electrons begin moving at the same instant? How is this analogous to the motion of particles in a rod that is being pushed, or pulled, at one point from a rest position? In such a circuit, what happens to charge densities (before and after the switch is closed) and to charge conservation? (See Problem 21 and Topical Appendix A.)

5. In Example 2, does the case $\theta = 180°$ differ from the case $\theta = 0°$? Does the case $\theta = 270°$ differ from the case $\theta = 90°$?

6. Resolve the apparent paradox between the requirement $E_\parallel{}' = E_\parallel$ of Eq. 4-6 and the result of Example 2, part *a*. (*Hint.* Consider the relativity of simultaneity and the relation between r and r'.)

7. If magnetic fields are of the second order compared to electrical forces, why is it that we observe magnetic forces without great difficulty?

8. Historically, relativity arose from electromagnetic theory. Considering that they are in complete agreement, could electromagnetic theory have been developed starting with relativity as given? What minimum information would we need other than relativity?

9. Does each new level, from the supermacroscopic to the submicroscopic domain, necessarily require a revision of the theory found adequate at an adjacent level? Could a level be *defined* by the need for a new theory there? That is, does it make any sense to talk about different levels if the same theory is equally applicable to each?

Problems

1. Show directly that $c^2\rho^2 - (j_x{}^2 + j_y{}^2 + j_z{}^2)$ is an invariant quantity equal to $c^2\rho_0{}^2$.

2. The nonrelativistic limit of Eqs. 4-4 (i.e., the results when $v/c \ll 1$) gives $\rho \cong \rho'$ and $j_x = j_x{}' + \rho'v$. Check this and interpret the terms physically.

3. Carry out the operations indicated prior to Eqs. 4-7 to confirm the results of the magnetic component transformation.

4. Prove that Eqs. 4-6 are consistent with (equivalent to) Eqs. 4-5. Do likewise for Eqs. 4-8 and Eqs. 4-7.

5. What is the nonrelativistic limit of the transformation equations for the electromagnetic field listed in Table 4-1? Do your results make sense physically?

6. Show that $E^2 - c^2B^2$ is an invariant quantity under a Lorentz transformation. Then argue that, if $E = cB$ in one inertial frame, $E' = cB'$ in any other inertial frame, and that if $E > cB$ in one inertial frame, then $E' > cB'$ in any other inertial frame.

7. Show that $\mathbf{E} \cdot \mathbf{B}$ is an invariant quantity under a Lorentz transformation. Then argue that if the electric and magnetic fields are perpendicular to one another in one inertial frame, they are perpendicular in all frames.

8. (a) Evaluate the invariants $E^2 - c^2B^2$ and $\mathbf{E} \cdot \mathbf{B}$ for a plane electromagnetic wave in vacuum. (b) Show that plane waves in one inertial frame transform to plane waves in another inertial frame.

9. Show that for a given electromagnetic field, we can find an inertial frame in which either $\mathbf{E} = 0$ (if $E < cB$) or $\mathbf{B} = 0$ (if $E > cB$) at a given point if, and only if, $\mathbf{E} \cdot \mathbf{B} = 0$ at that point. That is, if (and only if) $\mathbf{E}$ and $\mathbf{B}$ are perpendicular to one another, we can find a frame in which we have either no electric field or else no magnetic field. Use the results of earlier problems (6 and 7) and the field component transformations.

10. Show explicitly that the inverse transformations in Table 4-1 follow directly from inversion of the original transformations (i.e., solve for the unprimed fields in terms of the primed ones).

11. Show (from Eqs. 4-12 and 4-14) that (a)

$$\mathbf{B} = \frac{q\mathbf{u} \times \mathbf{r}}{4\pi\epsilon_0 c^2 \gamma^2 r^3 [1 - (u^2/c^2)\sin^2\theta]^{3/2}},$$

and that (b), in the limit of low speeds, this expression (using $c = 1/\sqrt{\mu_0\epsilon_0}$) reduces to the Biot-Savart law,

$$\mathbf{B} = \frac{\mu_0}{4\pi}\frac{q\mathbf{u} \times \mathbf{r}}{r^3}.$$

12. Plot the magnitude of the electric field of a high-speed charged particle as a function of the angle θ made with the direction of motion of the charge, for a given distance r (see Eq. 4-15). Assume $\beta = v/c = 0.95$ and take $0 \le \theta \le 90°$.

13. Refer to Fig. 4-3b in which the electric field of a high-speed charge is shown not to be spherically symmetric. Show that the electrostatic result $\oint \mathbf{E} \cdot d\mathbf{l} = 0$ does *not* hold so that the electric field is not conservative. Is there a changing magnetic field connected with the moving charge? Would you expect $\mathbf{E}$ to be conservative then?

14. A particle of charge q moves with uniform velocity **u** in inertial frame S. Consider a frame S', moving with uniform velocity **u** relative to S, in which the charge is at rest and the force on the charge is $\mathbf{F}' = q\mathbf{E}'$. Show that the force on the particle in frame S is the Lorentz force, $\mathbf{F} = q(\mathbf{E} + \mathbf{u} \times \mathbf{B})$, by using the tranformations for the components of force and the transformations for the components of **E** and **B**.

15. Use the force transformations to show that, if the source charge (the source of the field) moves with speed v relative to a test charge (the charge acted on by the field), either toward or away from it along the line connecting the two charges, the force on the test charge is $(1 - v^2/c^2)$ times the ordinary Coulomb force. (*Hint.* Transform from a frame in which the source charge is at rest and remember the space contraction effect.)

16. Use the force transformations to show that, if the source charge moves with a speed v relative to a test charge at right angles to their transverse separation, the force on the test charge, at the instant the line connecting them is at right angles to **v**, is $1/\sqrt{1 - v^2/c^2}$ times the ordinary Coulomb force. Compare this to the results of the previous problem.

17. Prove the result in Section 4-5 that $\mathbf{F} = 0$ required $\mathbf{F}' = 0$ by using the force transformations rather than the field component transformations.

18. In the example in the text of two charges, at rest in frame S' (the proper frame) separated by a distance r', viewed in a frame S (the laboratory frame) moving perpendicular to the line connecting the charges with a speed v, notice that the mutual force is smaller in the laboratory frame than in the proper frame. Find the force in both the laboratory frame and in the proper frame for two electrons moving along the axis of a linear accelerator in parallel paths separated by 5.00×10^{-9} meter at speeds given by $\beta = v/c = 0.999$.

19. Consider the example of two charges at rest in frame S' separated by a distance r'. Transform the static Coulomb force found there to a frame S which moves parallel to the line connecting the charges with a speed v and find the mutual force measured in this frame.

20. Consider two long parallel wires separated by a distance $2a$ and bearing equal and opposite uniform charge distributions (see Fig. 4-7). In frame S, at rest with respect to the wires, there is no current flowing and the linear charge density is λ.

    (*a*) Calculate the electric and magnetic fields in frame S at a point P midway between the wires.

    (*b*) Frame S' moves at a velocity v parallel to the length of the wires (the x direction). Find the linear charge density λ' and the current in the wires i' (if any) as measured in frame S'.

    (*c*) Using the results of (*b*), calculate the electric and magnetic fields measured in frame S' at a point midway between the wires.

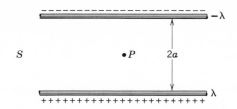

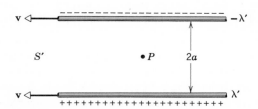

Fig. 4-7. Problem 20.

(*d*) Using the field transformation equations and the results of (*a*), calculate the electric and magnetic fields measured in frame S' at a point midway between the wires. Does this result agree with your answer to (*c*)?

21. Consider the space-time diagram (see Topical Appendix A) of the current in a segment of wire, Fig. 4-8.

(*a*) Show that the world lines of the electrons are parallel to the *ct* axis *before* the emf is applied at $t = 0$.

(*b*) Show that the world lines of the electrons are inclined to the *ct* axis *after* the emf is applied at $t = 0$.

(*c*) Show that the world lines of the positive ions are parallel to the *ct* axis when $t < 0$ *and* $t > 0$.

(*d*) Show that the diagram corresponds to all electrons starting to move simultaneously in S.

(*e*) Show that, in S, the separation of electrons is the *same* after the motion begins as before.

(*f*) Show that in S' the farther out electrons are from 0 the sooner they start moving.

(*g*) Show that in S' the separations are different from those in S, the positive ions being closer and the electrons farther apart. (The wire has a *positive* charge density in S', although neutral in S.)

(*h*) Finally, consider another segment of the circuit in which the electrons move in S opposite to the direction shown in the diagram. Draw in the world lines for $t > 0$ and show that this segment of the wire has a *negative* density in S', although neutral in S.

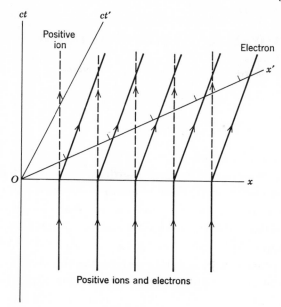

Fig. 4-8. Problem 21.

References

1. R. S. Shankland, "Michelson-Morley Experiment," *Am. J. Phys.*, **32** (1), 16 (1964).
2. R. Fleischmann and R. Kollath, "Method for Measurement of the Charge of Fast Moving Electrons," *Z. Physik*, **134,** 526 (1953); and R. Kollath and D. Menzel, "Measurement of the Charge of Fast Moving Electrons," *Z. Physik*, **134,** 530 (1953).
3. Edward M. Purcell, *Electricity and Magnetism*, McGraw-Hill, New York, 1965.
4. D. Halliday and R. Resnick, *Physics*, Part II, John Wiley, 1966, p. 773.
5. Supplementary Topic V of Ref. 4.
6. D. I. Blokhintsev, "Basis for Special Relativity Theory Provided by Experiments in High Energy Physics," *Soviet Phys. Usp.*, **9** (3), 405 (1966).

Supplementary Topic A

The Geometric Representation
of Space-Time

A-1 *Space-Time Diagrams*

In classical physics, the time coordinate is unaffected by a transformation from one inertial frame to another. The time coordinate, t', of one inertial system does not depend on the space coordinates, x, y, z of another inertial system, the transformation equation being $t' = t$. In relativity, however, space and time are interdependent. The time coordinate of one inertial system depends on both the time and the space coordinates of another inertial system, the transformation equation being $t' = [t - (v/c^2)x]/\sqrt{1 - v^2/c^2}$. Hence, instead of treating space and time separately, as is quite properly done in classical theory, it is natural in relativity to treat them together. H. Minkowski [1] was first to show clearly how this could be done.

In what follows, we shall consider only one space axis, the x-axis, and shall ignore the y and z axes. We lose no generality by this algebraic simplification and this procedure will enable us to focus more clearly on the interdependence of space and time and its geometric representation. The coordinates of an event are given then by x and t. All possible space-time coordinates can be represented on a space-time diagram in which the space axis is horizontal and the time axis is vertical. It is convenient to keep the dimensions of the coordinates the same; this is easily done by multiplying the time t by the universal constant c, the velocity of light. Let ct be represented by the symbol w. Then, the Lorentz transformation equations (see Table 2-1) can be written as follows:

$$x' = \frac{x - \beta w}{\sqrt{1 - \beta^2}} \qquad x = \frac{x' + \beta w'}{\sqrt{1 - \beta^2}} \qquad \text{(A-1)}$$

$$w' = \frac{w - \beta x}{\sqrt{1 - \beta^2}} \qquad w = \frac{w' + \beta x'}{\sqrt{1 - \beta^2}}$$

Notice the symmetry in this form of the equations.

To represent the situation geometrically, we begin by drawing the x

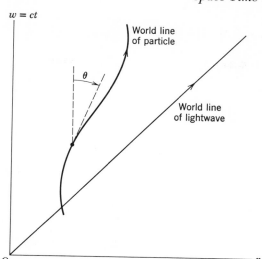

$w = ct$

World line
of particle

θ

World line
of lightwave

O x

Fig. A-1.

and w axes of frame S orthogonal (perpendicular) to one another (Fig. A-1). If we wanted to represent the motion of a particle in this frame, we would draw a curve, called a *world line*, which gives the loci of space-time points corresponding to the motion.* The tangent to the world line at any point, being $dx/dw = \dfrac{1}{c}(dx/dt)$, is always inclined at an angle less than 45° with the time axis. For this angle (see Fig. A-1) is given by $\tan \theta = dx/dw = u/c$ and we must have $u < c$ for a material particle. The world line of a light wave, for which $u = c$, is a straight line making a 45° angle with the axes.

Consider now the primed frame (S') which moves relative to S with a velocity **v** along the common x-x' axis. The equation of motion of S' relative to S can be obtained by setting $x' = 0$ (which locates the origin of S'); from Eq. A-1, we see that this corresponds to $x = \beta w\ (= vt)$. We draw the line $x' = 0$ (that is, $x = \beta w$) on our diagram (Fig. A-2) and note that, since $v < c$ and $\beta < 1$, the angle which this line makes with the w-axis, $\phi(= \tan^{-1} \beta)$, is less than 45°. Just as the w-axis corresponds to $x = 0$ and is the time axis in frame S, so the line $x' = 0$ gives the time axis

---

* Minkowski referred to space-time as "the world." Hence, events are world points and a collection of events giving the history of a particle is a world line. Physical laws on the interaction of particles can be thought of as the geometric relations between their world lines. In this sense, Minkowski may be said to have geometrized physics.

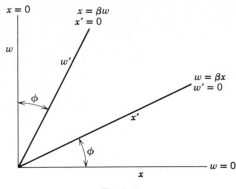

Fig. A-2.

w' in S'. Now, if we draw the line $w' = 0$ (giving the location of clocks which read $t' = 0$ in S'), we shall have the space axis x'. That is, just as the x-axis corresponds to $w = 0$, so the x'-axis corresponds to $w' = 0$. But, from Eq. A-1, $w' = 0$ gives us $w = \beta x$ as the equation of this axis on our w-x diagram (Fig. A-2).* The angle between the space axes is the same as that between the time axes.

From Fig. A-2, we see that in four-space (x,y,z,t) the Lorentz equations involve transforming from an orthogonal system to a nonorthogonal system. We can use this representation to show the relativity of simultaneity and to give a geometrical interpretation of the space-contraction and time-dilation effects, as well as to illustrate their reciprocal nature. To do all this clearly, let us first represent the situation on a new diagram (Fig. A-3). Here we draw the two branches of the hyperbola $w^2 - x^2 = 1$, and the two branches of the hyperbola $x^2 - w^2 = 1$. These lines, whose meaning will soon be clear, approach asymptotically the $45°$ light ray world-lines. We also draw in the x, w axes of S and the x', w' axes of S'.

The space-time point P_1 is the intersection of the right branch of hyperbola $x^2 - w^2 = 1$ with the x'-axis given by $w = \beta x$. Hence, P_1 is on both these lines and its coordinates (obtained by combining the equations of the lines) are

---

* For simplicity, we deal only with the quadrant in which x and w are positive. A light wave proceeding to increasing values of x as time goes on bisects the x-w axes in the third quadrant (x and w both negative) as well as the first quadrant. A light wave proceeding to decreasing values of x as time goes on bisects the x-w axes in the second and fourth quadrants (see, e.g. the dashed lines of Fig. A-3). Similar extensions and additions apply to the world line of a particle and to the primed axes when negative space-time coordinates are involved or when the primed frame moves in the opposite direction ($\beta < 0$) relative to the unprimed one.

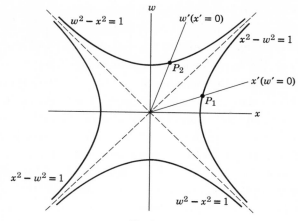

Fig. A-3.

$$w = \frac{\beta}{\sqrt{1 - \beta^2}} \qquad \text{and} \qquad x = \frac{1}{\sqrt{1 - \beta^2}}. \tag{A-2}$$

But, comparison of Eq. A-2 with Eq. A-1 shows that Eq. A-2 represents unit length (i.e., $x' = 1$) and zero time (i.e., $w' = 0$) in the S' frame. That is, the interval $0P_1$ gives unit length along the x'-axis. Similarly, the space-time point P_2 is the intersection of the upper branch of hyperbola $w^2 - x^2 = 1$ with the w'-axis given by $x = \beta w$. Hence, P_2 is on both these lines and its coordinates (obtained by combining the equations of the lines) are

$$w = \frac{1}{\sqrt{1 - \beta^2}} \qquad \text{and} \qquad x = \frac{\beta}{\sqrt{1 - \beta^2}}. \tag{A-3}$$

Comparison of Eq. A-3 with Eq. A-1 shows that Eq. A-3 represents unit time (i.e., $w' = 1$) and zero length (i.e., $x' = 0$) in the S' frame. That is, the interval $0P_2$ gives unit time along the w'-axis.

The hyperbolas are often referred to as calibration curves. Consider the upper hyperbola, for example. At $x = 0$, we have $w = 1$, which (in units of ct) is unit time in S. At any other point x we have $c^2 t^2 - x^2 = c^2(t^2 - x^2/c^2) = c^2 \tau^2 = 1$. Thus, points on the upper hyperbola give unit time on the clock at rest in S'; that is, the proper time in units of $c\tau$ is equal to one. Whatever the relative velocity of S' to S, the intersection of the time axis with this hyperbola will give the unit time in S'. Similarly, for the right hyperbola we have $x = 1$ at $w = 0$, which is unit length in S (measured from the origin). At any other value of w, points on the hyperbola represent unit length at rest in a frame S', the velocity of S' relative to S being determined by the inclination of the space axis, which intersects the hyperbola at the point in question.

Let us suppose now that we observe events from two inertial frames, S and S', whose relative velocity we know. The hyperbolic calibration curves determine the unit time interval and unit length interval on the axes of these frames; once the hyperbolas have served this purpose, we can dispense with them. In Fig. A-4 we show the calibration of the axes S and S', the unit time interval along w' being a longer line segment than the unit time interval along w and the unit length interval along x' being a longer line segment than the unit length interval along x. The first thing we must be able to do is to determine the space-time coordinates of an event, such as P, from the Minkowski diagram. To find the space coordinate of the event, we simply draw a line parallel to the time axis from P to the space axis. The time coordinate is given similarly by a line parallel to the space axis from P to the time axis. The rules hold equally well for the primed frame as for the unprimed frame. In Fig. A-4, for example, the event P has space-time coordinates $x = 3$, $w = 2.5$ in S (dashed lines), and space-time coordinates $x' = 2$, $w' = 1.5$ in S' (dotted lines). It is as though the rectangular grid of coordinate lines of S (Fig. A-5a) become squashed toward the bisecting 45° line when the coordinate lines of S' are put on the same graph (Fig. A-5b); clearly the Lorentz equations transform an orthogonal system to a nonorthogonal one.

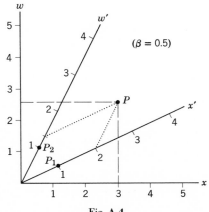

Fig. A-4.

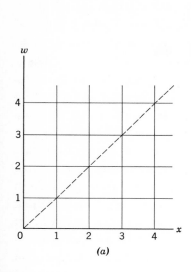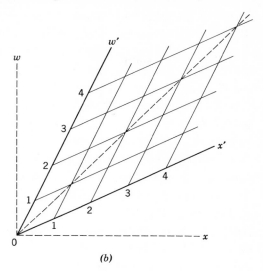

(a)   *(b)*

Fig. **A-5.**

A-2 *Simultaneity, Contraction, and Dilation*

Now we can easily show the relativity of simultaneity. As measured in S', two events will be simultaneous if they have the same time coordinate w'. Hence, if the events lie on a line parallel to the x'-axis they are simultaneous to S'. In Fig. A-6, for example, events Q_1 and Q_2 are simultaneous in S'; they obviously are not simultaneous in S, occurring at different times w_1 and w_2 there. Similarly, two events R_1 and R_2, which are simultaneous in S, are separated in time in S'.

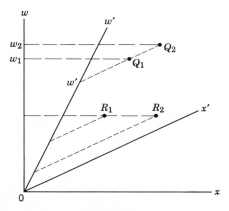

Fig. **A-6.**

As for the space contraction, consider Fig. A-7a. Let a meter stick be at rest in the S-frame, its end points being at $x = 3$ and $x = 4$, for example. As time goes on, the world-line of each end point traces out a vertical line parallel to the w-axis. The length of the stick is defined as the distance between the end points measured simultaneously. In S, the rest frame, the length is the distance in S between the intersections of the world lines with the x-axis, or any line parallel to the x-axis, for these intersecting points represent simultaneous events in S. The rest length is one meter. To get the length of the stick in S', where the stick moves, we must obtain the distance in S' between end points measured simultaneously. This will be the separation in S' of the intersections of the world lines with the x'-axis, or any line parallel to the x'-axis, for these intersecting points represent simultaneous events in S'. The length of the (moving) stick is clearly less than one meter in S'. (see Fig. A-7a).

Notice how very clearly Fig. A-7a reveals that it is a disagreement about the simultaneity of events that leads to different measured lengths. Indeed, the two observers do not measure the same pair of events in determining the length of a body (e.g., the S-observer uses E_1 and E_2, say, whereas the S'-observer would use E_1 and E_3, or E_2 and E_4) for events which are simultaneous to one inertial observer are *not* simultaneous to the other (see Ref. 2 for a forceful presentation of this point). We should also note that the x'-coordinate of each endpoint decreases as time goes on (simply project from successive world-line points parallel to w' onto the x'-axis), consistent with the fact that the stick which is at rest in S moves towards the left in S'.

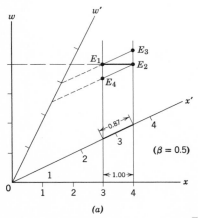 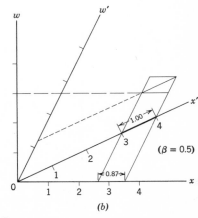

Fig. A-7.

The reciprocal nature of this result is shown in Fig. A-7b. Here, we have a meter stick at rest in S' and the world lines of its end points are parallel to w' (the end points are always at $x' = 3$ and $x' = 4$, say). The rest length is one meter. In S, where the stick moves to the right, the measured length is the distance in S between intersections of these world lines with the x-axis, or any line parallel to the x-axis. The length of the (moving) stick is clearly less than one meter in S (see Fig. A-7b).

It remains now to demonstrate the time-dilation result geometrically. For this purpose consider Fig. A-8. Let a clock be at rest in frame S, ticking off units of time there. The solid vertical line in Fig. A-8, at $x = 2.3$, is the world line corresponding to such a single clock. T_1 and T_2 are the events of ticking at w ($= ct$) $= 2$ and w ($= ct$) $= 3$, the time interval in S between ticks being unity. In S', this clock is moving to the left so that it is at a different place there each time it ticks. To measure the time interval between events T_1 and T_2 in S', we use two different clocks, one at the location of event T_1 and the other at the location of event T_2. The difference in reading of these clocks in S' is the difference in times between T_1 and T_2 as measured in S'. From the graph, we see that this interval is greater than unity. Hence, from the point of view of S', the moving S-clock appears slowed down. During the interval that the S-clock registered unit time, the S'-clock registered a time greater than one unit.

The reciprocal nature of the time-dilation result is also shown in Fig.

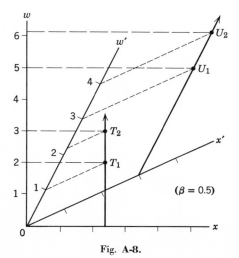

Fig. A-8.

A-8. The student should construct the detailed argument. Here a clock at rest in S' emits ticks U_1 and U_2 separated by unit proper time. As measured in S, the corresponding time interval exceeds one unit.

A-3   *The Time Order and Space Separation of Events*

We can also use the geometrical representation of space-time to gain further insight into the concepts of simultaneity and the time order of events which we discussed in Chapter Two. Consider the shaded area in Fig. A-9, for example. Through any point P in this shaded area, bounded by the world lines of light waves, we can draw a w'-axis from the origin; that is, we can find an inertial frame S' in which the events O and P occur at the same place ($x' = 0$) and are separated only in time. As shown in Fig. A-9, event P follows event O in time (it comes later on S' clocks), as is true wherever event P is in the upper half of the shaded area. Hence, events in the upper half (region 1 on Fig. A-10) are absolutely in the future relative to O and this region is called the Absolute Future. If event P is at a space-time point in the lower half of the shaded area (region 2 on Fig. A-10) then P will precede event O in time. Events in the lower half are absolutely in the past relative to O and this region is called the Absolute Past. In the shaded regions, therefore, there is a definite time order of events relative to O for we can always find a frame in which O and P occur at the same place; a single clock will determine absolutely the time order of the event at this place.

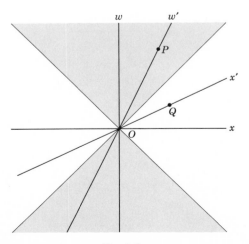

Fig. A-9.

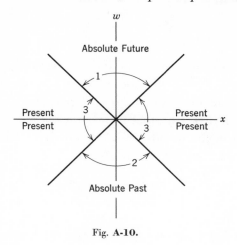

Fig. A-10.

Consider now the unshaded regions of Fig. A-9. Through any point Q we can draw an x'-axis from the origin; that is, we can find an inertial frame S' in which the events O and Q occur at the same time ($w' = ct' = 0$) and are separated only in space. We can always find an inertial frame in which events O and Q appear to be simultaneous for space-time points Q that are in the unshaded regions (region 3 of Fig. A-10), so that this region is called the Present. In other inertial frames, of course, O and Q are not simultaneous and there is no absolute time order of these events but a relative time order, instead.

If we ask about the space separation of events, rather than their time order, we see that events in the present are absolutely separated from O, whereas those in the absolute future or absolute past have no definite space order relative to O. Indeed, region 3 (present) is said to be "space-like" whereas regions 1 and 2 (absolute past or future) are said to be "timelike." That is, a world interval such as OQ is spacelike and a world interval such as OP is timelike.

The geometrical considerations that we have presented are connected with the invariant nature of proper time, that is, with the relation $d\tau^2 = dt^2 - (1/c^2)(dx^2 + dy^2 + dz^2)$. We can illustrate as follows. In

$$(\tau_2 - \tau_1)^2 = (t_2 - t_1)^2 - \frac{1}{c^2}[(x_2 - x_1)^2 + (y_2 - y_1)^2 + (z_2 - z_1)^2]$$

let subscript one refer to the origin ($t_1 = 0 = x_1 = y_1 = z_1$) and let subscript two refer to any other space-time point, so that

$$\tau^2 = t^2 - \frac{x^2 + y^2 + z^2}{c^2}.$$

Now, in our case, we have ignored y and z so that the appropriate expression is $\tau^2 = t^2 - x^2/c^2$. We can write this conveniently as $c^2\tau^2 = c^2t^2 - x^2$ which, in our terminology, is simply $c^2\tau^2 = w^2 - x^2$. The quantity $c^2\tau^2$ is an invariant, that is, $w^2 - x^2 = w'^2 - x'^2$ for the same two events. Hence, the quantity $-c^2\tau^2$, which we shall call σ^2, is also invariant. We have then the two relations:

$$c^2\tau^2 = w^2 - x^2$$

and
$$\sigma^2 = x^2 - w^2.$$

Now consider Figs. A-9 and A-10. In regions 1 and 2 we have space-time points for which $w > x$ (that is, $ct > x$), so that $c^2\tau^2 = w^2 - x^2 > 0$. The proper time is a real quantity, $c^2\tau^2$ being positive, in these regions. In regions 3 we have space-time points for which $x > w$ (that is, $x > ct$), so that $c^2\tau^2 = w^2 - x^2 < 0$. The proper time is an imaginary quantity, $c^2\tau^2$ being negative, in these regions. However, the quantity σ is real here for $\sigma^2 = x^2 - w^2 > 0$ in regions 3. Hence, either τ or σ is real for any two events (i.e., the event at the origin and the event elsewhere in space-time) and either τ or σ may be called the space-time interval between the two events. When τ is real the interval is called "timelike"; when σ is real the interval is called "spacelike." Because σ and τ are invariant properties of two events, it does not depend at all on what inertial frame is used to specify the events whether the interval between them is spacelike or timelike.

In the spacelike region we can find a frame in which the two events are simultaneous, so that σ can be thought of as the spatial interval between the events in that frame (i.e., $\sigma^2 = x^2 - w^2 = x'^2 - w'^2$. But $w' = 0$ in S' so that $\sigma = x'$). In the timelike region we can find a frame in which the two events occur at the same place, so that τ can be thought of as the time interval between the events in that frame (i.e., $\tau^2 = t^2 - (x^2/c^2) = t'^2 - (x'^2/c^2)$. But $x' = 0$ in S' so that $\tau = t'$).

What can we say about points on the 45° lines? For such points, $x = w$. Therefore, the proper time interval between two events on these lines vanishes, for $c^2\tau^2 = w^2 - x^2 = 0$ if $x = w$. We have seen that such lines represent the world lines of light rays and give the limiting velocity ($v = c$) of relativity. On one side of these 45° lines (shaded regions in

Fig. A-9) the proper time interval is real, on the other side (unshaded regions), it is imaginary. An imaginary value of τ would correspond to a velocity in excess of c. But no signals can travel faster than c. All this is relevant to an interesting question that can be posed about the unshaded regions.

In this region, which we have called the Present, there is no absolute time order of events; event O may precede event Q in one frame but follow event Q in another frame. What does this do to our deep-seated notions of cause and effect? Does relativity theory negate the causality principle? To test cause and effect, we would have to examine the events at the same place so that we could say absolutely that Q followed O, or that O followed Q, in each instance. But in the Present, or spacelike, region these two events occur in such rapid succession that the time difference is less than the time needed by a light ray to traverse the spatial distance between two events. We cannot fix the time order of such events absolutely, for no signal can travel from one event to the other faster than c. In other words, no frame of reference exists with respect to which the two events occur at the same place; thus, we simply cannot test causality for such events even in principle. Therefore, there is no violation of the law of causality implied by the relative time order of O and events in the spacelike region. We can arrive at this same result by an argument other than this operational one. If the two events, O and Q, are related causally, then they must be capable of interacting physically. But no physical signal can travel faster than c so that events O and Q cannot interact physically. Hence, their time order is immaterial for they cannot be related causally. Events that can interact physically with O are in regions other than the Present. For such events, O and P, relativity gives an unambiguous time order. Therefore, relativity is completely consistent with the causality principle.

Questions and Problems

1. Derive equations A-1, A-2, and A-3.

2. Two inertial observers, with physically identical sets of clocks synchronized by the same procedures, are in relative motion. *Each* observer finds, on measurement, that the *other* observer's clocks run slow. Explain this apparent paradox.

3. Read again problems 10 and 11 of Chapter Two. (a) Draw a world diagram for the problem, including on it the world lines for observers A, B,

C, D, and E. Label the points AD, BD, AC, BC, and EC. (*b*) Show, by means of the diagram, that the clock at A records a shorter time interval for the events AD, AC than do clocks at D and C. (*c*) Show that, if observers on the cart try to measure the length DC by making simultaneous markings on a measuring stick in their frame, they will measure a length shorter than the rest length DC. Explain this result in terms of simultaneity using the diagram.

For convenience, in the above problem, take $v = \frac{1}{2}c$.

4. In addition to timelike and spacelike intervals, we might talk about "lightlike" intervals. What value would τ or σ have for such intervals? Explain.

5. Do Problem 12, Chapter Two by means of a Minkowski diagram. Check your results by calculating the invariants $c^2\tau^2$ or σ^2.

6. Do Problem 13, Chapter Two, by means of a Minkowski diagram. Check your results by calculating the invariants $c^2\tau^2$ or σ^2.

7. The world diagrams drawn in the text have been from the point of view of the unprimed frame. Consider a system S' moving at speed $v = \frac{1}{2}c$ to the right relative to system S. (*a*) Draw the world diagram for these two frames from the point of view of the primed frame S' (i.e., make the x'-ct' axes the orthogonal ones. Note that the velocity of the S frame with respect to the S' frame is $-v$). (*b*) Verify that the three phenomena —relativity of simultaneity, length contraction, and time dilation—still hold.

8. Given a system S' moving to the right relative to S at a speed $\frac{3}{5}c$, and another system S'' moving to the right relative to S at a speed $\frac{1}{3}c$, (*a*) using the Minkowski diagram find the velocity of S'' relative to frame S'. (*b*) Repeat with S'' moving at a speed $+\frac{1}{2}c$ relative to S. (Hint: construct lines of constant x' and t' on the diagram. Using this gridwork of lines, find the slope of the world line for $\beta = \frac{1}{3}$ and for $\beta = \frac{1}{2}$.)

9. Do Problem 21, Chapter 4.

10. Discuss Questions 3 and 4, Chapter 4.

References

1. H. Minkowski, "Space and Time" (a translation of an address given September 21, 1908) in *The Principle of Relativity*, Dover Publications, Inc.
2. A. Gamba, "Physical Quantities in Different Reference Systems According to Relativity," *Am. J. Phys.*, **35**, 83 (1967).

The Twin Paradox

B-1 *Introduction*

Much has been written recently on what is called the twin paradox, or the clock paradox [see Ref. 1]. Einstein, in 1911 [2], specifically predicted that:

"If we placed a living organism in a box ... one could arrange that the organism, after any arbitrary lengthy flight, could be returned to its original spot in a scarcely altered condition, while corresponding organisms which had remained in their original positions had already long since given way to new generations. For the moving organism the lengthy time of the journey was a mere instant, provided the motion took place with approximately the speed of light."

If the stationary organism is a man and the traveling one is his twin, then the traveler returns home to find his twin brother much aged compared to himself. The paradox centers around the contention that, in relativity, either twin could regard the other as the traveler, in which case each should find the other younger—a logical contradiction. This contention assumes that the twins' situations are symmetrical and interchangeable, an assumption that is not correct. Furthermore, the accessible experiments have been done and support Einstein's prediction. In succeeding sections, we look with some care into the many aspects of this problem.

B-2 *The Route Dependence of Proper Time*

Consider a space-time diagram (Fig. B-1a) which is relevant to our problem. We can connect events P and Q by different possible world lines (1 and 2 in Fig. B-1a). We are not surprised that the distance traveled between P and Q (the odometer reading) depends on the route we take. It is also true, however, that the time recorded by the traveling clocks depends on the route taken. Let us illustrate this result directly. The time recorded by a clock attached to the object tracing out a world line is the proper time. We have seen (Eq. 2-12) that the relationship between the proper time τ and the time t is $d\tau = dt\sqrt{1 - v^2/c^2}$. For

201

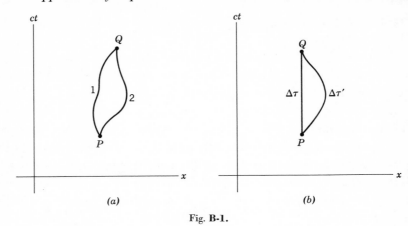

Fig. **B-1.**

motion in one space dimension we can write this also as $d\tau = \sqrt{dt^2 - dx^2/c^2}$. The elapsed proper time between events P and Q then is simply

$$\Delta\tau = \int_P^Q \sqrt{dt^2 - \frac{dx^2}{c^2}}$$ (B-1)

where we integrate along the (world line) path from P to Q. Consider now the particular case, Fig. B-1b, in which one world line represents a clock at rest on the x-axis; this gives a vertical line. Suppose now that we have a second path by which an identical second clock is taken from P to Q. Such a clock moves away from the first one and then returns to it, the clocks being coincident at P and at Q. The elapsed proper time along the first world line is

$$\Delta\tau = \int_P^Q \sqrt{dt^2 - \frac{dx^2}{c^2}} = \int_P^Q \sqrt{dt^2 - 0} = \int_P^Q dt = t_Q - t_P,$$

for dx is zero along this path and the proper time coincides with the time interval, $t_Q - t_P$, recorded by the rest clocks. Along the second world line, however, the elapsed proper time is

$$\Delta\tau' = \int_P^Q \sqrt{dt^2 - dx^2/c^2}.$$

$\Delta\tau'$ will *not* equal $\Delta\tau$. In fact, since dx^2 is always positive, we find that

$$\Delta\tau' < \Delta\tau.$$ (B-2)

The clocks will read different times when brought back together, the traveling clock running behind (recording a smaller time difference than) the stay-at-home clock.

We should note here that the *x-t* frame is an inertial frame. The motion of the traveling clock is represented in this frame by a curved world line, for this clock undergoes accelerated motion rather than motion with uniform velocity. It could not return to the stationary clock, for example, without reversing its velocity. The special theory of relativity can predict the behavior of accelerated objects as long as, in the formulation of the physical laws, we take the view of the inertial (unaccelerated) observer. This is what we have done so far. A frame attached to the clock traveling along its round-trip path would not be an inertial frame. We could reformulate the laws of physics so that they have the same form for accelerated (noninertial) observers—this is the program of general relativity theory—but it is unnecessary to do so to explain the twin paradox. All we wish to point out here is that the situation is *not* symmetrical with respect to the clocks (or twins); one is always in a single inertial frame and the other is not.

B-3 *Space-Time Diagram of the "Twin Paradox"*

In our earlier discussions of time dilation, we spoke of "moving clocks running slow." What is meant by that phrase is that a clock moving at a constant velocity **u** relative to an inertial frame containing synchronized clocks will be found to run slow by the factor $\sqrt{1 - u^2/c^2}$ *when timed by those clocks.* That is, to time a clock moving at constant velocity relative to an inertial frame, we need at least *two* synchronized clocks in that frame. We found this result to be reciprocal in that a single *S'*-clock is timed as running slow by the many *S*-clocks, and a single *S*-clock is timed as running slow by the many *S'*-clocks.

The situation in the twin paradox is different. If the traveling twin traveled always at a constant speed in a straight line, he would never get back home. And each twin would indeed claim that the other's clock runs slow compared to the synchronized clocks in his own frame. To get back home—that is, to make a round trip—the traveling twin would have to change his velocity. What we wish to compare in the case of the twin paradox is a single moving clock with a *single* clock at rest. To do this we must bring the clocks into coincidence twice—they must come back together again. It is not the idea that we regard one clock as moving and the other at rest that leads to the different clock readings, for if each of two observers seems to the other to be moving at constant speed in a straight line they cannot absolutely assert who is moving and who is not. Instead, it is because one clock has *changed* its velocity and the other has not that makes the situation unsymmetrical.

Now you may ask how the twins can tell who has changed his velocity. This is clearcut. Each twin can carry an accelerator. If he changes his speed or the direction of his motion, the acceleration will be detected. We may not be aware of an airplane's motion, or a train's motion, if it is one of uniform velocity; but let it move in a curve, rise and fall, speed up or slow down and we are our own accelerometer as we get thrown around. Our twin on the ground watching us does not experience these feelings— his accelerometer registers nothing. Hence, we can tell the twins apart by the fact that the one who makes the round-trip experiences and records accelerations whereas the stay-at-home does not.

A numerical example, suggested by Darwin [3], is helpful in fixing the ideas. We imagine that, on New Year's Day, Bob leaves his twin brother Dave, who is at rest on a space ship floating in free space. Bob, in another space ship, fires rockets that get him moving at a speed of $0.8c$ relative to Dave and by his own clock travels away for three years. He then fires more powerful rockets that exactly reverse his motion and gets to Dave after another three years by his clock. By firing rockets a third time he comes to rest beside Dave and compares clock readings. Bob's clock says he has been away for six years, but Dave's clock says ten years have elapsed. Let us see how this comes about.

First, we can simplify matters by ignoring the effect of the accelerations on the traveling clock. Bob can turn off his clock during the three acceleration periods, for example. The error thereby introduced can be made very small compared to the total time of the trip, for we can make the trip as far and as long as we wish without changing the acceleration intervals. It is the total time that is at issue here in any case.* We do not destroy the asymmetry, for even in the ideal simplification of Fig. B-2 (where the world lines are straight lines rather than curved ones) Dave is always in one inertial frame whereas Bob is definitely in two different

---

*An analogy is that the total distance traveled by two drivers between the same two points, one along the hypotenuse of a right triangle and the other along the other two sides of the triangle, can be quite different. One driver always moves along a straight line whereas the other makes a right turn to travel along two straight lines. We can make the distance between the two points as long as we wish without altering the fact that only one turn must be made. The difference in mileage traveled by the drivers certainly is not acquired at the turn that one of them makes.

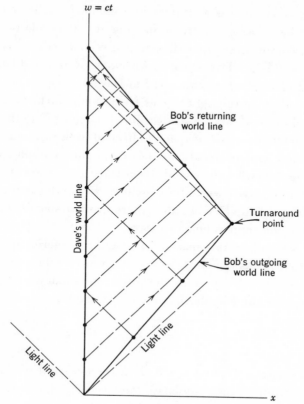

Fig. **B-2.**

inertial frames—one going out ($0.8c$) and another coming in ($-0.8c$).

Let the space ships be equipped with identical clocks which send out light signals at one-year intervals. Dave receives the signals arriving from Bob's clock and records them against the annual signals of his own clock; likewise, Bob receives the signals from Dave's clock and records them against the annual signals of his clock.

In Fig. B-2, Dave's world line is straight along the ct-axis:, he is at $x = 0$ and we mark off ten years (in terms of ct), a dot corresponding to the annual New Year's Day signal of his clock. Bob's world line at first is a straight line inclined to the ct-axis, corresponding to a ct'-axis of a frame moving at $+0.8c$ relative to Dave's frame. We mark off three years (in terms of ct'), a dot corresponding to the annual New Year's Day signal of his clock. After three of Bob's years, he switches to another inertial frame whose world line is a straight line inclined to the *ct*-axis, corresponding to the *ct″*-axis of a frame moving at $-0.8c$ relative to Dave's frame. We mark off three years (in terms of *ct″*), a dot corresponding to the annual New Year's Day signal of his clock. Note the dilation of the time interval of Bob's clock compared to Dave's.

Let us now draw in the light signals from Bob's clock. From each dot on Bob's world line we draw a straight line inclined 45° to the axes (corresponding to a light signal of speed *c*) headed back to Dave on the line at $x = 0$. There are six signals, the last one emitted when Bob returns home to Dave. Likewise, the signals from Dave's clock are straight lines, from each dot on Dave's world line, inclined 45° to the axes and headed out to Bob's spaceship. We see that there are ten signals, the last one emitted when Bob returns home to Dave.

How can we confirm this space-time diagram numerically? Simply by the Doppler effect. As the clocks recede from each other, the frequency of their signals is reduced from the proper frequency by the Doppler effect. In this case the Doppler factor (see Eq. 2-29) is

$$\sqrt{\frac{c - v}{c + v}} = \sqrt{\frac{c - 0.8c}{c + 0.8c}} = \sqrt{\frac{0.2}{1.8}} = \sqrt{\frac{1}{9}} = \frac{1}{3}.$$

Hence, Bob receives the first signal from Dave after three of his years, just as he is turning back. Similarly, Dave receives messages from Bob on the way out once every three of his years, receiving three signals in nine years. As the clocks approach one another, the frequency of their signals is increased from the proper frequency by the Doppler effect. In this case the Doppler factor (see Eq. 2-28) is

$$\sqrt{\frac{c + v}{c - v}} = \sqrt{\frac{1.8}{0.2}} = \sqrt{9} = 3.$$

Thus, Bob receives nine signals from Dave in his three-year return journey. Altogether, Bob receives ten signals from Dave. Similarly, Dave receives three signals from Bob in the last year before Bob is home. Altogether, Dave receives six signals from Bob.

There is no disagreement about the signals: Bob sends six and Dave receives six; Dave sends ten and Bob receives ten. Everything works out, each seeing the correct Doppler shift of the other's clock and each agreeing to the number of signals that the other sent. The different total times recorded by the twins corresponds to the fact that Dave sees Bob recede for nine years and return in one year, although Bob both receded for three of his years and returned for three of his years. Dave's records will show that he received signals at a slow rate for nine years and at a rapid rate for one year. Bob's records will show that he received signals at a slow rate for three years and at a rapid rate for another three years. The essential asymmetry is thereby revealed by a Doppler effect analysis. When Bob and Dave compare records, they will agree that Dave's clock recorded ten years and Bob's recorded only six. Ten years have passed for Dave during Bob's six-year round trip.

B-4 *Some Other Considerations*

Will Bob really be four years younger than his twin brother? Since for the word "clock" we could have substituted any periodic natural phenomena, such as heart-beat or pulse rate, the answer is yes. We might say that Bob lived at a slower rate then Dave during his trip, his bodily functions proceeding at the same slower rate as his physical clock. Biological clocks behave in this respect the same as physical clocks. There is no evidence that there is any difference in the physics of organic processes and the physics of the inorganic materials involved in these processes. If motion affects the rate of a physical clock, we expect it to effect a biological clock in the same way.

It is of interest to note the public acceptance of the idea that human life processes can be slowed down by refrigeration, so that a corresponding different aging of twins can be achieved by temperature differences. What is paradoxical about the relativistic case, in which the different aging is due to the difference in motion, is that since (uniform) motion is relative, the situation appears (incorrectly) to by symmetrical. But, just as the temperature differences are real, measurable, and agreed upon by the twins in the foregoing example, so are the differences in motion real, measurable, and agreed upon in the relativistic case—the changing of inertial frames, that is the accelerations, are not symmetrical. The results are absolutely agreed upon.

Although there is no need to invoke general relativity theory in explaining the twin paradox, the student may wonder what the outcome of the analysis would be if we knew how to deal with accelerated reference frames. We could then use Bob's space ship as our reference frame, so that Bob is the stay-at-home, and it would be Dave who, in this frame, makes the round-trip space journey. We would find that we must have a gravitational field in this frame to account for the accelerations that Bob feels and the fact that Dave feels no accelerations even though he makes a round trip. If, as required in general relativity, we then compute the frequency shifts of light in this gravitational field, we come to the same conclusion as in special relativity [see Ref. 4].

B-5 *An Experimental Test*

The experiments accessible to us are not those of spacemen traveling at speeds near that of light; they are instead radioactive nuclei whose change in ticking (photon decay rate) at different speeds can be measured to an extremely high accuracy. A radioactive source of gamma ray photons can be tuned to resonance with an absorber of such photons to within a very sharp frequency interval (Mössbauer effect). A source (radioactive iron-57 nuclei) mounted at the center of a rotor and a resonant absorber on the perimeter are used, the measurements being made as a function of the angular velocity of the rotor. The experiment can be analyzed in the inertial frame of the source using special relativity or in the reference frame of the accelerated absorber using general relativity. The measurements may be regarded as a transverse Doppler effect or a time dilation produced by gravitation, each expressing the same fact that the clock that is accelerated is slowed down compared to the clock at rest. One twin stays at home; the other literally makes a round trip. The results of these experiments [Refs. 5 to 7] show that a group of radioactive nuclei on the perimeter of the turning rotor undergo fewer decays than an identical set of radioactive nuclei at rest at the center of the rotor. The round-trip twin ages less than his stay-at-home brother and, within the limits of experimental error, by exactly the amount predicted by relativity theory.

Questions and Problems

1. A straight-line path between two points in (Euclidean) space is of shorter length than a curved path connecting these points. Is a straight world line between two events in (Minkowski) space of shorter or longer proper time than a curved world line connecting these same events? Explain.

2. Is asymmetric aging associated with acceleration? Explain your answer.

3. Explain (in terms of heartbeats, physical and mental activities, and so on) why the younger returning twin has not lived any longer than his own

proper time even though stay-at-homes may say that he has. Hence, explain the phrase "you age according to your own proper time."

4. Time dilation is a symmetric (reciprocal) effect. The twin-paradox result is asymmetric (nonreciprocal). In what sense are these effects related?

References

1. Many articles on this topic are reproduced in *Special Relativity Theory—Selected Reprints*, edited by Gerald Holton and published by the American Institute of Physics, New York, 1963.
2. Quoted from A. Einstein, *Vierteljahrachrift der Naturforsh. Gesellsch. in Zurich*, **56** (1911). A. Kopff, *The Mathematical Theory of Relativity*, (trans. H. Levy), London, 1923, p. 52, by C. J. Whitrow in *The Natural Philosophy of Time*, Harper Torchbooks, New York, 1961, p. 215.
3. C. G. Darwin, "The Clock Paradox in Relativity," *Nature*, **180**, 976 (1957).
4. O. R. Frisch, "Time and Relativity: Part II," *Contemporary Physics*, **3**, 194 (1962). See also, O. R. Frisch, "Time and Relativity: Part I," *Contemporary Physics*, **3**, 16 (1961). These articles are outstanding expositions of the problem.
5. J. J. Hay, J. P. Schiffer, T. E. Cranshaw, and P. A. Egelstaff, *Phys. Rev. Letters*, **4**, 165 (1960), discussed in Reference 6.
6. J. Bronowski, "The Clock Paradox," *Scientific American*, February, 1963.
7. Walter Kundig, *Phys. Rev.*, **129**, 2371 (1963).

The Principle of Equivalence and General Relativity

C-1 *Introduction*

We have seen that special relativity requires us to modify the classical laws of motion. However, the classical laws of electromagnetism, including the Lorentz force law, remain valid relativistically. What about the gravitational force, that is, Newton's law of gravitation—does relativity require us to modify that? Despite its great success in harmonizing the experimental observations, Newton's theory of gravitation is suspect conceptually if for no other reason than that it is an action-at-a-distance theory (see Section 3-1). The gravitational force of interaction between bodies is assumed to be transmitted instantaneously, that is, with infinite speed, in contradiction to the relativistic requirement that the limiting speed of a signal is c, the velocity of light. And there are worrisome features about the interpretation of the masses in the law of gravitation. For one thing, there is the equality of inertial and gravitational mass, which in the classical theory, is apparently an accident [see Ref. 1]. Surely there must be some physical significance to this equality. For another thing, the relativistic concept of mass-energy suggests that even particles of zero rest mass will exhibit masslike properties (e.g., inertia and weight). But such particles are excluded from the classical theory. If gravity acts on them, we must find how to incorporate this fact in a theory of gravitation.

In 1911 Einstein advanced his principle of equivalence, which became the starting point for a new theory of gravitation. In 1916, he published his theory of general relativity, in which gravitational effects propagate with the speed of light and the laws of physics are reformulated so as to be invariant with respect to accelerated (noninertial) observers. The equivalence principle is strongly confirmed by experiment. Let us examine this first.

C-2 *The Principle of Equivalence*

Consider two reference frames: (1) a nonaccelerating (inertial) reference frame S in which there is a uniform gravitational field, and (2) a reference frame S', which is accelerating uniformly with respect to an inertial frame but in which there is no gravitational field. Two such frames are physically equivalent; that is, experiments carried out under otherwise identical conditions in these two frames should give the same results. This is Einstein's *principle of equivalence.*

For example, imagine a spaceship to be at rest in an inertial reference frame S in which there is a uniform gravitational field, say at the surface of the earth. Inside the spaceship, objects that are released will fall with an acceleration, say g, in the gravitational field; an object which is at rest, such as an astronaut sitting on the floor, will experience a force opposing its weight. Now let the spaceship proceed to a region of outer space where there is no gravitational field. Its rockets are accelerating the spaceship, our new frame S', with $a = -g$ with respect to the inertial frame S. In other words, the ship is accelerating away from the earth beyond the region where the earth's field (or any other gravitational field) is appreciable. The conditions in the spaceship will now be like those in the spaceship when it was at rest on the surface of the earth. Inside the ship an object released by the astronaut will accelerate downward relative to the spaceship with an acceleration g. And an object at rest relative to the spaceship, for instance, the astronaut sitting on the floor, will experience a force indistinguishable from that which balanced its weight before. From observations made in his own frame, the astronaut could not tell the difference between a situation in which his ship was accelerating relative to an inertial frame in a region having no gravitational field and a situation in which the spaceship was unaccelerated in an inertial frame in which a uniform gravitational field existed. The two situations are exactly equivalent.

Indeed, it follows that if a body is in a uniform gravitational field—such as an elevator in a building on earth—and is at the same time accelerating in the direction of the field with an acceleration whose magnitude equals that due to the field—such as the same elevator in free fall—then particles in such a body will behave as though they are in an inertial reference frame with no gravitational field. They will be free of acceleration unless a force is impressed on them. This is the situation inside an artificial earth satellite in which objects released by the astronaut will not fall relative to the satellite (they appear to float in space) and the astronaut himself will be free of the force which countered the pull of gravity before launching (he feels weightless).

Einstein pointed out that, from the principle of equivalence, it follows that we cannot speak of the absolute acceleration of a reference frame, only a relative one, just as it followed from the special theory of relativity that we cannot speak of the absolute velocity of a reference frame, only a relative one. This analogy to special relativity is a formal one, for there is no absolute acceleration provided that we grant that there is also no absolute gravitational field. It also follows from the principle of equivalence (it is *not* an accident) that inertial mass and gravitational mass are equal (see Question 1).

C-3 *The Gravitational Red Shift*

Now let us apply the principle of equivalence to see what gravitational effects there might be that are not accounted for in the classical theory. Consider a pulse of radiation (a photon) emitted by an atom A at rest in frame S (a space ship at rest on the earth's surface, e.g.). A uniform gravitationl field $\mathbf{g}$ is directed downward in S, the photon falling down a distance d through this field before it is absorbed by the detector D (see Fig. C-1a). To analyze what effect gravity has on the photon, let us consider the equivalent situation, shown in Fig. C-1b. Here we have an atom and a detector separated by a distance d in a frame S' in which there is no gravitational field, the frame S' (a spaceship in outer space, e.g.) accelerating uniformly upward relative to S with $a = g$. When the photon is emitted, the atom has some speed u in this frame. The speed of the detector, when the photon reaches it, is $u + at$, where t is the time of flight of the photon. But (see Question 2) t is (approximately) d/c and $a = g$ so that the detector's speed on absorption is $u + g\,d/c$. In effect, the detector has an approach velocity relative to the emitter of $v = g\,d/c$, independent of u. Hence, the frequency received, ν', is greater than that emitted, ν, the Doppler formula giving us

$$\frac{\nu'}{\nu} = \sqrt{\frac{c + v}{c - v}} = \sqrt{\frac{c + g\,d/c}{c - g\,d/c}} \cong 1 + g\,d/c^2. \qquad \text{(C-1)}$$

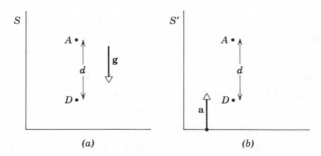

(a)   (b)

Fig. C-1.

By the principle of equivalence, we should obtain this same result in frame S. In this frame, however, A and D are at rest and there is no Doppler effect to explain the increase in frequency. There is a gravitational field, however, and the result in S' suggests that this field might act on the photon. Let us explore this possibility by ascribing to the photon a *gravitational mass* equal to its inertial mass, E/c^2. Then, in falling a distance d in a gravitational field of strength g, the photon gains energy $(E/c^2)g\,d$. How can we connect the energy E to the frequency ν? In the quantum theory, the connection is $E = h\nu$, where h is a constant called Planck's constant. For the moment, let us use this relation so that the energy of the photon on absorption at D is its initial emission energy plus the energy gained in falling from A to D, or $h\nu + (h\nu/c^2)g\,d$. If we call this absorption energy $E' = h\nu'$, then we have

$$h\nu' = h\nu + \frac{h\nu g\,d}{c^2}$$

or
$$\frac{\nu'}{\nu} = 1 + \frac{g\,d}{c^2}, \tag{C-2}$$

the same result obtained in frame S' (Eq. C-1).

Actually, it is not necessary to use quantum theory. We can show in relativity itself that E is proportional to ν, because it follows, from the relativistic transformation of energy and momentum, that the energy in an electromagnetic pulse changes by the same factor as its frequency when observed in a different reference frame (see Question 3). The conclusion then is that, in falling through a gravitational field, light gains energy and frequency (its wavelength decreases and we say it is shifted toward the blue). Clearly, had we reversed emitter and detector, we would have concluded that in rising against a gravitational field light loses energy and frequency (its wavelength increases and we say it is shifted toward the red).

The predicted fractional change in frequency, $(\nu' - \nu)/\nu$ or $\Delta\nu/\nu$, is $g\,d/c^2$, and even with d being the distance from sea level to the top of the highest mountains on earth, its value is only about 10^{-12}. Nevertheless, Pound and Rebka [2] in 1960 were able to confirm the prediction using the 74 ft high Jefferson tower at Harvard! For such a small distance we have

$$\frac{\Delta\nu}{\nu} = \frac{g\,d}{c^2} = \frac{(9.8 \ \text{m/sec}^2)(22.5 \ \text{m})}{(3 \times 10^8 \ \text{m/sec})^2} \cong 2.5 \times 10^{-15},$$

an incredibly small effect. By using the Mössbauer effect (which permits a highly sensitive measurement of frequency shifts) with a gamma ray source, and taking admirable care to control the competing variables, Pound and Rebka observed this gravitational effect on photons and confirmed the quantitative prediction. Their result, comparing experimental observation to theoretical calculation, was

$$\frac{(\Delta\nu)_{\text{exp}}}{(\Delta\nu)_{\text{theory}}} = 1.05 \pm 0.10.$$

In a subsequent refinement of the original experiment, Pound and Snider [3] in 1965 found

$$\frac{(\Delta\nu)_{\text{exp}}}{(\Delta\nu)_{\text{theory}}} = 0.9990 \pm 0.0076.$$

We can easily generalize our result (Eqs. C-1 and C-2) to photons emitted from the surface of stars and observed on earth. Here we assume that the gravitational field need not be uniform and that the result depends only on the difference in gravitational potential between the source and the observer. Then, in place of gd we have GM_s/R_s, where M_s is the mass of the star of radius R_s, and because the photon *loses* energy in rising through the gravitational field of the star, we obtain

$$\nu' \cong \nu\left(1 - \frac{GM_s}{R_s c^2}\right). \tag{C-3}$$

This effect is known as the *gravitational red shift*, for light in the visible part of the spectrum will be shifted in frequency toward the red end. This effect is distinct from the Doppler red shift from receding stars. Indeed, because the Doppler shift is much larger, the gravitational red shift has not been confirmed with certainty.

C-4   *General Relativity Theory*

Let us return to Fig. C-1a in which D measures a greater frequency than A emits. It may appear strange that a frequency can increase with no relative motion of source and detector. After all, D surely receives the same *number* of vibrations that A sent out. Even the distance of separation remains constant between A and D, so how do we interpret the measured frequency increase? The answer, once again, is that there is a disagreement about time. That is, frequency is the number of vibrations per unit time so that the frequency difference must be due to a time difference; the rate of A's clock must differ from the rate of D's clock.

We say that clocks in the region of high gravitational potential run faster than those in a region of low gravitational potential. Let the emitting atom be the clock, for example, its rate being the frequency of radiation. Then the higher up in the gravitational field the atom is, the higher its frequency appears to be to D (i.e., compared to the same atom radiating at D). Similarly, if we reverse A and D, then the lower down in the gravitational field the atom is the lower its frequency appears to be to D (i.e., compared to the same atom radiating at D). It is the frequency shifts produced by the (equivalent) gravitational fields that lead us to the same result in the "twin-paradox" as that obtained in special relativity when we take the point of view of the noninertial frame rather than the inertial one (see Ref. 4 of Appendix B).

It was Einstein who postulated the principle of the equivalence of a system in a uniform gravitational field to a uniformly accelerated reference system for all physical processes. He, too, derived the result that the rate of clocks is slower in regions of lower gravitational potential than in regions of higher gravitational potential. Furthermore, he called attention to the gravitational red shift required from the theory and to the need to ascribe gravitational mass $m = E/c^2$ to an energy E. Still another of his results was that the direction of the velocity of light is not constant in a gravitational field; indeed, light rays *bend* in a gravitational field because of their gravitational mass and Einstein predicted that this bending would cause a displacement in the position of fixed stars that are seen near the edge of the sun.

From all this, we see that special relativity can only be correct in the absence of a gravitational field, since the definition of simultaneity upon which the Lorentz transformations are based is contradicted by the dependence of the velocity of light and of the rate of clocks on the gravitational potential. Hence, a more general theory is needed* which takes into account the principle of equivalence and which generalizes even that principle to nonuniform (inhomogeneous) gravitational fields. Furthermore, gravitational effects themselves must be treated by a field theory in which the propagation speed is finite. In a series of papers [4] Einstein formulated such a general theory of relativity.

We shall mention only some features of general relativity theory. The

---

* Just as Galilean relativity is a special case of Einstein's special relativity, so special relativity is a special case of general relativity. The gravitational field (as near the earth) is usually so weak that there are no observable discrepancies between special relativity and general relativity. In most cases we operate in the special relativistic limit of general relativity.

subject is clearly beyond the scope of a book at this level.** First, inhomogeneous gravitational fields can be transformed away, or imitated, by having at *each* point in the field a *different* accelerated frame that replaces the local (infinitesimal) field there. In such local frames, the special theory of relativity *is* valid so that the invariance of the laws of physics under a Lorentz transformation applies to infinitesimal regions. Second, through an invariant space-time metric that follows from this, we can link geometry to gravitation and geometry becomes non-Euclidean. That is, the presence of a large body of matter causes space-time to warp in the region near it so that space-time becomes non-Euclidean. This warping is equivalent to the gravitational field. The curvature of space-time in general relativity replaces the gravitational field of classical theory. Hence, the geometry of space-time is determined by the presence of matter. In this sense, geometry becomes a branch of physics. The fact that special relativity is valid in small regions corresponds to the fact that Euclidean geometry is valid over small parts of a curved surface. In large regions, special relativity and Euclidean geometry need not apply so that the world lines of light rays and inertial motion need not be straight; instead, they are geodetic, that is, as straight as possible. Third, the laws of physics are postulated to be invariant with respect to transformations between all reference frames, however they move. Hence, *all* observers are equivalent. Finally, a specific theory of gravitation is proposed, consistent with the other requirements, in which gravitational effects propagate with the speed of light.

Other specific theories of gravitation have been proposed in recent times (see Ref. 6, e.g.). The Einstein Theory has the appeal of being the simplest in form. And theories at variance with some of the basic features of general relativity are also advocated [7 and 8]. All of these theories are difficult to put to the test of experiment (see Refs. 9 and 10 for summaries and interpretation of the experiments). Two major predictions of Einstein's theory are (1) that the precession of the perihelion of the planet Mercury (Fig. C-2a) should differ from the classical prediction, the difference being about 43 seconds of arc per century, and (2) that the positions of stars whose light passes near the edge of the sun (observed, say, during a solar eclipse) should be displaced (due to deflection by the gravitational field of the sun) by 1.75 seconds of arc from their positions

** See Refs. 5 for some good elementary discussions.

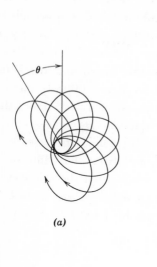

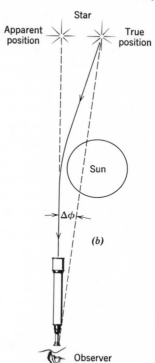

Fig. C-2. (*a*) A planet moving in a precessing orbit about a fixed center of force. The perhelion, or point of closest approach, shifts by an angle θ after each excursion. In the case of Mercury, the orbit is nearly circular and the precession of perhelion is very small—only 5600 seconds of arc per century. All but about 40 seconds of this is due to the gravitational attractions of the other planets and can be deduced classically. The remainder is in agreement with Einstein's general theory. (*b*) Light passing the sun from a star to the earth is deflected toward the sun, making the star appear displaced away from the sun by an angle $\Delta\varphi = 1.75$ seconds of arc. The drawing is schematic only, obviously not to scale.

observed at night (Fig. C-2b). The experimental results are compatible with Einstein's predictions. In the case of the first prediction the results are known to great accuracy but interpretations other than Einstein's have been advanced. In the case of the second prediction, the accuracy of the results is uncertain. Much experimental work is now underway to clarify the situation. There is universal agreement, however, that Einstein's equivalence principle (confirmed, e.g., by Pound's experiments) is valid. As for his specific theory of gravitation, the story is still unfolding.

The general theory of relativity is one of the greatest intellectual achievements of all time. Its originality and unorthodox approach exceed that of special relativity. And far more so than special relativity, it was almost completely the work of a single man, Albert Einstein. The philosophic impact of relativity theory on the thinking of man has been profound and the vistas of science opened by it are literally endless. To quote Max Born [5]: "The idea first expressed by Ernst Mach, that the inertial forces are due to the total system of fixed stars, suggests the application of the theory of general relativity to the whole universe. This step was actually made by Einstein in 1917, and from that time dates the modern development of cosmology and cosmogony, the sciences of the structure and genesis of the cosmos. This development is still in full swing and rich in important results, though far from final conclusions."

Questions and Problems

1. Starting from the fact that all bodies that are free of forces move with uniform velocity relative to an inertial frame, then considering the motion of these bodies in an accelerated frame, and finally using the principle of equivalence, show that all bodies fall with the same acceleration in a uniform gravitational field—hence, the equality of inertial and gravitational mass.

2. Why is the relation $t = d/c$, used for the photon's time of flight in frame S' of Fig. C-1b, only approximate, rather than exact?

3. Prove that special relativity is consistent with quantum physics in regard to the proportionality of E and v for a photon.

4. Can gravity be regarded as a "fictitous" force, arising from the acceleration of one's reference frame relative to an inertial reference frame, rather than a "real" force?

References

1. See Section 16-4 "*Physics*," Part I, R. Resnick and D. Halliday, John Wiley and Sons, Inc., New York (1966).
2. R. V. Pound and G. A. Rebka, Jr., "Apparent Weight of Photons," *Phys. Rev. Letters*, **4**, 337 (1960).
3. R. V. Pound and J. L. Snider, "Effect of Gravity on Gamma Radiation," *Phys. Rev.*, **140**, B-788 (1965).
4. A. Einstein, "Die Grundlagen der allgemeinen Relativitatstheorie," *Ann. Phys. Lpz.* **49**, 769 (1916), translated, along with other papers, into English in *The Principle of Relativity* by Einstein and others, Dover Publications, Inc., 1923.

5. Max Born, *Einstein's Theory of Relativity*, Chapter VII, Dover Publications, Inc. New York (1962).

Albert Einstein, *Relativity, The Special and General Theory*, Crown Publishers, Inc. (1961). A reprinting of the fifteenth edition (1952) of a 1916 translation.

6. R. H. Dicke, "The Richtmeyer Memorial Lecture—Gravitation and Cosmic Physics," *Am. J. Phys.*, **35**, 559 (1967).

7. Some are discussed in "A Crucial Test of Relativity Theory," by Robert Bernhard in *Scientific Research*, August, 1967, p. 62.

8. C. Alton Coulter, "Spin-$\frac{1}{2}$ Particles in a Gravitational Field," *Am. J. Phys.*, **35**, 603 (1967).

9. L. Witten (ed.), *Gravitation: An Introduction to Current Research*, John Wiley and Sons, Inc., New York, 1962.

10. R. H. Dicke, *The Theoretical Significance of Experimental Relativity*, by Gordon and Breach, New York, 1964.

Answers to Problems

Chapter 1
15. (a) Same, (b) sound, (c) bullet.

Chapter 2
1. (a) 4.00×10^{-13} sec; (b) zero.
4. $x' = 2520$ km, $y' = 10$ km, $z' = 1$ km, $t' = -7.70 \times 10^{-4}$ sec.
5. (a) $45/c = 1.5 \times 10^{-7}$ sec; (b) $190/c = 6.3 \times 10^{-7}$ sec; (c) $170/c = 5.7 \times 10^{-7}$ sec.
6. (a) $0.0447c = 1.44 \times 10^{7}$ m/sec; (b) $0.141c = 4.23 \times 10^{7}$ m/sec; (c) $0.436c = 1.31 \times 10^{8}$ m/sec.
9. (a) No, (b) $\dfrac{v/c^2}{\sqrt{1 - \beta^2}} [(x_1 - x_2)^2 + (y_1 - y_2)^2 + (z_1 - z_2)^2]^{1/2}$.
10. (a) AD, AC; (b) $\Delta t \sqrt{1 - \beta^2}$; (c) No, BC before AD.
12. (a) Yes, $v = c/2$ in the direction of positive x, 519 m.
13. (a) 3.74 sec, (b) zero sec, (c) undefined.
15. (a) $u = c/3$, (b) $c/3$.
18. (a) $\Delta L/L_0 = 2.2 \times 10^{-12}$ m, (b) 4.54×10^{5} sec $= 5.26$ days.
19. (a) $L - L_0 = 6.40 \times 10^{-5}$ km.
20. Exceeds speed limit by 40 mph.   21. 2.12×10^{-2} m.
22. (a) $0.866c = 2.60 \times 10^{8}$ m/sec; (b) ship's clocks will go half as fast.
23. (a) Yes, (b) $v = 0.9999990c$.
24. (a) 3.94×10^{7} m/sec, (b) 2.54×10^{-6} sec.
26. (a) 1.67 m, (b) 1.67 m.
27. (a) (i) zero; (ii) 517 m; (iii) 1420 m; (iiii) 4840 m.
    (b) (i) zero; (ii) 414 m; (iii) 622 m; (iiii) 683 m.
28. 199, 947 m.   29. $0.99c$.
33. $0.946c$.   34. One part in 10^9.
38. (a) $0.817c$ in the direction of positive x;
    (b) $0.801c$, $86.4°$ from the x-axis;
    (c) $0.799c$, $86.4°$ from the x'-axis.
40. $L' = L \sqrt{1 - \beta^2 \cos^2 \theta}$; $\tan \theta' = \dfrac{\tan \theta}{\sqrt{1 - \beta^2}}$.
41. $u' = \dfrac{[u^2 + v^2 + 2uv \cos \theta - (uv/c)^2 \sin^2 \theta]^{1/2}}{1 + (uv/c) \cos \theta}$

$\tan \theta' = \dfrac{u \sin \theta \sqrt{1 - (v/c)^2}}{v + u \cos \theta}$.
44. (a) 6 min, (b) 12 min, (c) 6 min.
45. (a) $\tau_0/\sqrt{1 - \beta^2}$.   47. Green.
48. (i) 560 Å; (ii) 2040 Å; (iii) 3930 Å.
49. (i) 13 Å; (ii) 66 Å; (iii) 690 Å.
50. $\Delta\lambda = 29$ Å.

Chapter 3

1. (a) $abc \sqrt{1 - \beta^2}$, (b) $m_0 / \sqrt{1 - \beta^2}$, (e) $\rho' = \dfrac{\rho_0}{\sqrt{1 - \beta^2}}$.

3. $0.867c$, no.

4. (a) $0.948c = 2.84 \times 10^8$ m/sec; (b) $621\ m_e$; (c) 212 Mev, 1.62×10^{-19} kg-m/sec.

5. (a) $1962\ m_e$; (b) $0.99999987c$; (c) $2.96\ m_e$, $v = 0.942c$.

6. (a) $0.99882c$; (b) $0.1c$; (c) 20.6 (electron), 1.01 (proton).

13. (a) 2.56×10^5 volts; (b) $0.6c$; (c) 1.43×10^{-30} kg, $4.1 \times 10^{-14} j$.

18. (a) 0.145 webers/m², (b) 1.98.   **19.** 663 km.

21. 1.82×10^{20} m.   **22.** $267\ m_e$; pi meson.

23. 114.2 km above sea level.

24. (a) 4.42×10^{-36} kg; (b) 2.208×10^{-32} kg.

25. $4.4 \times 10^{-6}\ nt/m^2$.   **26.** 5.62×10^{26} Mev.

27. $\Delta m = 4.22 \times 10^{-12}$ kg; $4.64 \times 10^{-13}\%$.

28. (b) 0.51 Mev (electron); 938.2 Mev (proton).

29. (a) 2.7×10^{14} joules, (b) 1.79×10^7 kg.

30. 92.162 Mev.

31. 0.51 Mev; 2.72×10^{-22} kg-m/sec.   **32.** (a) $c/3$; (b) $2.12\ m_0$.

34. (a) 2.36×10^{-21} kg-m/sec; (b) 8.78×10^{-4} Mev.

36. 29.58 Mev (neutrino); 4.22 Mev (muon).

38. (a) 4.38 Mev.

41. (a) 3.63×10^{-22} kg-m/sec; 0.850 Mev.

(b) $p_x' = 1.15 \times 10^{-22}$ kg-m/sec; $p_y' = p_z' = 0$; 0.552 Mev.

Chapter 4

8. (a) zero for both.

18. $F_y' = 9.22 \times 10^{-12}\ nt$; $F_y = 4.12 \times 10^{-13}\ nt$.

20. (a) $E_x = E_z = 0$; $E_y = \dfrac{\lambda}{\pi\epsilon_0 a}$, $B_x = B_y = B_z = 0$;

(b) $\lambda' = \lambda\gamma$; $i' = \gamma\lambda v$;

(c) $E_x' = E_z' = 0$, $E_y' = \dfrac{\lambda'}{\pi\epsilon_0 a}$, $B_x' = B_y' = 0$, $B_z' = -\dfrac{\mu_0 i'}{\pi a}$.

Supplementary Topic A

8. (a) $-c/3$, (b) $-c/7$.

Index